GLOBAL COMMONS
MANAGEMENT
AND
GOVERNANCE

GLOBAL COMMONS
MANAGEMENT
AND
GOVERNANCE

By
N Jawadekar

2008

SBS Publishers & Distributors Pvt. Ltd.
New Delhi

ISBN 10 : 81-89741-61-6
ISBN 13 : 978-81-89741-61-7

Indian Price - INR 995.00
Foreign Price - USD 50.00

First Published in India in 2008

© Reserved

Published by:
SBS PUBLISHERS & DISTRIBUTORS PVT. LTD.
2/9, Ground Floor, Ansari Road, Darya Ganj,
New Delhi - 110002, INDIA
Tel: 23289119, 41563911
Email: mail@sbspublishers.com
www.sbspublishers.com

Printed in India by SALASAR IMAGING SYSTEMS.

Preface

The term "Global Commons" has usually referred to those parts of international space that are beyond national jurisdiction: the deep seabed, the troposphere, stratosphere and near outer space and, arguably, Antarctica. These have sometimes been termed "the common heritage of mankind", in Arvid Pardo's eloquent formulation. Even this formulation has a bit of the realist model in it: by referring to national jurisdiction, there is an implication of the right of the nation-state to control physical territory. However, given that the basis of jurisdiction has historically been the ability (or potential ability) of States to control territory, it is possible to propose a modified concept of the commons. An entry point, to determining what the global commons can mean, it is necessary to return to the United Nations Charter, and the fundamental purposes of the organization set out in it:

❑ To employ international machinery for the promotion of the economic and social advancement of all peoples;
❑ To achieve international cooperation in solving international problems of an economic, social, cultural or humanitarian character; and
❑ To be a centre for harmonizing the actions of nations for the attainment of these common ends.

Global commons, in general, is a term used by environmentalists and others to describe the relationship of the global environment and human activity. "Global commons" recognizes that the ecosystem is shared by all and implies that there is a common responsibility to maintain it. Common pool resources present some of the most intellectually interesting and practically demanding resource management problems in the world today. The management requirements of other types of resources are reasonably well understood, at least in principle, if rarely attained in practice But "absolute sovereignty is an idea whose time has passed" and an understanding of the issues associated with the global commons - the final frontier on the planet - is of increasing relevance as population levels and per capita consumption continue to grow and put increasing pressure on the resource. The problem does not appear to be a lack of environmental attention. Although the environmental field is new, more than a thousand multilateral and bilateral environmental agreements have been concluded in the last several decades. Nevertheless, environmental law — particularly at the international level — is still in an emerging phase. Efforts to promote international cooperation have been hampered by the limits of international law generally and the pressures of national sovereignty more specifically. With regard to a number of aspects of the global natural commons, treaties and other international compacts exist. But these agreements often offer little more than a framework for international cooperation. Because of the constraint of sovereignty, substantive commitments to actions that will make an on-the-ground difference are only undertaken with unanimous consent. This means the process moves only as quickly as the most hesitant or recalcitrant actors are willing to proceed. In recent years, in the face of the difficulty of achieving consensus on concrete actions, a number of governments have turned to a "partnership" approach that engages a subset of countries willing to act. Such an approach makes good sense for issues of limited scope. But for truly global-scale problems, relying on "coalitions of the willing" is unlikely to be successful, especially where significant harm-causers decline to participate or "free riding" is otherwise prevalent. In many cases, moreover, international "rules" arise as guidelines and not binding obligations. While international standards that emerge as "soft law" may harden over time into more enforceable obligations, the lack of binding regulations—and thus the inability to deter "free riding"—hampers progress in many realms.

The difficulty of promoting international environmental cooperation at the global scale is not just a function of a lack of a lawmaking capacity. Constraints on executive authority in the international domain and the hesitancy to enforce international standards also limit environmental progress. In this regard, the environmental regime lags other elements of the international order. The trade regime, for example, has developed quite a robust institutional architecture in the World Trade Organization with systematic structures for negotiation, rulemaking, and administration. In contrast, the international regime for the environment remains ad hoc, fragmented, and largely ineffectual. The pattern of institutional weakness leading to substantive poor performance is especially notable with regard to settlement of international environmental disputes. While there exists an Environmental Chamber at the International Court of Justice, it has never been used, perhaps because jurisdiction is only by consent. With no other well-established international environmental dispute resolution mechanism, issues go unresolved or emerge as "trade and environment" problems that fall to trade institutions to address. In contrast, the international trading system (including both the WTO and many regional trade agreements) has dispute settlement procedures that are frequently used and generally well respected.

In true sense global commons include acid rain, air pollution, air slots, atmosphere, carbon sequestration; climate change, electro-magnetic spectrum, governance and management of Arctic and Antarctic regions; global warming, greenhouse effect; international treaties; oceans, outer space; governance, law and management of transboundary resources; transboundary disputes, radio spectrum, etc. However, this book examines the major natural global commons cases, such as; the Antarctica; the gene pool; the high seas and the deep seabed; the outer space, moon and other celestial bodies; the international freshwater resources; and the transboundary groundwater. These share a number of ownership and international management characteristics. The development of the accepted international law and the present status of international treaties governing each is outlined and analyzed.

This book titled "Global Commons Management and Governance: International Guidelines & Frameworks" provides a clear, useful introduction to the subject that will be of interest to general readers as well as to students in international relations and international environmental law, and in environmental law and policy generally. In sum, this book is a unique initiative to help provide the most comprehensive coverage to the subject area in question. It accounts for an integrative approach and user-friendly methodology. The editors believe that this book will prove itself a milestone in times to come for addressing the issue of global commons. This book is of great contemporary relevance. It will serve as a reference book on the said subject and tends to acquaint readers with both in-depth and extensive knowledge of the subject concerned. This book is user friendly and comes with select acronym, glossary, bibliography and index. This book is an attempt to address the most important environment issues of current period dealing with major natural global commons.

Author

Contents

1

Antarctica:
Environmental Management and Resource Governance in Polar Regions

THE ANTARCTIC TREATY

The Antarctic Treaty, the earliest of the post-World War II arms limitation agreements, has significance both in itself and as a precedent. It internationalized and demilitarized the Antarctic Continent and provided for its cooperative exploration and future use. It has been cited as an example of nations exercising foresight and working in concert to prevent conflict before it develops. Based on the premise that to exclude armaments is easier than to eliminate or control them once they have been introduced, the treaty served as a model, in its approach and even provisions, for later "nonarmament" treaties—the treaties that excluded nuclear weapons from outer space, from Latin America, and from the seabed.

By the 1950s seven nations—Argentina, Australia, Chile, France, New Zealand, Norway, and the United Kingdom—claimed sovereignty over areas of Antarctica, on the basis of discovery, exploration, or geographic propinquity. Claims of Argentina, Chile, and the United Kingdom overlapped. Eight other nations—the United States, the Soviet Union, Belgium, Germany, Poland, Sweden, Japan, and South Africa—had engaged in exploration but had put forward no specific claims. The United States did not recognize the claims of other governments and reserved the right to assert claims based on exploration by its citizens. The Soviet Union took a similar position.

Activities in the Antarctic had generally been conducted peacefully and cooperatively. Yet the possibility that exploitable economic resources might be found meant the possibility of future rivalry for their control. Moreover, isolated and uninhabited, the continent might at some time become a potential site for emplacing nuclear weapons.

Fortunately, scientific interests rather than political, economic, or military concerns dominated the expeditions sent to Antarctica after World War II. Fortunately, too, international scientific associations were able to work out arrangements for effective cooperation. In 1956 and 1957, for example, American meteorologists "wintered over" at the Soviet post Mirnyy, while Soviet meteorologists "wintered over" at Little America. These cooperative activities culminated in the International Geophysical Year of 1957-1958 (IGY), a joint scientific effort by 12 nations—Argentina, Australia, Belgium, Chile, France, Japan, New Zealand, Norway, South Africa, the Soviet Union, the United Kingdom, and the United States—to conduct studies of the Earth and its cosmic environment.

In these years the desire to keep the continent demilitarized was general and some diplomatic discussion of the possibility had taken place. On 3 May, 1958, the United States proposed to the other 11 nations participating in the IGY that a conference be held, based on the points of agreement that had been reached in informal discussions:

1. that the legal *status quo* of the Antarctic Continent remain unchanged;
2. that scientific cooperation continue;
3. that the continent be used for peaceful purposes only.

All accepted the U.S. invitation. The Washington Conference on Antarctica met from 15 October to 1 December, 1959. No insurmountable conflicts or issues divided the conference, and negotiations culminated in a treaty signed by all 12 nations on 1 December, 1959. Approved by the U.S. Senate, U.S. ratification was deposited 18 August, 1960, and the treaty entered into force on 23 June, 1961, when the formal ratifications of all the participating nations had been received.

The treaty provides that Antarctica shall be used for peaceful purposes only. It specifically prohibits "any measures of a military nature, such as the establishment of military bases and fortifications, the carrying out of military maneuvers, as well as the testing of any type of weapons." Military personnel or equipment, however, may be used for scientific research or for any other peaceful purpose. Nuclear explosions and the disposal of radioactive waste material in Antarctica are prohibited, subject to certain future international agreements on these subjects. All Contracting Parties entitled to participate in the meetings referred to in Article IX of the treaty have the right to designate observers to carry out inspections in all areas of Antarctica, including all stations, installations and equipment, and ships and aircraft at discharge or embarkation points. Each observer has complete freedom of access at any time to any or all areas of Antarctica. Contracting Parties may also carry out aerial inspections. There are provisions for amending the treaty; for referring disputes that cannot be handled by direct talks, mediation, arbitration, or other peaceful means to the International Court of Justice; and for calling a conference in 30 years to review the operation of the treaty if any parties request it.

Argentina, Australia, New Zealand, the Soviet Union, the United Kingdom, and the United States have all exercised the right of inspection. The United States conducted inspections in 1971, 1975, 1977, 1980, 1983, 1985, and 1989. All American inspections included Soviet facilities. The 1985 inspection concentrated on the Antarctic Peninsula area where the U.S. team inspected stations belonging to the United Kingdom, the Soviet Union, the Peoples Republic of China, Argentina, Chile, and Poland. The 1989 inspection was conducted in the Ross Sea area, visiting six (only five are named) stations of France, Italy, New Zealand, the Federal Republic of Germany, and the Soviet Union, as well as 12 sites of historic and scientific interest. In February, 1995, the 10th inspection since inspections began in 1963 was conducted. In a circumnavigation of the South Pole, eight sites were visited to allow teams to observe environmental conditions at research stations. No military activities, armaments, or prohibited nuclear activities were observed, and all scientific programs were in accord with previously published plans. The observed activities at each station were in compliance with the provisions and spirit of the Antarctic Treaty.

Fifteen consultative meetings have been held in accordance with Article IX of the treaty. Numerous recommendations on measures in furtherance of the principles and objectives of the treaty have been adopted, many of which have now entered into force. There are now 24 Contracting Parties entitled to participate in these meetings: the original 12 signatory states plus Brazil, China, Germany, Finland, India, Italy, Republic of Korea, Peru, Poland, Spain, Sweden, and Uruguay.

THE ANTARCTIC TREATY

Signed at Washington 1 December, 1959
Ratification advised by U.S. Senate 10 August, 1960
Ratified by U.S. President 18 August, 1960
U.S. ratification deposited at Washington 18 August, 1960
Proclaimed by U.S. President 23 June, 1961
Entered into force 23 June, 1961

The Governments of Argentina, Australia, Belgium, Chile, the French Republic, Japan, New Zealand, Norway, the Union of South Africa, the Union of Soviet Socialist Republics, the United Kingdom of Great Britain and Northern Ireland, and the United States of America,

Recognizing that it is in the interest of all mankind that Antarctica shall continue forever to be used exclusively for peaceful purposes and shall not become the scene or object of international discord;

Acknowledging the substantial contributions to scientific knowledge resulting from international cooperation in scientific investigation in Antarctica;

Convinced that the establishment of a firm foundation for the continuation and development of such cooperation on the basis of freedom of scientific investigation in Antarctica as applied during the International Geophysical Year accords with the interests of science and the progress of all mankind;

Convinced also that a treaty ensuring the use of Antarctica for peaceful purposes only and the continuance of international harmony in Antarctica will further the purposes and principles embodied in the Charter of the United Nations;

Have agreed as follows:

Article I

1. Antarctica shall be used for peaceful purposes only. There shall be prohibited, *inter alia*, any measures of a military nature, such as the establishment of military bases and fortifications, the carrying out of military maneuvers, as well as the testing of any type of weapons.
2. The present treaty shall not prevent the use of military personnel or equipment for scientific research or for any other peaceful purposes.

Article II

Freedom of scientific investigation in Antarctica and cooperation toward that end, as applied during the International Geophysical Year, shall continue, subject to the provisions of the present treaty.

Article III

1. In order to promote international cooperation in scientific investigation in Antarctica, as provided for in Article II of the present treaty, the Contracting Parties agree that, to the greatest extent feasible and practicable:
   (a) information regarding plans for scientific programs in Antarctica shall be exchanged to permit maximum economy and efficiency of operations;
   (b) scientific personnel shall be exchanged in Antarctica between expeditions and stations;
   (c) scientific observations and results from Antarctica shall be exchanged and made freely available.
2. In implementing this Article, every encouragement shall be given to the establishment of cooperative working relations with those Specialized Agencies of the United Nations and other international organizations having a scientific or technical interest in Antarctica.

Article IV

1. Nothing contained in the present treaty shall be interpreted as:

(a) a renunciation by any Contracting Party of previously asserted rights of or claims to territorial sovereignty in Antarctica;

(b) a renunciation or diminution by any Contracting Party of any basis of claim to territorial sovereignty in Antarctica which it may have whether as a result of its activities or those of its nationals in Antarctica, or otherwise;

(c) prejudicing the position of any Contracting Party as regards its recognition or non-recognition of any other States right of or claim or basis of claim to territorial sovereignty in Antarctica.

2. No acts or activities taking place while the present treaty is in force shall constitute a basis for asserting, supporting or denying a claim to territorial sovereignty in Antarctica or create any rights of sovereignty in Antarctica. No new claim, or enlargement of an existing claim, to territorial sovereignty in Antarctica shall be asserted while the present treaty is in force.

Article V

1. Any nuclear explosions in Antarctica and the disposal there of radioactive waste material shall be prohibited.

2. In the event of the conclusion of international agreements concerning the use of nuclear energy, including nuclear explosions and the disposal of radioactive waste material, to which all of the Contracting Parties whose representatives are entitled to participate in the meetings provided for under Article IX are parties, the rules established under such agreements shall apply in Antarctica.

Article VI

The provisions of the present treaty shall apply to the area south of 60° South Latitude, including all ice shelves, but nothing in the present treaty shall prejudice or in any way affect the rights, or the exercise of the rights, of any State under international law with regard to the high seas within that area.

Article VII

1. In order to promote the objectives and ensure the observance of the provisions of the present treaty, each Contracting Party whose representatives are entitled to participate in the meetings referred to in Article IX of the treaty shall have the right to designate observers to carry out any inspection provided for by the present Article. Observers shall be nationals of the Contracting Parties which designate them. The names of observers shall be communicated to every other Contracting Party having the right to designate observers, and like notice shall be given of the termination of their appointment.

2. Each observer designated in accordance with the provisions of paragraph 1 of this Article shall have complete freedom of access at any time to any or all areas of Antarctica.

3. All areas of Antarctica, including all stations, installations and equipment within those areas, and all ships and aircraft at points of discharging or embarking cargoes or personnel in Antarctica, shall be open at all times to inspection by any observers designated in accordance with paragraph 1 of this Article.

4. Aerial observation may be carried out at any time over any or all areas of Antarctica by any of the Contracting Parties having the right to designate observers.

5. Each Contracting Party shall, at the time when the present treaty enters into force for it, inform the other Contracting Parties, and thereafter shall give them notice in advance, of

   (a) all expeditions to and within Antarctica, on the part of its ships or nationals, and all expeditions to Antarctica organized in or proceeding from its territory;

   (b) all stations in Antarctica occupied by its nationals; and

   (c) any military personnel or equipment intended to be introduced by it into Antarctica subject to the conditions prescribed in paragraph 2 of Article I of the present treaty.

Article VIII

1. In order to facilitate the exercise of their functions under the present treaty, and without prejudice to the respective positions of the Contracting Parties relating to jurisdiction over all other persons in Antarctica, observers designated under paragraph 1 of Article VII and scientific personnel exchanged under subparagraph 1(b) of Article III of the treaty, and members of the staffs accompanying any such persons, shall be subject only to the jurisdiction of the Contracting Party of which they are nationals in respect of all acts or omissions occurring while they are in Antarctica for the purpose of exercising their functions.

Without prejudice to the provisions of paragraph 1 of this Article, and pending the adoption of measures in pursuance of subparagraph 1(e) of Article IX, the Contracting Parties concerned in any case of dispute with regard to the exercise of jurisdiction in Antarctica shall immediately consult together with a view to reaching a mutually acceptable solution.

Article IX

1. Representatives of the Contracting Parties named in the preamble to the present treaty shall meet at the City of Canberra within two months after the date of entry into force of the treaty, and thereafter at suitable intervals and places, for the purpose of exchanging information, consulting together on matters of common interest pertaining to Antarctica, and formulating and considering, and recommending to their Governments, measures in furtherance of the principles and objectives of the treaty, including measures regarding:
    (a) use of Antarctica for peaceful purposes only;
    (b) facilitation of scientific research in Antarctica;
    (c) facilitation of international scientific cooperation in Antarctica;
    (d) facilitation of the exercise of the rights of inspection provided for in Article VII of the treaty;
    (e) questions relating to the exercise of jurisdiction in Antarctica;

(f) preservation and conservation of living resources in Antarctica.

2. Each Contracting Party which has become a party to the present treaty by accession under Article XIII shall be entitled to appoint representatives to participate in the meetings referred to in paragraph 1 of the present Article, during such time as that Contracting Party demonstrates its interest in Antarctica by conducting substantial scientific research activity there, such as the establishment of a scientific station or the dispatch of a scientific expedition.

3. Reports from the observers referred to in Article VII of the present treaty shall be transmitted to the representatives of the Contracting Parties participating in the meetings referred to in paragraph 1 of the present Article.

4. The measures referred to in paragraph 1 of this Article shall become effective when approved by all the Contracting Parties whose representatives were entitled to participate in the meetings held to consider those measures.

5. Any or all of the rights established in the present treaty may be exercised from the date of entry into force of the treaty whether or not any measures facilitating the exercise of such rights have been proposed, considered or approved as provided in this Article.

Article X

Each of the Contracting Parties undertakes to exert appropriate efforts, consistent with the Charter of the United Nations, to the end that no one engages in any activity in Antarctica contrary to the principles or purposes of the present treaty.

Article XI

1. If any dispute arises between two or more of the Contracting Parties concerning the interpretation or application of the present treaty, those Contracting Parties shall consult among themselves with a view to having the

dispute resolved by negotiation, inquiry, mediation, conciliation, arbitration, judicial settlement or other peaceful means of their own choice.

2. Any dispute of this character not so resolved shall, with the consent, in each case, of all parties to the dispute, be referred to the International Court of Justice for settlement; but failure to reach agreement on reference to the International Court shall not absolve parties to the dispute from the responsibility of continuing to seek to resolve it by any of the various peaceful means referred to in paragraph 1 of this Article.

Article XII

1. (a) The present treaty may be modified or amended at any time by unanimous agreement of the Contracting Parties whose representatives are entitled to participate in the meetings provided for under Article IX. Any such modification or amendment shall enter into force when the depositary Government has received notice from all such Contracting Parties that they have ratified it.

    (b) Such modification or amendment shall thereafter enter into force as to any other Contracting Party when notice of ratification by it has been received by the depositary Government. Any such Contracting Party from which no notice of ratification is received within a period of two years from the date of entry into force of the modification or amendment in accordance with the provisions of subparagraph 1(a) of this Article shall be deemed to have withdrawn from the present treaty on the date of the expiration of such period.

2. (a) If after the expiration of thirty years from the date of entry into force of the present treaty, any of the Contracting Parties whose representatives are entitled to participate in the meetings provided for under Article IX so requests by a communication addressed to the depositary Government, a Conference of all the Contracting Parties shall be held as soon as practicable to review the operation of the treaty.

    (b) Any modification or amendment to the present treaty

which is approved at such a Conference by a majority of the Contracting Parties there represented, including a majority of those whose representatives are entitled to participate in the meetings provided for under Article IX, shall be communicated by the depositary Government to all the Contracting Parties immediately after the termination of the Conference and shall enter into force in accordance with the provisions of paragraph 1 of the present Article.

(c) If any such modification or amendment has not entered into force in accordance with the provisions of subparagraph 1(a) of this Article within a period of two years after the date of its communication to all the Contracting Parties, any Contracting Party may at any time after the expiration of that period give notice to the depositary Government of its withdrawal from the present treaty; and such withdrawal shall take effect two years after the receipt of the notice of the depositary Government.

Article XIII

1. The present treaty shall be subject to ratification by the signatory States. It shall be open for accession by any State which is a Member of the United Nations, or by any other State which may be invited to accede to the treaty with the consent of all the Contracting Parties whose representatives are entitled to participate in the meetings provided for under Article IX of the treaty.

2. Ratification of or accession to the present treaty shall be effected by each State in accordance with its constitutional processes.

3. Instruments of ratification and instruments of accession shall be deposited with the Government of the United States of America, hereby designatèd as the depositary Government.

4. The depositary Government shall inform all signatory and acceding States of the date of each deposit of an instrument of ratification or accession, and the date of entry into force of the treaty and of any modification or amendment thereto.

5. Upon the deposit of instruments of ratification by all the signatory States, the present treaty shall enter into force for those States and for States which have deposited instruments of accession. Thereafter the treaty shall enter into force for any acceding State upon the deposit of its instrument of accession.

6. The present treaty shall be registered by the depositary Government pursuant to Article 102 of the Charter of the United Nations.

Article XIV

The present treaty, done in the English, French, Russian and Spanish languages, each version being equally authentic, shall be deposited in the archives of the Government of the United States of America, which shall transmit duly certified copies thereof to the Governments of the signatory and acceding States.

IN WITNESS WHEREOF the undersigned Plenipotentiaries, duly authorized, have signed the present treaty.

DONE at Washington this first day of December, one thousand nine hundred and fifty-nine.

The Antarctic Treaty

Country	Date of Signature	Date of Deposit of Ratification	Date of Deposit of Accession
Argentina	12/01/59	06/23/61	–
Australia	12/01/59	06/23/61	–
Austria	–	–	08/25/87
Belgium	12/01/59	07/26/60	–
Brazil	–	–	05/16/75
Bulgaria	–	–	09/11/78
Chile	12/01/59	06/23/61	–
China	–	–	06/08/83
Cuba	–	–	08/16/84
Czechoslovakia	–	–	06/14/62
Denmark	–	–	05/20/65
Ecuador	–	–	09/15/87
Finland	–	–	05/15/84
France	12/01/59	09/16/60	–
German Democratic			

(Contd.)

(*Contd.*)

Country	Date of Signature	Date of Deposit of Ratification	Date of Deposit of Accession
Republic	–	–	11/19/74
Germany, Federal Republic of	–	–	02/05/79
Greece	–	–	01/08/87
Hungary	–	–	01/27/84
India	–	–	08/19/83
Italy	–	–	03/18/81
Japan	12/01/59	08/04/60	–
Korea, Democratic Peoples Republic of	–	–	01/21/87
Korea, Republic of	–	–	11/28/86
Netherlands	–	–	03/30/67
New Zealand	12/01/59	11/01/60	–
Norway	12/01/59	08/24/60	–
Papua New Guinea	–	–	03/16/81
Peru	–	–	04/10/81
Poland	–	–	06/08/61
Romania	–	–	09/15/71
South Africa	12/01/59	06/21/60	–
Spain	–	–	03/31/82
Sweden	–	–	04/24/84
Union of Soviet Socialist Republics	12/01/59	11/02/60	–
United Kingdom	12/01/59	05/31/60	–
United States	12/01/59	08/18/60	–
Uruguay	–	–	01/11/80
Total	**12**	**12**	**25**

CONSERVATION OF
ANTARCTIC FLORA AND FAUNA

Preamble

The Governments participating in the Third Consultative Meeting under Article IX of the Antarctic Treaty,

Desiring to implement the principles and purposes of the Antarctic Treaty;

Recognizing the scientific importance of the study of Antarctic fauna and flora, their adaptation to their rigorous environment, and their inter-relationship with that environment;

Considering the unique nature of these fauna and flora, their circumpolar range, and particularly their defenselessness and susceptibility to extermination;

Desiring by further international collaboration within the framework of the Antarctic Treaty to promote and achieve the objectives of protection, scientific study, and rational use of these fauna and flora; and

Having particular regard to the conservation principles developed by the Scientific Committee on Antarctic Research (SCAR) of the International Council of Scientific Unions;

Hereby consider the Treaty Area as a Special Conservation Area and have agreed on the following measures:

Article I: Area of Application

1. These Agreed Measures shall apply to the same area to which the Antarctic Treaty is applicable (hereinafter referred to as the Treaty Area) namely the area south of 60° South Latitude, including all ice shelves.
2. However, nothing in these Agreed Measures shall prejudice or in any way affect the rights, or the exercise of the rights, of any State under international law with regard to the high seas within the Treaty Area, or restrict the implementation of the provisions of the Antarctic Treaty with respect to inspection.
3. The Annexes to these Agreed Measures shall form an integral part thereof, and all references to the Agreed Measures shall be considered to include the Annexes.

Article II: Definitions

For the purposes of these Agreed Measures:

(a) 'Native mammal' means any member, at any stage of its life cycle, of any species belonging to the Class Mammalia indigenous to the Antarctic or occurring there through natural agencies of dispersal, excepting whales.

(b) 'Native bird' means any member, at any stage of its life cycle (including eggs), of any species of the Class Aves indigenous to the Antarctic or occurring there through natural agencies of dispersal.

(c) 'Native plant' means any kind of vegetation at any stage of its life cycle (including seeds), indigenous to the Antarctic or occurring there through natural agencies of dispersal.

(d) 'Appropriate authority' means any person authorized by a Participating Government to issue permits under these Agreed Measures. The functions of an authorised person will be carried out within the framework of the Antarctic Treaty. They will be carried out exclusively in accordance with scientific principles and will have as their sole purpose the effective protection of Antarctic fauna and flora in accordance with these Agreed Measures.

(e) 'Permit' means a formal permission in writing issued by an appropriate authority as defined at paragraph (d) above.

(f) 'Participating Government' means any Government for which these Agreed Measures have become effective in accordance with Article XIII of these Agreed Measures.

Article III: Implementation

Each Participating Government shall take appropriate action to carry out these Agreed Measures.

Article IV: Publicity

The Participating Governments shall prepare and circulate to members of expeditions and stations information to ensure understanding and observance of the provisions of these Agreed Measures, setting forth in particular prohibited activities, and providing lists of specially protected species and specially protected areas.

Article V: Cases of Extreme Emergency

The provisions of these Agreed Measures shall not apply in cases of extreme emergency involving possible loss of human life or involving the safety of ships or aircraft. Article VI Protection of native fauna

1. Each Participating Government shall prohibit within the Treaty Area the killing, wounding, capturing or molesting of any native mammal or native bird, or any attempt at any such act, except in accordance with a permit.

2. Such permits shall be drawn in terms as specific as possible and issued only for the following purposes:

    (a) to provide indispensable food for men or dogs in the Treaty Area in limited quantities, and in conformity with the purposes and principles of these Agreed Measures;

    (b) to provide specimens for scientific study or scientific information;

    (c) to provide specimens for museums, zoological gardens, or other educational or cultural institutions or uses.

3. Permits for Specially Protected Areas shall be issued only in accordance with the provisions of Article VIII.

4. Participating Governments shall limit the issue of such permits so as to ensure as far as possible that:

    (a) no more native mammals or birds are killed or taken in any year than can normally be replaced by natural reproduction in the following breeding season;

    (b) the variety of species and the balance of the natural ecological systems existing within the Treaty Area are maintained.

5. The species of native mammals and birds listed in Annex A of these Measures shall be designated 'Specially Protected Species', and shall be accorded special protection by Participating Governments.

6. A Participating Government shall not authorize an appropriate authority to issue a permit with respect to a Specially Protected Species except in accordance with paragraph 7 of this Article.

7. A permit may be issued under this Article with respect to a Specially Protected Species, provided that:

    (a) it is issued for a compelling scientific purpose, and

    (b) the actions permitted thereunder will not jeopardize

the existing natural ecological system or the survival of that species.

Article VII: Harmful Interference

1. Each Participating Government shall take appropriate measures to minimize harmful interference within the Treaty Area with the normal living conditions of any native mammal or bird, or any attempt at such harmful interference, except as permitted under Article VI.
2. The following acts and activities shall be considered harmful interference:
   (a) flying helicopters or other aircraft in a manner which would unnecessarily disturb bird and seal concentrations, or landing close to such concentrations (eg within 200 m),
   (c) driving vehicles unnecessarily close to concentrations of birds and seals (eg within 200 m),
   (d) use of explosives close to concentrations of birds and seals,
   (e) discharge of firearms close to bird and seal concentrations (eg. within 300 m),
   (f) any disturbance of bird and seal colonies during the breeding period by persistent attention from persons on foot.

However, the above activities, with the exception of those mentioned in (a) and (e) may be permitted to the minimum extent necessary for the establishment, supply and operation of stations.

3. Each Participating Government shall take all reasonable steps towards the alleviation of pollution of the waters adjacent to the coast and ice shelves.

Article VIII: Specially Protected Areas

1. The areas of outstanding scientific interest listed in Annex B shall be designated 'Specially Protected Area' and shall be accorded special protection by the Participating Governments in order to preserve their unique natural ecological system.
2. In addition to the prohibitions and measures of protection

dealt with in other Articles of these Agreed Measures, the Participating Governments shall in Specially Protected Areas further prohibit:

    (a) the collection of any native plant, except in accordance with a permit;

    (b) the driving of any vehicle.

    (c) entry by their nationals, except in accordance with a permit issued under Article VI or under paragraph 2(a) of the present Article or in accordance with a permit issued for some other compelling scientific purpose;

3.   A permit issued under Article IV shall not have effect within a Specially Protected Area except in accordance with paragraph 4 of the present Article.

4.   A permit shall have effect within a Specially Protected Area provided that:

    (a) it was issued for a compelling scientific purpose which cannot be served elsewhere; and

    (b) the actions permitted thereunder will not jeopardize the natural ecological system existing in that Area.

Article IX: Introduction of Non-indigenous Species, Parasites and Diseases

1.   Each Participating Government shall prohibit the bringing into the Treaty Area of any species of animal or plant not indigenous to that Area, except in accordance with a permit.

2.   Permits under paragraph 1 of this Article shall be drawn in terms as specific as possible and shall be issued to allow the importation only of the animals and plants listed in Annex C. When any such animal or plant might cause harmful interference with the natural system if left unsupervised within the Treaty Area, such permits shall require that it be kept under controlled conditions and, after it has served its purpose, it shall be removed from the Treaty Area or destroyed.

3.   Nothing in paragraphs 1 and 2 of this Article shall apply to the importation of food into the Treaty Area so long as animals and plants used for this purpose are kept under controlled conditions.

4. Each Participating Government undertakes to ensure that all reasonable precautions shall be taken to prevent the accidental introduction of parasites and diseases into the Treaty Area. In particular, the precautions listed in Annex D shall be taken.

Article X: Activities Contrary to the Principles and Purposes of These Measures

Each Participating Government undertakes to exert appropriate efforts, consistent with the Charter of the United nations, to the end that no one engages in any activity in the Treaty Area contrary to the principles or purposes of these Agreed Measures.

Article XI: Ships' Crews

Each Participating Government whose expeditions use ships sailing under flags of nationalities other than its own shall, as far as feasible, arrange with the owners of such ships that the crews of these ships observe these Agreed Measures.

Article XII: Exchange of Information

1. The Participating Governments may make such arrangements as may be necessary for the discussion of such matters as:
   (a) the collection and exchange of records (including records of permits) and statistics concerning the numbers of each species of native mammal and bird killed or captured annually in the Treaty Area;
   (b) the obtaining and exchange of information as to the status of native mammals and birds in the Treaty Area, and the extent to which any species needs protection;
   (c) the number of native mammals or birds which should be permitted to be harvested for food, scientific study, or other uses in the various regions;
   (d) the establishment of a common form in which this information shall be submitted by Participating Governments in accordance with paragraph 2 of this Article.

2. Each Participating Government shall inform the other Governments in writing before the end of November each year of the steps taken and information collected in the preceding period of 1 July to 30 June relating to the implementation of these Agreed Measures. Governments exchanging information under paragraph 5 of Article VII of the Antarctic Treaty may at the same time transmit the information relating to the implementation of these Agreed Measures.

Article XIII: Formal Provisions

1. After the receipt by the Government designated in Recommendation I-XIV(5) of notification of approval by all Governments whose representatives are entitled to participate in meetings provided for under Article IX of the Antarctic Treaty, these Agreed Measures shall become effective for those Governments.
2. Thereafter any other Contracting Party to the Antarctic Treaty may, in consonance with the purposes of Recommendation III-VII, accept these Agreed Measures by notifying the designated Government of its intention to apply the Agreed Measures and to be bound by them. The Agreed Measures shall become effective with regard to such Governments on the date of receipt of such notification.
3. The designated Government shall inform the Governments referred to in paragraph 1 of this Article of each notification of approval, the effective date of these Agreed Measures and of each notification of acceptance. The designated Government shall also inform any Government which has accepted these Agreed Measures of each subsequent notification of acceptance.

Article XIV: Amendment

1. These Agreed Measures may be amended at any time by unanimous agreement of the Governments whose Representatives are entitled to participate in meetings under Article IX of the Antarctic Treaty.

2. The Annexes, in particular, may be amended as necessary through diplomatic channels.
3. An amendment proposed through diplomatic channels shall be submitted in writing to the designated Government which shall communicate it to the Governments referred to in paragraph 1 of the present Article for approval; at the same time, it shall be communicated to the other Participating Governments.
4. Any amendment shall become effective on the date on which notifications of approval have been received by the designated Government and from all of the Governments referred to in paragraph 1 of this Article.
5. The designated Government shall notify those same Governments of the date of receipt of each approval communicated to it and the date on which the amendment will become effective for them.
6. Such amendment shall become effective on that same date for all other Participating Governments, except those which before the expiry of two months after that date notify the designated Government that they do not accept it.

ANNEXES TO
THESE AGREED MEASURES

Annex A: Specially Protected Species

All species of the genus *Arctocephalus*, Fur Seals.
Ommatophoca rossii, Ross Seal.

Annex B: Importation of Animals and Plants

The following animals and plants may be imported into the Treaty Area in accordance with permits issued under Article I2 of these Agreed Measures:

(a) sledge dogs
(b) domestic animals and plants
(c) laboratory animals and plants including viruses, bacteria, yeasts and fungi.

Annex C: Precautions to Prevent Accidental Introduction of Parasites and Diseases into the Treaty Area

The following precautions shall be taken:
1. *Dogs*: All dogs imported into the Treaty Area shall be inoculated against the following diseases:
    (a) distemper
    (b) contagious canine hepatitis
    (c) rabies
    (d) leptospirosis (*L. canicola* and *L. icterohaemorragicae*)

Each dog shall be inoculated at least two months before the time of its arrival in the Treaty Area

2. *Poultry*: Notwithstanding the provisions of Article I3 of these Agreed Measures, no living poultry shall be brought into the Treaty Area after 1 July, 1966.

MEASURES RELATED TO
THE AGREED MEASURES

Introductory Note

The adoption of the Agreed Measures required that each country should legislate, in accordance with their respective constitutional practices, to give legal effect to them. It was therefore agreed (Rec. III-IX) to recommend that the Agreed Measures be considered as guidelines in the interim period. A similar Recommendation (IV-20) was adopted in relation to the first nineteen Recommendations of the Fourth ATCM dealing with Specially Protected Species, Specially Protected Areas and other matters related to the Agreed Measures.

Practical experience of the application of the Agreed Measures and increasing knowledge of the Antarctic environment brought about four developments in the Agreed Measures: cooperation between nearby stations to minimize impact on local fauna and flora (Rec. IV-18), standardization of the format for the exchange of information on animals killed or captured (Rec. IV-19), which resulted four years later, in a request to SCAR to publish exchanged information and report on its significance (Rec. VI-9).

III-IX: Interim Guidelines for the Conservation of Fauna and Flora

The Representatives recommend to their Governments that until such time as the Agreed Measures on the Conservation of Antarctic Fauna and Flora may become effective in accordance with Article IX of the Antarctic Treaty, these Agreed Measures as far as feasible be considered as guide lines in this interim period.

III-X: Interest of SCAR in the conservation of Antarctic fauna and flora

Recognizing the initiative already taken by the Scientific Committee on Antarctic Research (SCAR) on matters relating to the conservation of Antarctic fauna and flora, and considering its role as defined in Recommendation I-IV, the Representatives recommend to their Governments that they encourage SCAR to continue its interest in those matters and to prepare reports from time to time on this subject, and especially at this time on the matters that it considers should be listed in the Annexes of the Agreed Measures for the Conservation of Antarctic Fauna and Flora.

IV-18: Cooperation in implementing Article VI of the Agreed Measures for the Conservation of Antarctic Fauna and Flora (Recommendation III-8)

The Representatives, taking into consideration Article VI of the Agreed Measures for the Conservation of Antarctic Fauna and Flora (Recommendation III-8), recommend to their Governments that in cases where expeditions of more than one Participating Government may be working in the same region of the Treaty Area, the Governments involved should arrange to cooperate as far as practicable in limiting the issuance of permits in accordance with Article VI to ensure that the total number of native mammals and birds killed or captured accords with the requirements of paragraphs 4 and 7(b) of Article VI and paragraph 4(b) of Article VIII of the Agreed Measures.

IV-19: Implementation of Article XII(d) of the Agreed Measures

The Representatives recommend to their Governments that for the effective implementation of the provision of Article XII of the Agreed Measures for the Conservation of Antarctic Fauna and Flora, documents exchanged annually by Participating Governments on the matters set down in paragraph 1(a) of that Article should follow the pattern of the form annexed hereto p. 2054]. Recognizing the role of the Scientific Committee on Antarctic Research (SCAR), as defined in Recommendation I-IV, the Representatives further welcome the decision of SCAR to study the status of species, their need for protection and numbers of each species which might be harvested for food, study or other uses, as outlined in paragraph 1(b) and (c) of Article XII of the Agreed Measures.

IV-20: Interim Guide Lines for the Conservation of Fauna and Flora

The Representatives recommend to their Governments that, until such time as the Agreed Measures on the Conservation of Antarctic Fauna and Flora may become effective in accordance with Article IX of the Antarctic Treaty, the following Recommendations as far as feasible be considered as guide lines in the interim period. Recommendations IV-1 to IV-19 inclusive.

VI-9: Data on the Conservation of Fauna and Flora

The Representatives,
Recalling Recommendations III-10 and IV-19;
Noting that:

1. information is already being exchanged in accordance with the interim guidelines contained in Recommendation IV-20;
2. this information may be freely published and it is desirable that it should be amalgamated in the form most useful for scientific analysis;

Recommend to their Governments that:

1. They transmit the information exchanged under Recommendation IV-19 to their National Antarctic Committees;
2. They invite the Scientific Committee on Antarctic Research, through their National Committees, to assemble the information exchanged under Article XII of the Agreed Measures for the Conservation of Antarctic Fauna and Flora, to arrange for its publication and, in accordance with Recommendation IV-19, to prepare reports from time to time on the status of species.

Extract from Report of VIth ATCM

The Meeting considered that on the occasion of the exchanges of information under the provisions of Article XII of the Agreed Measures on the Conservation of Antarctic Fauna and Flora or under any amendment to that Article by a subsequent Recommendation, it would be desirable that Consultative Parties which have no information to report should indicate this formally.

Extract from Report of VIIth ATCM

The Meeting noted that, in response to the invitations initiated by Recommendation VI-9, the Scientific Committee on Antarctic Research (SCAR) had tabulated and had arranged for the publication of the statistics exchanged under Article XII of the Agreed Measures for the Conservation of Antarctic Fauna and Flora on the seals and birds killed and captured in the Antarctic Treaty Area during the period 1964-69. Those tabulated statistics would continue to be published, together with the comments of the relevant SCAR group on any changes in the status of species that could be attributed to the numbers killed. The Representatives were pleased to note, from information drawn to their attention during the meeting, an authoritative opinion that there is at present no serious direct threat to Antarctic seals and birds and in particular that no species is endangered, although the possibility of over-exploitation of some local populations of seals cannot be entirely ruled out.

The Meeting reviewed the legislative and/or administrative action taken by Consultative Parties, or in preparation, to conserve fauna and flora in the Treaty Area, and expressed satisfaction at the consider able progress made towards the harmonization of national regulations. The need to expedite approval of the Agreed Measures for the Conservation of Fauna and Flora, and to give effect to the provisions thereof throughout the Treaty Area in accordance with their terms, was also stressed.

Extract from Report of VIIIth ATCM

A desire was expressed that Consultative Parties which had not yet approved certain Recommendations of previous Consultative Meetings, and especially Recommendation III-8, should take appropriate steps for the earliest possible approval of such Recommendations. The Meeting noted with satisfaction statements by some Representatives that action for approval of Recommendation III-8 is imminent and also that the Agreed Measures for the Conservation of Antarctic Fauna and Flora are being voluntarily implemented pending unanimous approval and entry into force of Recommendation III-8.

CONSERVATION OF ANTARCTIC SEALS

The Contracting Parties,
Recalling the Agreed Measures for the Conservation of Antarctic Fauna and Flora, adopted under the Antarctic Treaty signed at Washington on 1 December, 1959; (1)
Recognizing the general concern about the vulnerability of Antarctic seals to commercial exploitation and the consequent need for effective conservation measures;
Recognizing that the stocks of Antarctic seals are an important living resource in the marine environment which requires an international agreement for its effective conservation;
Recognizing that this resource should not be depleted by over-exploitation, and hence that any harvesting should be regulated so as not to exceed the levels of the optimum sustainable yield;
Recognizing that in order to improve scientific knowledge and so place exploitation on a rational basis, every effort should be made both to encourage biological and other research on Antarctic

seal populations and to gain information from such research and from the statistics of future sealing operations, so that further suitable regulations may be formulated;

Noting that the Scientific Committee on Antarctic Research of the International Council of Scientific Unions (SCAR) is willing to carry out the tasks requested of it in this Convention;

Desiring to promote and achieve the objectives of protection, scientific study and rational use of Antarctic seals, and to maintain a satisfactory balance within the ecological system,

Have agreed as follows:

Article 1: Scope

1. This Convention applies to the seas south of 60deg. South Latitude, in respect of which the Contracting Parties affirm the provisions of Article IV of the Antarctic Treaty.
2. This Convention may be applicable to any or all of the following species:

   Southern elephant seal *Mirounga leonina,*
   Leopard seal *Hydrurga leptonyx,*
   Weddell seal *Leptonychotes weddelli,*
   Crabeater seal *Lobodon carcinophagus,*
   Ross seal *Ommatophoca rossi,*
   Southern fur seals *Arctocephalus* sp.

3. The Annex to this Convention forms and integral part thereof.

Article 2: Implementation

1. The Contracting Parties agree that the species of seals enumerated in Article 1 shall not be killed or captured within the Convention area by their nationals or vessels under their respective flags except in accordance with the provisions of this Convention.
2. Each Contracting Party shall adopt for its nationals and for vessels under its flag such laws, regulations and other measures, including a permit system as appropriate, as may be necessary to implement this Convention.

Article 3: Annexed Measures

1. This Convention includes an Annex specifying measures which the Contracting Parties hereby adopt. Contracting Parties may from time to time in the future adopt other measures with respect to the conservation, scientific study and rational and humane use of seal resources, prescribing inter alia:

   (a) permissible catch;
   (b) protected and unprotected species;
   (c) open and closed seasons;
   (d) open and closed areas, including the designation of reserves;
   (e) the designation of special areas where there shall be no disturbance of seals;
   (f) limits relating to sex, size, or age for each species;
   (g) restrictions relating to time of day and duration, limitations of effort and methods of sealing;
   (h) types and specifications of gear and apparatus and appliances which may be used;
   (i) catch returns and other statistical and biological records;
   (j) procedures for facilitating the review and assessment of scientific information;
   (k) other regulatory measures including an effective system of inspection.

2. The measures adopted under paragraph (1) of this Article shall be based upon the best scientific and technical evidence available.

3. The Annex may from time to time be amended in accordance with the procedures provided for in Article 9.

Article 4: Special Permits

1. Notwithstanding the provisions of this Convention, and Contracting Party may issue permits to kill or capture seals in limited quantities and in conformity with the objectives and principles of this Convention for the following purposes:

   (a) to provide indispensable food for men or dogs;

    (b) to provide for scientific research; or

    (c) to provide specimens for museums, educational or cultural institutions.

2. Each Contracting Party shall, as soon as possible, inform the other Contracting Parties and SCAR of the purpose and content of all permits issued under paragraph (1) of this Article and subsequently of the numbers of seals killed or captured under these permits.

Article 5: Exchange of Information and Scientific Advice

1. Each Contracting Party shall provide to the other Contracting Parties and to SCAR the information specified in the Annex within the period indicated therein.

2. Each Contracting Party shall also provide to the other Contracting Parties and to SCAR before 31 October each year information on any steps it has taken in accordance with Article 2 of this Convention during the preceding period 1 July to 30 June.

3. Contracting Parties which have no information to report under the two preceding paragraphs shall indicate this formally before 31 October each year.

4. SCAR is invited:

    (a) to assess information received pursuant to this Article; encourage exchange of scientific data and information among the Contracting Parties; recommend programmes for scientific research; recommend statistical and biological data to be collected by sealing expeditions within the Convention area; and suggest amendments to the Annex; and

    (b) to report on the basis of the statistical, biological and other evidence available when the harvest of any species of seal in the Convention area is having a significantly harmful effect on the total stocks of such species or on the ecological system in any particular locality.

5. SCAR is invited to notify the Depositary which shall report to the Contracting Parties when SCAR estimates in any sealing season that the permissible catch limits for any species are likely to be exceeded and, in that case, to provide an estimate of the date upon which the permissible

catch limits will be reached. Each Contracting Party shall then take appropriate measures to prevent its nationals and vessels under its flag from killing or capturing seals of that species after the estimated date until the Contracting Parties decide otherwise.

6. SCAR may if necessary seek the technical assistance of the Food and Agriculture Organization of the United Nations in making its assessments.

7. Notwithstanding the provisions of paragraph (1) of Article 1 the Contracting Parties shall, in accordance with their internal law, report to each other and to SCAR, for consideration, statistics relating to the Antarctic seals listed in paragraph (2) of Article 1 which have been killed or captured by their nationals and vessels under their respective flags in the area of floating sea ice north of 60deg. South Latitude.

Article 6: Consultations between Contracting Parties

1. At any time after commercial has begun a Contracting Party may propose through the Depositary that a meeting of Contracting Parties be convened with a view to:

    (a) establishing by a two-thirds majority of the Contracting Parties, including the concurring votes of all States signatory to this Convention present at the meeting, an effective system of control, including inspection, over the implementation of the provisions of this Convention;

    (b) establishing a commission to perform such functions under this Convention as the Contracting Parties may deem necessary; or

    (c) considering other proposals, including:

        (i)   the provision of independent scientific advice;

        (ii) the establishment, by a two-thirds majority, of a scientific advisory committee which may be assigned some or all of the functions requested of SCAR under this Convention, if commercial sealing reaches significant proportions;

        (iii) the carrying out of scientific programmes with the participation of the Contracting Parties; and

        (iv) the provision of further regulatory measures, including moratoria.

2. If one-third of the Contracting Parties indicate agreement the Depositary shall convene such a meeting, as soon as possible.

3. A meeting shall be held at the request of any Contracting Party, if SCAR reports that the harvest of any species of Antarctic seal in the area to which this Convention applies is having a significantly harmful effect on the total stocks or the ecological system in any particular locality.

Article 7: Review of Operations

The Contracting Parties shall meet within five years after the entry into force of this Convention and at least every five years thereafter to review the operation of the Convention.

Article 8: Amendments to the Convention1

1. This Convention may be amended at any time. The text of any amendment proposed by a Contracting Party shall be submitted to the Depositary, which shall transmit it to all the Contracting Parties.

2. If one-third of the Contracting Parties request a meeting to discuss the proposed amendment the Depositary shall call such a meeting.

3. An amendment shall enter into force when the Depositary has received instruments of ratification or acceptance thereof from all the Contracting Parties.

Article 9: Amendments to the Annex

1. Any Contracting Party may propose amendments to the Annex to this Convention. The text of any such proposed amendment shall be submitted to the Depositary which shall transmit it to all Contracting Parties.

2. Each such proposed amendment shall become effective for all Contracting Parties six months after the date appearing on the notification from the Depositary to the Contracting Parties, if within 120 days of the notification

date, no objection has been received and two-thirds of the Contracting Parties have notified the Depositary in writing of their approval.

3. If an objection is received from any Contracting Party within 120 days of the notification date, the matter shall be considered by the Contracting Parties at their next meeting. If unanimity on the matter is not reached at the meeting, the Contracting Parties shall notify the Depositary within 120 days from the date of closure of the meeting of their approval or rejection of the original amendment or of any new amendment proposed by the meeting. If, by the end of this period, two-thirds of the Contracting Parties have approved such amendment, it shall become effective six months from the date of the closure of the meeting for those Contracting Parties which have by then notified their approval.

4. Any Contracting Party which has objected to a proposed amendment may at any time withdraw that objection, and the proposed amendment shall become effective with respect to such Party immediately if the amendment is already in effect, or at such time as it becomes effective under the terms of this Article.

5. The Depositary shall notify each Contracting Party immediately upon receipt of each approval or objection, of each withdrawal of objection, and of the entry into force of any amendment.

6. Any State which becomes a Party to this Convention after an amendment to the Annex has entered into force shall be bound by the Annex as so amended. Any State which becomes a Party to this Convention during the period when a proposed amendment is pending may approve or object to such an amendment within the time limits applicable to other Contracting Parties.

Article 10: Signature

This Convention shall be open for signature at London from 1 June to 31 December, 1972 by States participating in the Conference on the Conservation of Antarctic Seals held at London from 3 to 11 February, 1972.

Article 11: Ratification

This Convention is subject to ratification or acceptance. Instruments of ratification or acceptance shall be deposited with the Government of the United Kingdom of Great Britain and Northern Ireland, hereby designated as the Depositary.

Article 12: Accession

This Convention shall be open for accession by any State which may be invited to accede to this Convention with the consent of the Contracting Parties.

Article 13: Entry into Force

1. This Convention shall enter into force on the thirtieth day following the date of deposit of the seventh instrument of ratification or acceptance.
2. Thereafter this Convention shall enter into force for each ratifying, accepting or acceding State on the thirtieth day after deposit by such State of its instrument of ratification, acceptance or accession.

Article 14: Withdrawal

Any Contracting Party may withdraw from this Convention on 30 June of any year by giving notice on or before 1 January of the same year to the Depositary, which upon receipt of such a notice shall at once communicate it to the other Contracting Parties. Any other Contracting Party may, in like manner, within one month of the receipt of a copy of such a notice from the Depositary, give notice of withdrawal, so that the Convention shall cease to be in force on 30 June of the same year with respect to the Contracting Party giving such notice.

Article 15: Notifications by the Depositary

The Depositary shall notify all signatory and acceding States of the following:

    (a)   signatures of this Convention, the deposit of instruments of ratification, acceptance or accession and notices of withdrawal:

    (b)   the date of entry into force of this Convention and of any amendments to it or its Annex.

Article 16: Certified Copies and Registration1

1. This Convention, done the English, French, Russian and Spanish languages, each version being equally authentic, shall be deposited in the archives of the Government of the United Kingdom of Great Britain and Northern Ireland, which shall transmit duly certified copies thereof to all signatory and acceding States.

2. This Convention shall be registered by the Depositary pursuant to Article 102 of the Charter of the United Nations.

In witness whereof, the undersigned, duly authorized, have signed this Convention.

Done at London, this 1st day of June, 1972.

ANNEX

1. Permissible Catch

The Contracting Parties shall in any one year, which shall run from 1 July to 30 June inclusive, restrict the total number of seals of each species killed or captured to the numbers specified below. These numbers are subject to review in the light of scientific assessments:

    (a)   in the case of Crabeater seals *Lobodon carcinophagus*, 175,000;

    (b)   in the case of Leopard seals *Hydrurga leptonyx*, 12,000;

    (c)   in the case of Weddell seals *Leptonychotes weddelli*, 5,000.

2. Protected Species

    (a)   It is forbidden to kill or capture Ross seals *Ommatophoca rossi,* Southern elephant seals *Mirounga leonina,* or fur seals of the genus *Arctocephalus.*

(b) In order to protect the adult breeding stock during the period when it is most concentrated and vulnerable, it is forbidden to kill or capture any Weddell seal *Leptonychotes weddelli* one year old or older between 1 September and 31 January inclusive.

3. Closed Season and Sealing Season

The period between 1 March and 31 August inclusive is a Closed Season, during which the killing or capturing of seals is forbidden. The period 1 September to the last day in February constitutes a Sealing Season.

4. Sealing Zones

Each of the sealing zones listed in this paragraph shall be closed in numerical sequence to all sealing operations for the seal species listed in paragraph 1 of this Annex for the period 1 September to the last day of February inclusive. Such closures shall begin with the same zone as is closed under paragraph 2 of Annex B to Annex 1 of the Report of the Fifth Antarctic Treaty Consultative Meeting at the moment the Convention enters into force. Upon the expiration of each closed period, the affected zone shall reopen:

Zone 1 : between 60deg. and 120deg. West Longitude
Zone 2 : between 0deg. and 60deg. West Longitude, together with that part of the Weddell Sea lying westward of 60deg. West Longitude
Zone 3 : between 0deg. and 70deg. East Longitude
Zone 4 : between 70deg. and 130deg. East Longitude
Zone 5 : between 130deg. East Longitude and 170deg. West Longitude
Zone 6 : between 120deg. and 170deg. West Longitude.

5. Seal Reserves

It is forbidden to kill or capture seals in the following reserves, which are seal breeding areas or the site of long-term scientific research:

  (a) The area around the South Orkney Islands between 60deg.20′ and 60deg.56′ South Latitude and 44deg.05′ and 46deg.25′ West Longitude.

  (b) The area of the southwestern Ross Sea south of 76deg. South Latitude and west of 170deg. East Longitude.

  (c) The area of Edisto Inlet south and west of a line drawn between Cape Hallett at 72deg.19′ South Latitude, 170deg.18′ East Longitude, and Helm Point, at 72deg.11′ South Latitude, 170deg.00′ East Longitude.

6. Exchange of Information

  (a) Contracting Parties shall provide before 31 October each year to other Contracting Parties and to SCAR a summary of statistical information on all seals killed or captured by their nationals and vessels under their respective flags in the Convention area, in respect of the preceding period 1 July to 30 June. This information shall include by zones and months:

    (i) The gross and net tonnage, brake horse-power, number of crew, and number of days' operation of vessels under the flag of the Contracting Party;

    (ii) The number of adult individuals and pups of each species taken.

When specially requested, this information shall be provided in respect of each ship, together with its daily position at noon each operating day and the catch on that day.

  (b) When an industry has started, reports of the number of seals of each species killed or captured in each zone shall be made to SCAR in the form and at the intervals (not shorter than one week) requested by that body.

  (c) Contracting Parties shall provide to SCAR biological information, in particular:

    (i) Sex

    (ii) Reproductive condition

    (iii) Age

SCAR may request additional information or material with the approval of the Contracting Parties.

(d) Contracting Parties shall provide to other Contracting Parties and to SCAR at least 30 days in advance of departure from their home ports, information on proposed sealing expeditions.

7. Sealing Methods

(a) SCAR is invited to report on methods of sealing and to make recommendations with a view to ensuring that the killing or capturing of seals is quick, painless and efficient. Contracting Parties, as appropriate, shall adopt rules for their nationals and vessels under their respective flags engaged in the killing and capturing of seals, giving due consideration to the views of SCAR.

(b) In the light of the available scientific and technical data, Contracting Parties agree to take appropriate steps to ensure that their nationals and vessels under their respective flags refrain from killing or capturing seals in the water, except in limited quantities to provide for scientific research in conformity with the objectives and principles of this Convention. Such research shall include studies as to the effectiveness of methods of sealing from the viewpoint of the management and humane and rational utilization of the Antarctic seal resources for conservation purposes. The undertaking and the results of any such scientific programme shall be communicated to SCAR and the Depositary which shall transmit them to the Contracting Parties.

ANTARCTIC MARINE
LIVING RESOURCES CONSERVATION

The Convention on the Conservation of Antarctic Marine Living Resources came into force in 1982, as part of the Antarctic Treaty System. It was established mainly in response to concerns that an increase in krill catches in the Southern Ocean could have a serious effect on populations of krill and other marine life; particularly on birds, seals and fish which mainly depend on krill for food.

The aim of the Convention is to conserve marine life. This does not exclude harvesting as long as such harvesting is carried out in a rational manner. The Convention defines a Commission and a Scientific Committee to work together to manage marine living resources in the Southern Ocean.

The Southern Ocean surrounds the continent of Antarctica and is clearly delimited by the Antarctic Convergence, which is formed where the cold Antarctic waters meet the warmer waters to the north. The Antarctic Convergence acts as an effective biological barrier and the Southern Ocean is therefore substantially a closed ecosystem.

The Commission for the Conservation of Antarctic Marine Living Resources (CCAMLR) and its Scientific Committee were a pioneer in the development of what has become known as the 'ecosystem approach' to the regulation of fisheries. An ecosystem approach does not concentrate solely on the species fished, but also seeks to avoid situations in which fisheries have a significant adverse effect on 'dependent and related species'. CCAMLR has to develop management approaches that assess the status of the ecosystem and its health. In the application of this ecosystem approach, CCAMLR has tackled with the difficulty of describing the full complexity of marine ecosystems.

Statement by the Chairman of the Conference on the Conservation of Antarctic Marine Living Resources

The Contracting Parties,

Recognising the importance of safeguarding the environment and protecting the integrity of the ecosystem of the seas surrounding Antarctica;

Noting the concentration of marine living resources found in Antarctic waters and the increased interest in the possibilities offered by the utilisation of these resources as a source of protein;

Conscious of the urgency of ensuring the conservation of Antarctic marine living resources;

Considering that it is essential to increase knowledge of the Antarctic marine ecosystem and its components so as to be able to base decisions on harvesting on sound scientific information;

Believing that the conservation of Antarctic marine living resources calls for international co-operation with due regard for the provisions of the Antarctic Treaty and with the active involvement of all States engaged in research or harvesting activities in Antarctic waters;

Recognising the prime responsibilities of the Antarctic Treaty Consultative Parties for the protection and preservation of the Antarctic environment and, in particular, their responsibilities under Article IX, paragraph 1(f) of the Antarctic Treaty in respect of the preservation and onservation of living resources in Antarctica;

Recalling the action already taken by the Antarctic Treaty Consultative Parties including in particular the Agreed Measures for the Conservation of Antarctic Fauna and Flora, as well as the provisions of the Convention for the Conservation of Antarctic Seals;

Bearing in mind the concern regarding the conservation of Antarctic marine living resources expressed by the Consultative Parties at the Ninth Consultative Meeting of the Antarctic Treaty and the importance of the provisions of Recommendation IX-2 which led to the establishment of the present Convention; Convention

Believing that it is in the interest of all mankind to preserve the waters surrounding the Antarctic continent for peaceful purposes only and to prevent their becoming the scene or object of international discord;

Recognising, in the light of the foregoing, that it is desirable to establish suitable machinery for recommending, promoting, deciding upon and co-ordinating the measures and scientific studies needed to ensure the conservation of Antarctic marine living organisms;

Have Agreed as follows:

Article I

1. This Convention applies to the Antarctic marine living resources of the area south of 60° South latitude and to the Antarctic marine living resources of the area between that latitude and the Antarctic Convergence which form part of the Antarctic marine ecosystem.
2. Antarctic marine living resources means the populations of fin fish, molluscs, crustaceans and all other species of

living organisms, including birds, found south of the Antarctic Convergence.

3. The Antarctic marine ecosystem means the complex of relationships of Antarctic marine living resources with each other and with their physical environment.

4. The Antarctic Convergence shall be deemed to be a line joining the following points along parallels of latitude and meridians of longitude: 50°S, 0°; 50°S, 30°E; 45°S, 30°E; 45°S, 80°E; 55°S, 80°E; 55°S, 150°E; 60°S, 150°E; 60°S, 50°W; 50°S, 50°W; 50°S, 0°.

Article II

1. The objective of this Convention is the conservation of Antarctic marine living resources.

2. For the purposes of this Convention, the term 'conservation' includes rational use.

3. Any harvesting and associated activities in the area to which this Convention applies shall be conducted in accordance with the provisions of this Convention and with the following principles of conservation:

   (a) prevention of decrease in the size of any harvested population to levels below those which ensure its stable recruitment. For this purpose its size should not be allowed to fall below a level close to that which ensures the greatest net annual increment;

   (b) maintenance of the ecological relationships between harvested, dependent and related populations of Antarctic marine living resources and the restoration of depleted populations to the levels defined in subparagraph (a) above; and

   (c) prevention of changes or minimisation of the risk of changes in the marine ecosystem which are not potentially reversible over two or three decades, taking into account the state of available knowledge of the direct and indirect impact of harvesting, the effect of the introduction of alien species, the effects of associated activities on the marine ecosystem and of the effects of environmental changes, with the aim of making possible the sustained conservation of Antarctic marine living resources.

Article III

The Contracting Parties, whether or not they are Parties to the Antarctic Treaty, agree that they will not engage in any activities in the Antarctic Treaty area contrary to the principles and purposes of that Treaty and that, in their relations with each other, they are bound by the obligations contained in Articles I and V of the Antarctic Treaty.

Article IV

1. With respect to the Antarctic Treaty area, all Contracting Parties, whether or not they are Parties to the Antarctic Treaty, are bound by Articles IV and VI of the Antarctic Treaty in their relations with each other.
2. Nothing in this Convention and no acts or activities taking place while the present Convention is in force shall:
   (a) constitute a basis for asserting, supporting or denying a claim to territorial sovereignty in the Antarctic Treaty area or create any rights of sovereignty in the Antarctic Treaty area;
   (b) be interpreted as a renunciation or diminution by any Contracting Party of, or as prejudicing, any right or claim or basis of claim to exercise coastal state jurisdiction under international law within the area to which this Convention applies;
   (c) be interpreted as prejudicing the position of any Contracting Party as regards its recognition or non-recognition of any such right, claim or basis of claim;
   (d) affect the provision of Article IV, paragraph 2, of the Antarctic Treaty that no new claim, or enlargement of an existing claim, to territorial sovereignty in Antarctica shall be asserted while the Antarctic Treaty is in force.

Article V

1. The Contracting Parties which are not Parties to the Antarctic Treaty acknowledge the special obligations and responsibilities of the Antarctic Treaty Consultative Parties

for the protection and preservation of the environment of the Antarctic Treaty area.

2. The Contracting Parties which are not Parties to the Antarctic Treaty agree that, in their activities in the Antarctic Treaty area, they will observe as and when appropriate the Agreed Measures for the Conservation of Antarctic Fauna and Flora and such other measures as have been recommended by the Antarctic Treaty Consultative Parties in fulfilment of their responsibility for the protection of the Antarctic environment from all forms of harmful human interference.

3. For the purposes of this Convention, 'Antarctic Treaty Consultative Parties' means the Contracting Parties to the Antarctic Treaty whose Representatives participate in meetings under Article IX of the Antarctic Treaty.

Article VI

Nothing in this Convention shall derogate from the rights and obligations of Contracting Parties under the International Convention for the Regulation of Whaling and the Convention for the Conservation of Antarctic Seals.

Article VII

1. The Contracting Parties hereby establish and agree to maintain the Commission for the Conservation of Antarctic Marine Living Resources (hereinafter referred to as 'the Commission').

2. Membership in the Commission shall be as follows:

   (a) each Contracting Party which participated in the meeting at which this Convention was adopted shall be a Member of the Commission;

   (b) each State Party which has acceded to this Convention pursuant to Article XXIX shall be entitled to be a Member of the Commission during such time as that acceding Party is engaged in research or harvesting activities in relation to the marine living resources to which this Convention applies;

   (c) each regional economic integration organisation

which has acceded to this Convention pursuant to Article XXIX shall be entitled to be a Member of the Commission during such time as its States members are so entitled;

(d) a Contracting Party seeking to participate in the work of the Commission pursuant to sub-paragraphs (b) and (c) above shall notify the Depositary of the basis upon which it seeks to become a Member of the Commission and of its willingness to accept conservation measures in force. The Depositary shall communicate to each Member of the Commission such notification and accompanying information. Within two months of receipt of such communication from the Depositary, any Member of the Commission may request that a special meeting of the Commission be held to consider the matter. Upon receipt of such request, the Depositary shall call such a meeting. If there is no request for a meeting, the Contracting Party submitting the notification shall be deemed to have satisfied the requirements for Commission Membership.

3. Each Member of the Commission shall be represented by one representative who may be accompanied by alternate representatives and advisers.

Article VIII

The Commission shall have legal personality and shall enjoy in the territory of each of the States Parties such legal capacity as may be necessary to perform its function and achieve the purposes of this Convention. The privileges and immunities to be enjoyed by the Commission and its staff in the territory of a State Party shall be determined by agreement between the Commission and the State Party concerned.

Article IX

1. The function of the Commission shall be to give effect to the objective and principles set out in Article II of this Convention. To this end, it shall:

(a) facilitate research into and comprehensive studies of Antarctic marine living resources and of the Antarctic marine ecosystem;

(b) compile data on the status of and changes in population of Antarctic marine living resources and on factors affecting the distribution, abundance and productivity of harvested species and dependent or related species or populations;

(c) ensure the acquisition of catch and effort statistics on harvested populations;

(d) analyse, disseminate and publish the information referred to in sub-paragraphs (b) and (c) above and the reports of the Scientific Committee;

(e) identify conservation needs and analyse the effectiveness of conservation measures;

(f) formulate, adopt and revise conservation measures on the basis of the best scientific evidence available, subject to the provisions of paragraph 5 of this Article;

(g) implement the system of observation and inspection established under Article XXIV of this Convention;

(h) carry out such other activities as are necessary to fulfil the objective of this Convention.

2. The conservation measures referred to in paragraph 1(f) above include the following:

(a) the designation of the quantity of any species which may be harvested in the area to which this Convention applies;

(b) the designation of regions and sub-regions based on the distribution of populations of Antarctic marine living resources;

(c) the designation of the quantity which may be harvested from the populations of regions and sub-regions;

(d) the designation of protected species;

(e) the designation of the size, age and, as appropriate, sex of species which may be harvested;

(f) the designation of open and closed seasons for harvesting;

(g) the designation of the opening and closing of areas, regions or sub-regions for purposes of scientific study or conservation, including special areas for protection and scientific study;

(h) regulation of the effort employed and methods of harvesting, including fishing gear, with a view, inter alia, to avoiding undue concentration of harvesting in any region or sub-region;

(i) the taking of such other conservation measures as the Commission considers necessary for the fulfillment of the objective of this Convention, including measures concerning the effects of harvesting and associated activities on components of the marine ecosystem other than the harvested populations.

3. The Commission shall publish and maintain a record of all conservation measures in force.

4. In exercising its functions under paragraph 1 above, the Commission shall take full account of the recommendations and advice of the Scientific Committee.

5. The Commission shall take full account of any relevant measures or regulations established or recommended by the Consultative Meetings pursuant to Article IX of the Antarctic Treaty or by existing fisheries commissions responsible for species which may enter the area to which this Convention applies, in order that there shall be no inconsistency between the rights and obligations of a Contracting Party under such regulations or measures and conservation measures which may be adopted by the Commission.

6. Conservation measures adopted by the Commission in accordance with this Convention shall be implemented by Members of the Commission in the following manner:

(a) the Commission shall notify conservation measures to all Members of the Commission;

(b) conservation measures shall become binding upon all Members of the Commission 180 days after such notification, except as provided in subparagraphs (c) and (d) below;

(c) if a Member of the Commission, within ninety days following the notification specified in sub-paragraph (a), notifies the Commission that it is unable to accept the conservation measure, in whole or in part, the measure shall not, to the extent stated, be binding upon that Member of the Commission;

(d) in the event that any Member of the Commission invokes the procedure set forth in sub-paragraph (c) above, the Commission shall meet at the request of any Member of the Commission to review the conservation measure. At the time of such meeting and within thirty days following the meeting, any Member of the Commission shall have the right to declare that it is no longer able to accept the conservation measure, in which case the Member shall no longer be bound by such a measure.

Article X

1. The Commission shall draw the attention of any State which is not a Party to this Convention to any activity undertaken by its nationals or vessels which, in the opinion of the Commission, affects the implementation of the objective of this Convention.

2. The Commission shall draw the attention of all Contracting Parties to any activity which, in the opinion of the Commission, affects the implementation by a Contracting Party of the objective of this Convention or the compliance by that Contracting Party with its obligations under this Convention.

Article XI

The Commission shall seek to co-operate with Contracting Parties which may exercise jurisdiction in marine areas adjacent to the area to which this Convention applies in respect of the conservation of any stock or stocks of associated species which occur both within those areas and the area to which this Convention applies, with a view to harmonising the conservation measures adopted in respect of such stocks.

Article XII

1. Decisions of the Commission on matters of substance shall

be taken by consensus. The question of whether a matter is one of substance shall be treated as a matter of substance.

2. Decisions on matters other than those referred to in paragraph 1 above shall be taken by a simple majority of the Members of the Commission present and voting.

3. in Commission consideration of any item requiring a decision, it shall be made clear whether a regional economic integration organisation will participate in the taking of the decision and, if so, whether any of its Member States will also participate. The number of Contracting Parties so participating shall not exceed the number of Member States of the regional economic integration organisation which are Members of the Commission.

4. in the taking of decisions pursuant to this Article, a regional economic integration organisation shall have only one vote.

Article XIII

1. The headquarters of the Commission shall be established at Hobart, Tasmania, Australia.

2. The Commission shall hold a regular annual meeting. Other meetings shall also be held at the request of one-third of its Members and as otherwise provided in this Convention. The first meeting of the Commission shall be held within three months of the entry into force of this Convention, provided that among the Contracting Parties there are at least two States conducting harvesting activities within the area to which this Convention applies. The first meeting shall, in any event, be held within one year of the entry into force of this Convention. The Depositary shall consult with the signatory States regarding the first Commission meeting, taking into account that a broad representation of such States is necessary for the effective operation of the Commission.

3. The Depositary shall convene the first meeting of the Commission at the headquarters of the Commission. Thereafter, meetings of the Commission shall be held at its headquarters, unless it decides otherwise.

4. The Commission shall elect from among its Members a

Chairman and Vice-Chairman, each of whom shall serve for a term of two years and shall be eligible for reelection for one additional term. The first Chairman shall, however, be elected for an initial term of three years. The Chairman and Vice-Chairman shall not be representatives of the same Contracting Party.

5. The Commission shall adopt and amend as necessary the rules of procedure for the conduct of its meetings, except with respect to the matters dealt with in Article XII of this Convention.

6. The Commission may establish such subsidiary bodies as are necessary for the performance of its functions.

Article XIV

1. The Contracting Parties hereby establish the Scientific Committee for the Conservation of Antarctic Marine Living Resources (hereinafter referred to as 'the Scientific Committee') which shall be a consultative body to the Commission. The Scientific Committee shall normally meet at the headquarters of the Commission unless the Scientific Committee decides otherwise.

2. Each Member of the Commission shall be a Member of the Scientific Committee and shall appoint a representative with suitable scientific qualifications who may be accompanied by other experts and advisers.

3. The Scientific Committee may seek the advice of other scientists and experts as may be required on an *ad hoc* basis.

Article XV

1. The Scientific Committee shall provide a forum for consultation and co-operation concerning the collection, study and exchange of information with respect to the marine living resources to which this Convention applies. It shall encourage and promote cooperation in the field of scientific research in order to extend knowledge of the marine living resources of the Antarctic marine ecosystem.

2. The Scientific Committee shall conduct such activities as

the Commission may direct in pursuance of the objective of this Convention and shall:

(a) establish criteria and methods to be used for determinations concerning the conservation measures referred to in Article IX of this Convention;

(b) regularly assess the status and trends of the populations of Antarctic marine living resources;

(c) analyse data concerning the direct and indirect effects of harvesting on the populations of Antarctic marine living resources;

(d) assess the effects of proposed changes in the methods or levels of harvesting and proposed conservation measures;

(e) transmit assessments, analyses, reports and recommendations to the Commission as requested or on its own initiative regarding measures and research to implement the objective of this Convention;

(f) formulate proposals for the conduct of international and national programs of research into Antarctic marine living resources.

3. In carrying out its functions, the Scientific Committee shall have regard to the work of other relevant technical and scientific organisations and to the scientific activities conducted within the framework of the Antarctic Treaty.

Article XVI

1. The first meeting of the Scientific Committee shall be held within three months of the first meeting of the Commission. The Scientific Committee shall meet thereafter as often as may be necessary to fulfil its functions.

2. The Scientific Committee shall adopt and amend as necessary its rules of procedure. The rules and any amendments thereto shall be approved by the Commission. The rules shall include procedures for the presentation of minority reports.

3. The Scientific Committee may establish, with the approval of the Commission, such subsidiary bodies as are necessary for the performance of its functions.

Article XVII

1. The Commission shall appoint an Executive Secretary to serve the Commission and Scientific Committee according to such procedures and on such terms and conditions as the

Commission may determine. His term of office shall be for four years and he shall be eligible for re-appointment.

2. The Commission shall authorise such staff establishment for the Secretariat as may be necessary and the Executive Secretary shall appoint, direct and supervise such staff according to such rules, and procedures and on such terms and conditions as the Commission may determine.

3. The Executive Secretary and Secretariat shall perform the functions entrusted to them by the Commission.

Article XVIII

The official languages of the Commission and of the Scientific Committee shall be English, French, Russian and Spanish.

Article XIX

1. At each annual meeting, the Commission shall adopt by consensus its budget and the budget of the Scientific Committee.

2. A draft budget for the Commission and the Scientific Committee and any subsidiary bodies shall be prepared by the Executive Secretary and submitted to the Members of the Commission at least sixty days before the annual meeting of the Commission.

3. Each Member of the Commission shall contribute to the budget. Until the expiration of five years after the entry into force of this Convention, the contribution of each Member of the Commission shall be equal. Thereafter the contribution shall be determined in accordance with two criteria: the amount harvested and an equal sharing among all Members of the Commission. The Commission shall determine by consensus the proportion in which these two criteria shall apply.

4. The financial activities of the Commission and Scientific Committee shall be conducted in accordance with financial regulations adopted by the Commission and shall be subject to an annual audit by external auditors selected by the Commission.

5. Each Member of the Commission shall meet its own expenses arising from the attendance at meetings of the Commission and of the Scientific Committee.

6. A Member of the Commission that fails to pay its contributions for two consecutive years shall not, during the period of its default, have the right to participate in the taking of decisions in the Commission.

Article XX

1. The Members of the Commission shall, to the greatest extent possible, provide annually to the Commission and to the Scientific Committee such statistical, biological and other data and information as the Commission and Scientific Committee may require in the exercise of their functions.

2. The Members of the Commission shall provide, in the manner and at such intervals as may be prescribed, information about their harvesting activities, including fishing areas and vessels, so as to enable reliable catch and effort statistics to be compiled.

3. The Members of the Commission shall provide to the Commission at such intervals as may be prescribed information on steps taken to implement the conservation measures adopted by the Commission.

4. The Members of the Commission agree that in any of their harvesting activities, advantage shall be taken of opportunities to collect data needed to assess the impact of harvesting.

Article XXI

1. Each Contracting Party shall take appropriate measures within its competence to ensure compliance with the provisions of this Convention and with conservation

measures adopted by the Commission to which the Party is bound in accordance with Article IX of this Convention.

2. Each Contracting Party shall transmit to the Commission information on measures taken pursuant to paragraph 1 above, including the imposition of sanctions for any violation.

Article XXII

1. Each Contracting Party undertakes to exert appropriate efforts, consistent with the Charter of the United Nations, to the end that no one engages in any activity contrary to the objective of this Convention.
2. Each Contracting Party shall notify the Commission of any such activity which comes to its attention.

Article XXIII

1. The Commission and the Scientific Committee shall co-operate with the Antarctic Treaty Consultative Parties on matters falling within the competence of the latter.
2. The Commission and the Scientific Committee shall co-operate, as appropriate, with the Food and Agriculture Organisation of the United Nations and with other Specialised Agencies.
3. The Commission and the Scientific Committee shall seek to develop co-operative working relationships, as appropriate, with inter-governmental and nongovernmental organisations which could contribute to their work, including the Scientific Committee on Antarctic Research, the Scientific Committee on Oceanic Research and the International Whaling Commission.
4. The Commission may enter into agreements with the organisations referred to in this Article and with other organisations as may be appropriate. The Commission and the Scientific Committee may invite such organisations to send observers to their meetings and to meetings of their subsidiary bodies.

Article XXIV

1. In order to promote the objective and ensure observance
    of the provisions of this Convention, the Contracting
    Parties agree that a system of observation and inspection
    shall be established.

2. The·system of observation and inspection shall be
    elaborated by the Commission on the basis of the following
    principles:

    (a) Contracting Parties shall co-operate with each other
        to ensure the effective implementation of the system
        of observation and inspection, taking account of the
        existing international practice. This system shall
        include, inter alia, procedures for boarding and
        inspection by observers and nspectors designated by
        the Members of the Commission and procedures for
        flag state prosecution and sanctions on the basis of
        evidence resulting from such boarding and
        inspections. A report of such prosecutions and
        sanctions imposed shall be included in the information
        referred to in Article XXI of this Convention;

    (b) in order to verify compliance with measures adopted
        under this Convention, observation and inspection
        shall be carried out on board vessels engaged in
        scientific research or harvesting of marine living
        resources in the area to which this Convention applies,
        through observers and inspectors designated by the
        Members of the Commission and operating under
        terms and conditions to be established by the
        Commission;

    (c) designated observers and inspectors shall remain
        subject to the jurisdiction of the Contracting Party of
        which they are nationals. They shall report to the
        Member of the Commission by which they have been
        designated which in turn shall report to the
        Commission.

3. Pending the establishment of the system of observation
    and inspection, the Members of the Commission shall seek
    to establish interim arrangements to designate observers
    and

inspectors and such designated observers and inspectors shall be entitled to carry out inspections in accordance with the principles set out in paragraph 2 above.

Article XXV

1. If any dispute arises between two or more of the Contracting Parties concerning the interpretation or application of this Convention, those Contracting Parties shall consult among themselves with a view to having the dispute resolved by negotiation, inquiry, mediation, conciliation, arbitration, judicial settlement or other peaceful means of their own choice.
2. Any dispute of this character not so resolved shall, with the consent in each case of all Parties to the dispute, be referred for settlement to the International Court of Justice or to arbitration; but failure to reach agreement on reference to the International Court or to arbitration shall not absolve Parties to the dispute from the responsibility of continuing to seek to resolve it by any of the various peaceful means referred to in paragraph 1 above.
3. In cases where the dispute is referred to arbitration, the arbitral tribunal shall be constituted as provided in the Annex to this Convention.

Article XXVI

1. This Convention shall be open for signature at Canberra from 1 August to 31 December, 1980 by the States participating in the Conference on the Conservation of Antarctic Marine Living Resources held at Canberra from 7 to 20 May, 1980.
2. The States which so sign will be the original signatory States of the Convention.

Article XXVII

1. This Convention is subject to ratification, acceptance or approval by signatory States.
2. Instruments of ratification, acceptance or approval shall

be deposited with the Government of Australia, hereby designated as the Depositary.

Article XXVIII

1. This Convention shall enter into force on the thirtieth day following the date of deposit of the eighth instrument of ratification, acceptance or approval by States referred to in paragraph 1 of Article XXVI of this Convention.
2. With respect to each State or regional economic integration organisation which subsequent to the date of entry into force of this Convention deposits an instrument of ratification, acceptance, approval or accession, the Convention shall enter into force on the thirtieth day following such deposit.

Article XXIX

1. This Convention shall be open for accession by any State interested in research or harvesting activities in relation to the marine living resources to which this Convention applies.
2. This Convention shall be open for accession by regional economic integration organisations constituted by sovereign States which include among their members one or more States Members of the Commission and to which the States members of the Convention organisation have transferred, in whole or in part, competences with regard to the matters covered by this Convention. The accession of such regional economic integration organisations shall be the subject of consultations among Members of the Commission.

Article XXX

1. This Convention may be amended at any time.
2. If one-third of the Members of the Commission request a meeting to discuss a proposed amendment the Depositary shall call such a meeting.
3. An amendment shall enter into force when the

Depositary has received instruments of ratification, acceptance or approval thereof from all the Members of the Commission.

4. Such amendment shall thereafter enter into force as to any other Contracting Party when notice of ratification, acceptance or approval by it has been received by the Depositary. Any such Contracting Party from which no such notice has been received within a period of one year from the date of entry into force of the amendment in accordance with paragraph 3 above shall be deemed to have withdrawn from this Convention.

Article: XXXI

1. Any Contracting Party may withdraw from this Convention on 30 June of any year, by giving written notice not later than 1 January of the same year to the Depositary, which, upon receipt of such a notice, shall communicate it forthwith to the other Contracting Parties.
2. Any other Contracting Party may, within sixty days of the receipt of a copy of such a notice from the Depositary, give written notice of withdrawal to the Depositary in which case the Convention shall cease to be in force on 30 June of the same year with respect to the Contracting Party giving such notice.
3. Withdrawal from this Convention by any Member of the Commission shall not affect its financial obligations under this Convention.

Article XXXII

The Depositary shall notify all Contracting Parties of the following:

(a) signatures of this Convention and the deposit of instruments of ratification, acceptance, approval or accession;
(b) the date of entry into force of this Convention and of any amendment thereto.

Article XXXIII

1. This Convention, of which the English, French, Russian and Spanish texts are equally authentic, shall be deposited with the Government of Australia which shall transmit duly certified copies thereof to all signatory and acceding Parties.
2. This Convention shall be registered by the Depositary pursuant to Article 102 of the Charter of the United Nations.

Drawn up at Canberra this twentieth day of May, 1980.

ANNEX FOR
AN ARBITRAL TRIBUNAL

1. The arbitral tribunal referred to in paragraph 3 of Article XXV shall be composed of three arbitrators who shall be appointed as follows:
   (a) The Party commencing proceedings shall communicate the name of an arbitrator to the other Party which, in turn, within a period of forty days following such notification, shall communicate the name of the second arbitrator. The Parties shall, within a period of sixty days following the appointment of the second arbitrator, appoint the third arbitrator, who shall not be a national of either Party and shall not be of the same nationality as either of the first two arbitrators. The third arbitrator shall preside over the tribunal;
   (b) If the second arbitrator has not been appointed within the prescribed period, or if the Parties have not reached agreement within the prescribed period on the appointment of the third arbitrator, that arbitrator shall be appointed, at the request of either Party, by the Secretary-General of the Permanent Court of Arbitration, from among persons of international standing not having the nationality of a State which is a Party to this Convention.
2. The arbitral tribunal shall decide where its headquarters

will be located and shall adopt its own rules of procedure.

3. The award of the arbitral tribunal shall be made by a majority of its members, who may not abstain from voting.

4. Any Contracting Party which is not a Party to the dispute may intervene in the proceedings with the consent of the arbitral tribunal.

5. The award of the arbitral tribunal shall be final and binding on all Parties to the dispute and on any Party which intervenes in the proceedings and shall be complied with without delay. The arbitral tribunal shall interpret the award at the request of one of the Parties to the dispute or of any intervening Party.

6. Unless the arbitral tribunal determines otherwise because of the particular circumstances of the case, the expenses of the tribunal, including the remuneration of its members, shall be borne by the Parties to the dispute in equal shares.

Statement by the Chairman of the Conference on the Conservation of Antarctic Marine Living Resources

The Conference on the Conservation of Antarctic Marine Living Resources decided to include in the publication of the Final Act of the Conference the text of the following statement made by the Chairman on 19 May, 1980 regarding the application of the Convention on the Conservation of Antarctic Marine Living Resources to the waters adjacent to Kerguelen and Crozet over which France has jurisdiction and to waters adjacent to other islands within the area to which this Convention applies over which the existence of State sovereignty is recognised by all Contracting Parties.

'1. Measures for the conservation of Antarctic marine living resources of the waters adjacent to Kerguelen and Crozet, over which France has jurisdiction, adopted by France prior to the entry into force of the Convention, would remain in force after the entry into force of the Convention until modified by France acting within the framework of the Commission or otherwise.

2. After the Convention has come into force, each time the Commission should undertake examination of the

conservation needs of the marine living resources of the general Sarea in which the waters adjacent to Kerguelen and Crozet are to be found, it would be open to France either to agree that the waters in question should be included in the area of Sapplication of any specific conservation measure under consideration or to indicate that they should be excluded. In the latter event, the Commission would not proceed to the adoption of the specific conservation measure in a form applicable to the waters in question unless France removed its objection to it. France could also adopt such national measures as it might deem appropriate for the waters in question.

3. Accordingly, when specific conservation measures are considered within the frameworSk of the Commission and with the participation of France, then:

   (a) France would be bound by any conservation measures adopted by consensus with its participation for the duration of those measures. This would not prevent France from promulgating national measures that were more strict than the Commission's measures or which dealt with other matters;

   (b) in the absence of consensus, France could promulgate any national measures which it might deem appropriate.

4. Conservation measures, whether national measures or measures adopted by the Commission, in respect of the waters adjacent to Kerguelen and Crozet, would be enforced by France. The system of observation and inspection foreseen by the Convention would not be implemented in the waters adjacent to Kerguelen and Crozet except as agreed by France and in the manner so agreed.

5. The understandings, set forth in paragraphs 1 to 4 above, regarding the application of the Convention to waters adjacent to the islands of Kerguelen and Crozet, also apply to waters adjacent to the islands within the area to which this Convention applies over which the existence of State sovereignty is recognised by all Contracting Parties.'

No objection to the statement was made.

ENVIRONMENTAL PROTECTION TO
THE ANTARCTIC

Preamble

The States Parties to this Protocol to the Antarctic Treaty, hereinafter referred to as the Parties,

Convinced of the need to enhance the protection of the Antarctic environment and dependent and associated ecosystems;

Convinced of the need to strengthen the Antarctic Treaty system so as to ensure that Antarctica shall continue forever to be used exclusively for peaceful purposes and shall not become the scene or object of international discord;

Bearing in mind the special legal and political status of Antarctica and the special responsibility of the Antarctic Treaty Consultative Parties to ensure that all activities in Antarctica are consistent with the purposes and principals of the Antarctic Treaty;

Recalling the designation of Antarctica as a Special Conservation Area and other measures adopted under the Antarctic Treaty system to protect the Antarctic environment and dependent and associated ecosystems;

Acknowledging further the unique opportunities Antarctica offers for scientific monitoring of and research on processes of global as well as regional importance;

Reaffirming the conservation principles of the Convention on the Conservation of Antarctic Marine Living Resources;

Convinced that the development of a Comprehensive regime for the protection of the Antarctic environment and dependent and associated ecosystems is in the interest of mankind as a whole;

Desiring to supplement the Antarctic Treaty to this end;

Have agreed as follows:

Article 1: Definitions

For the purposes of this Protocol:

    (a) "The Antarctic Treaty" means the Antarctic Treaty done at Washington on 1 December, 1959;

    (b) "Antarctic Treaty area" means the area to which the provisions of the Antarctic Treaty apply in accordance with Article VI of that Treaty;

(c) "Antarctic Treaty Consultative Meetings" means the meetings referred to in Article IX of the Antarctic Treaty;

(d) "Antarctic Treaty Consultative Parties" means the Contracting Parties to the Antarctic Treaty entitled to appoint representatives to participate in the meetings referred to in Article IX of that Treaty;

(e) "Antarctic Treaty system" means the Antarctic Treaty, the measures in effect under that Treaty, its associated separate international instruments in force and the measures in effect under those instruments;

(f) "Arbitral Tribunal" means the arbitral Tribunal established in accordance with the Schedule to this Protocol, which forms an integral part thereof;

(g) "Committee" means the Committee for Environmental Protection established in accordance with Article 11.

Article 2: Objective and Designation

The Parties commit themselves to the comprehensive protection of the Antarctic environment and dependent and associated ecosystems and hereby designate Antarctica as a natural reserve, devoted to peace and science.

Article 3 : Environmental Principles

1. The protection of the Antarctic environment and dependent and associated ecosystems and the intrinsic value of Antarctica, including its wilderness and aesthetic values and its value as an area for the conduct of scientific research, in particular research essential to understanding the global environment, shall be fundamental considerations in the planning and conduct of all activities in the Antarctic Treaty area.

2. To this end:
   (a) activities in the Antarctic Treaty area shall be planned and conducted so as to limit adverse impacts on the Antarctic environment and dependent and associated ecosystems;
   (b) activities in the Antarctic Treaty area shall be planned and conducted so as to avoid:

    (i)   adverse effects on climate or weather patterns;

    (ii) significant adverse effects on air or water quality;

    (iii) significant changes in the atmospheric, terrestrial (including aquatic), glacial or marine environments;

    (iv) detrimental changes in the distribution, abundance or productivity of species of populations of species of fauna and flora;

    (v) further jeopardy to endangered or threatened species or populations of such species; or

    (vi) degradation of, or substantial risk to, areas of biological, scientific, historic, aesthetic or wilderness significance;

(c) activities in the Antarctic Treaty area shall be planned and conducted on the basis of information sufficient to allow prior assessments of, and informed judgments about, their possible impacts on the Antarctic environment and dependent and associated ecosystems and on the value of Antarctica for the conduct of scientific research; such judgments shall take account of:

    (i) the scope of the activity, including its area, duration and intensity;

    (ii) the cumulative impacts of the activity, both by itself and in combination with other activities in the Antarctic Treaty area;

    (iii) whether the activity will detrimentally affect any other activity in the Antarctic Treaty area;

    (iv) whether technology and procedures are available to provide for environmentally safe operations;

    (v) whether there exists the capacity to monitor key environmental parameters and ecosystem components so as to identify and provide early warning of any adverse effects of the activity and to provide for such modification of operating procedures as may be necessary in the light of the results of monitoring or increased knowledge of the Antarctic environment and dependent and associated ecosystems; and

(vi) whether there exists the capacity to respond promptly and effectively to accidents, particularly those with potential environmental effects;

(d) regular and effective monitoring shall take place to all assessment of the impacts of ongoing activities, including the verification of predicted impacts;

(e) regular and effective monitoring shall take place to facilitate early detection of the possible unforeseen effects of activities carried on both within and outside the Antarctic Treaty area on the Antarctic environment and dependent and associated ecosystems.

3. Activities shall be planned and conducted in the Antarctic Treaty area so as to accord priority to scientific research and to preserve the value of Antarctica as an area for the conduct of such research, including research essential to understanding the global environment.

4. Activities undertaken in the Antarctic Treaty area pursuant to scientific research programs, tourism and all other governmental and non-governmental activities in the Antarctic Treaty area for which advance notice is required in accordance with Article VII(5) of the Antarctic Treaty, including associated logistic activities, shall:

(a) take place in a manner consistent with the principles in this Article; and

(b) be modified, suspended or cancelled if they result in or threaten to result in impacts upon the Antarctic environment or dependent or associated ecosystems inconsistent with those principles.

Article 4: Relationship with other Components of the Antarctic Treaty System

1. This Protocol shall supplement the Antarctic Treaty and shall neither modify nor amend that Treaty.

2. Nothing in this Protocol shall derogate from the rights and obligations of the Parties to this Protocol under the other international instruments in force within the Antarctic Treaty system.

Article 5: Consistency with other Components of the Antarctic Treaty System

The Parties shall consult and cooperate with the Contracting Parties to the other international instruments in force within the Antarctic Treaty system and their respective institutions with a view to ensuring the achievement of the objectives and principles of this Protocol and avoiding any interference with the achievement of the objectives and principles of those instruments or any inconsistency between the implementation of those instruments and of this Protocol.

Article 6: Cooperation

1. The Parties shall cooperate in the planning and conduct of activities in the Antarctic Treaty area. To this end, each Party shall endeavour to:
   (a) promote cooperative programs of scientific, technical and ducational value, concerning the protection of the Antarctic environment and dependent and associated ecosystems;
   (b) provide appropriate assistance to other Parties in the preparation of environmental impact assessments;
   (c) provide to other Parties upon request information relevant to any potential environmental risk and assistance to minimise the effects of accidents which may damage the Antarctic environment or dependent and associated ecosystems;
   (d) consult with other Parties with regard to the choice of sites for prospective station sand other facilities so as to avoid the cumulative impacts caused by their excessive concentration in any location;
   (e) where appropriate, undertake joint expeditions and share the use of stations and other facilities; and
   (f) carry out such steps as may be agreed upon at Antarctic Treaty Consultative Meetings.
2. Each Party undertakes, to the extent possible, to share information that may be helpful to other Parties in planning and conducting their activities in the Antarctic Treaty area, with a view to the protection of the Antarctic environment and dependent and associated ecosystems.

3. The Parties shall co-operate with those Parties which may exercise jurisdiction in areas adjacent to the Antarctic Treaty area with a view to ensuring that activities in the Antarctic Treaty area do not have adverse environmental impacts on those areas.

Article 7: Prohibition of Mineral Resource Activities

Any activity relating to mineral resources, other than scientific research, shall be prohibited.

Article 8: Environmental Impact and Assessment

1. Proposed activities referred to in paragraph 2 below shall be subject to the procedures set out in Annex I for prior assessment of the impacts of those activities on the Antarctic environment or on dependent or associated ecosystems according to whether those activities are identified as having:
   (a) less than a minor or transitory impact;
   (b) a minor or transitory impact; or
   (c) more than a minor or transitory impact.
2. Each Party shall ensure that the assessment procedures set out in Annex I are applied in the planning processes leading to decisions about any activities undertaken in the Antarctic Treaty area pursuant to scientific research programs, tourism and all other governmental and non-governmental activities in the Antarctic Treaty area for which advance notice is required under Article VII(5) of the Antarctic Treaty, including associated logistic support activities.
3. The assessment procedures set out in Annex I shall apply to any change in an activity whether the change arises from an increase or decrease in the intensity of an existing activity, from the addition of an activity, the decommissioning of a facility, or otherwise.
4. Where activities are planned jointly by more than one Party, the Parties involved shall nominate one of their number to coordinate the implementation of the environmental impact assessment procedures set out in Annex I.

Article 9: Annexes

1. The Annexes to this Protocol shall form an integral part thereof.
2. Annexes, additional to Annexes I-IV, may be adopted and become effective in accordance with Article IX of the Antarctic Treaty.
3. Amendments and modifications to Annexes may be adopted and become effective in accordance with Article IX of the Antarctic Treaty, provided that any Annex may itself make provision for amendments and modifications to become effective on an accelerated basis
4. Annexes and any amendments and modifications thereto which have become effective in accordance with paragraphs 2 and 3 above shall, unless an Annex itself provides otherwise in respect of the entry into effect of any amendment or modification thereto, become effective for a Contracting Party to the Antarctic Treaty which is not an Antarctic Treaty Consultative Party, or which was not an Antarctic Treaty Consultative Party at the time of the adoption, when notice of approval of that Contracting Party has been received by the Depositary.
5. Annexes shall, except to the extent that an Annex provides otherwise, be subject to the procedures for dispute settlement set out in Articles 18 to 20.

Article 10: Antarctic Treaty Consultative Meetings

1. Antarctic Treaty Consultative Meetings shall, drawing upon the best scientific and technical advice available:
    (a) define, in accordance with the provisions of this Protocol, the general policy for the comprehensive protection of the Antarctic environment and dependent and associated ecosystems; and
    (b) adopt measures under Article IX of the Antarctic Treaty for the implementation of this Protocol.
2. Antarctic Treaty Consultative Meetings shall review the work of the Committee and shall draw fully upon its advice and recommendations in carrying out the tasks referred to in paragraph 1 above, as well as upon the advice of the Scientific Committee on Antarctic Research.

Article 11: Committee for Environmental Protection

1. There is hereby established the Committee for Environmental Protection.
2. Each Party shall be entitled to be a member of the Committee and to appoint a representative who may be accompanied by experts and advisers.
3. Observer status in the Committee shall be open to any Contracting Party to the Antarctic Treaty which is not a Party to this Protocol.
4. The Committee shall invite the President of the Scientific Committee on Antarctic Research and the Chairman of the Scientific Committee for the Conservation of Antarctic Marine Living Resources to participate as observers at its sessions. The Committee may also, with the approval of the Antarctic Treaty Consultative Meeting, invite such other relevant scientific, environmental and technical organisations which can contribute to its work to participate as observers at its sessions.
5. The Committee shall present a report on each of its sessions to the Antarctic Treaty Consultative Meeting. The report shall cover all matters considered at the session and shall reflect the views expressed. The report shall be circulated to the Parties and to observers attending the session, and shall thereupon be made publicly available.
6. The Committee shall adopt its rules of procedure which shall be subject to approval by the Antarctic Treaty Consultative Meeting.

Article 12: Functions of the Committee

1. The functions of the Committee shall be to provide advice and formulate recommendations to the Parties in connection with the implementation of this Protocol, including the operation of its Annexes, for consideration at Antarctic Treaty Consultative Meetings, and to perform such other functions as may be referred to it by the Antarctic Treaty Consultative Meetings. In particular, it shall provide advice on:
   (a) the effectiveness of measures taken pursuant to this

Protocol;

(b) the need to update, strengthen or otherwise improve such measures;

(c) the need for additional measures, including the need for additional Annexes, where appropriate;

(d) the application and implementation of the environmental impact assessment procedures set out in Article 8 and Annex I;

(e) means of minimising or mitigating environmental impacts of activities in the Antarctic Treaty area;

(f) procedures for situations requiring urgent action, including response action in environmental emergencies;

(g) the operation and further elaboration of the Antarctic Protected Area system;

(h) inspection procedures, including formats for inspection reports and checklists for the conduct of inspections;

(i) the collection, archiving, exchange and evaluation of information related to environmental protection;

(j) the state of the Antarctic environment; and

(k) the need for scientific research, including environmental monitoring, related to the implementation of this Protocol.

2. In carrying out its functions, the Committee shall, as appropriate, consult with the Scientific Committee on Antarctic Research, the Scientific Committee for the Conservation of Antarctic Marine Living Resources and other relevant scientific, environmental and technical organisations.

Article 13: Compliance with this Protocol

1. Each Party shall take appropriate measures within its competence, including the adoption of laws and regulations, administrative actions and enforcement measures, to ensure compliance with this Protocol.

2. Each Party shall exert appropriate efforts, consistent with the Charter of the United Nations, to the end that no one engages in any activity contrary to this Protocol.

3. Each Party shall notify all other Parties of the measures it takes pursuant to paragraphs 1 and 2 above.

4. Each Party shall draw the attention of all other Parties to

any activity which in its opinion affects the implementation of the objectives and principles of this Protocol.

5. The Antarctic Treaty Consultative Meetings shall draw the attention of any State which is not a Party to this Protocol to any activity undertaken by that State, its agencies, instrumentalities, natural or juridical persons, ships, aircraft or other means of transport which affects the implementation of the objectives and principles of this Protocol.

Article 14: Inspection

1. In order to promote the protection of the Antarctic environment and dependent and associated ecosystems, and to ensure compliance with this Protocol, the Antarctic Treaty Consultative Parties shall arrange, individually or collectively, for inspections by observers to be made in accordance with Article VII of the Antarctic Treaty.

2. Observers are:
   (a) observers designated by any Antarctic Treaty Consultative Party who shall be nationals of that Party; and
   (b) any observers designated at Antarctic Treaty Consultative Meetings to carry out inspections under procedures to be established by an Antarctic Treaty Consultative Meeting.

3. Parties shall co-operate fully with observers undertaking inspections, and shall ensure that during inspections, observers are given access to all parts of stations, installations, equipment, ships and aircraft open to inspection under Article VII(3) of the Antarctic Treaty, as well as to all records maintained thereon which are called for pursuant to this Protocol.

4. Reports of inspections shall be sent to the Parties whose stations, installations, equipment, ships or aircraft are covered by the reports. After those Parties have been given the opportunity to comment, the reports and any comments thereon shall be circulated to all the Parties and to the Committee, considered at Antarctic Treaty

Consultative Meeting, and thereafter made publicly available.

Article 15: Emergency Response Action

In order to respond to environmental emergencies in Antarctic Treaty area, each Party agrees to:

1. (a) provide for prompt and effective response action to such emergencies which might arise in the performance of scientific research programs, tourism and all other governmental and non-governmental activities in the Antarctic Treaty area for which advance notice is required under Article VII(5) of the Antarctic Treaty, including associated logistic support activities; and
    (b) establish contingency plans for response to incidents with potential adverse effects on the Antarctic environment or dependent and associated ecosystems.
2. To this end, the Parties shall:
    (a)　　　co-operate in the formulation and implementation of such contingency plans; and
    (b)　　　establish procedures for immediate notification of, and co-operative response to, environmental emergencies.
3. In the implementation of this Article, the Parties shall draw upon the advice of the appropriate international organisations.

Article 16: Liability

Consistent with the objectives of this Protocol for the comprehensive protection of the Antarctic environment and dependent and associated ecosystems, the Parties undertake to elaborate rules and procedures relating to liability for damage arising from activities taking place in the Antarctic Treaty area and covered by this Protocol. Those rules and procedures shall be included in one or more Annexes to be adopted in accordance with Article 9(2).

Article 17: Annual Report by Parties

1. Each Party shall report annually on the steps taken to

implement this Protocol. Such reports shall include notifications made in accordance with Article 13(3), contingency plans established in accordance with Article 15 and any other notifications and information called for pursuant to this Protocol for which there is no other provision concerning the circulation and exchange of information.

2. Reports made in accordance with paragraph 1 above shall be circulated to all Parties and to the Committee, considered at the next Antarctic Treaty Consultative Meeting, and made publicly available.

Article 18: Dispute Settlement

If a dispute arises concerning the interpretation or application of this Protocol, the parties to the dispute shall, at the request of any one of them, consult among themselves as soon as possible with a view to having the dispute resolved by negotiation, inquiry, mediation, conciliation, arbitration, and judicial settlement or other. Which the parties to the dispute agree.

Article 19: Choice of Dispute Settlement Procedure

1. Each Party, when signing, ratifying, accepting, approving or acceding to this Protocol, or at any time thereafter, may choose, by written declaration, one or both of the following means for the settlement of disputes concerning the interpretation or application of Articles 7, 8 and 15 and, except to the extent that an Annex provides otherwise, the provisions of any Annex and, insofar as it relates to these Articles and provisions, Article 13:
   (a) the International Court of Justice;
   (b) the Arbitral Tribunal.
2. declaration made under paragraph 1 above shall not affect the operation of Article 18 and Article 20(2).
3. A Party which has not made a declaration under paragraph 1 above or in respect of which a declaration is no longer in force shall be deemed to have accepted the competence of the Arbitral Tribunal.
4. If the parties to a dispute have accepted the same means

for the settlement of a dispute, the dispute may be submitted only to that procedure, unless the parties otherwise agree.

5. If the parties to a dispute have not accepted the same means for the settlement of a dispute, or if they have both accepted both means, the dispute may be submitted only to the Arbitral Tribunal, unless the parties otherwise agree.

6. A declaration made under paragraph 1 above shall remain in force until it expires in accordance with its terms or until three months after written notice of revocation has been deposited with the Depositary.

7. A new declaration, a notice of revocation or the expiry of a declaration shall not in any way affect proceedings pending before the International Court of Justice or the Arbitral Tribunal, unless the parties to the dispute otherwise agree.

8. Declarations and notices referred to in this Article shall be deposited with the Depositary who shall transmit copies thereof to all Parties.

Article 20: Dispute Settling Procedure

1. If the parties to a dispute concerning the interpretation or application of Articles 7, 8 or 15 or, except to the extent that an Annex provides otherwise, the provisions of any Annex or, insofar as it relates to these Articles and provisions, Article 13, have not agreed on a means for resolving it within 12 months of the request for consultation pursuant to Article 18, the dispute shall be referred, at the request of any party to the dispute, for settlement in accordance with the procedure determined by Article 19(4) and (5).

2. The Arbitral Tribunal shall not be competent to decide or rule upon any matter within the scope of Article IV of the Antarctic Treaty. In addition, nothing in this Protocol shall be interpreted as conferring competence or jurisdiction on the International Court of Justice or any other tribunal established for the purpose of settling disputes between Parties to decide or otherwise rule upon any matter within the scope of Article IV of the Antarctic Treaty.

Article 21: Signature

This Protocol shall be open for signature at Madrid on the 4th of October 1991 and thereafter at Washington until the 3rd of October 1992 by any State which is a Contracting Party to the Antarctic Treaty.

Article 22: Ratification, Acceptance, Approval or Accession

1. This Protocol is subject to ratification, acceptance or approval by signatory States.
2. After the 3rd of October 1992 this Protocol shall be open for accession by any State which is a Contracting Party to the Antarctic Treaty.
3. Instruments of ratification, acceptance, approval or accession shall be deposited with the Government of the United States of America, hereby designated as the Depository.
4. After the date on which this Protocol has entered into force, the Antarctic Treaty Consultative Parties shall not act upon a notification regarding the entitlement of a Contracting Party to the Antarctic Treaty to appoint representatives to participate in Antarctic Treaty Consultative Meetings in accordance with Article IX(2) of the Antarctic Treaty unless that Contracting Party has first ratified, accepted, approved or acceded to this Protocol.

Article 23: Entry into Force

1. This Protocol shall enter into force on the thirtieth day following the date of deposit of instruments of ratification, acceptance, approval or accession by all States which are Antarctic Treaty Consultative Parties at the date on which this Protocol is adopted.
2. For each Contracting Party to the Antarctic Treaty which, subsequent to the date of entry into force of this Protocol, deposits an instrument of ratification, acceptance, approval or accession, this Protocol shall enter into force on the thirtieth day following such deposit.

Article 24: Reservations

Reservations to this Protocol shall not be permitted.

Article 25: Modification or Amendment

1. Without prejudice to the provisions of Article 9, this Protocol may be modified or amended at any time in accordance with the procedures set forth in Article XII(1)(a) and (b) of the Antarctic Treaty.
2. If, after the expiration of 50 years from the date of entry into force of this Protocol, any of the Antarctic Treaty Consultative Parties so requests by a communication addressed to the Depositary, a conference shall be held as soon as practicable to review the operation of this Protocol.
3. A modification or amendment proposed at any Review Conference called pursuant to paragraph 2 above shall be adopted by a majority of the Parties, including three-quarters of the States which are Antarctic Treaty Consultative Parties at the time of adoption of this Protocol.
4. A modification or amendment adopted pursuant to paragraph 3 above shall enter into force upon ratification, acceptance, approval or accession by three-quarters of the Antarctic Treaty Consultative Parties, including ratification, acceptance, approval or accession by all States which are Antarctic Treaty Consultative Parties at the time of adoption of this Protocol.
5. (a) With respect to Article 7. the prohibition on Antarctic mineral resource activities contained therein shall continue unless there is in force a binding legal regime on Antarctic mineral resource activities that includes an agreed means for determining whether, and if so, under which conditions, any such activities would be acceptable. This regime shall fully safeguard the interests of all States referred to in Article IV of the Antarctic Treaty and apply the principles thereof. Therefore, if a modification or amendment to Article 7 is proposed at a Review Conference referred to in paragraph 2 above, it shall include such a binding legal regime.
    (b) If any such modification or amendment has not

entered into force within 3 years of the date of its adoption, any Party may at any time thereafter notify to the Depositary of its withdrawal from the Protocol, and such withdrawal shall take effect 2 years after receipt of the notification by the Depositary.

Article 26: Notifications by the Depositary

The Depositary shall notify all Contracting Parties to the Antarctic Treaty of the following:

(a) signatures of this Protocol and the deposit of instruments of ratification, acceptance, approval or accession;
(b) the date of entry into force of this Protocol and any additional Annex thereto;
(c) the date of entry into force of any amendment or modification to this Protocol;
(d) the deposit of declarations and notices pursuant to Article 19; and
(e) any notification received pursuant to Article 25 (5)(b).

Article 27: Authentic Texts and Registration with the United Nations

1. This Protocol, done in the English, French, Russian and Spanish languages, each version being equally authentic, shall be deposited in the archives of the Government of the United States of America, which shall transmit duly certified copies thereof to all Contracting Parties to the Antarctic Treaty.
2. This Protocol shall be registered by the Depositary pursuant to Article 102 of the Charter of the United Nations.

SCHEDULE TO THE PROTOCOL: ARBITRATION

Article 1

1. The Arbitral Tribunal shall be constituted and shall

function in accordance with the Protocol, including this Schedule.

2. The Secretary referred to in this Schedule is the Secretary General of the Permanent Court of Arbitration.

Article 2

1. Each Party shall be entitled to designate up to three Arbitrators, at least one of whom shall be designated within three months of the entry into force of the Protocol for that Party. Each Arbitrator shall be experienced in Antarctic affairs, have thorough knowledge of international law and enjoy the highest reputation for fairness, competence and integrity. The names of the persons so designated shall constitute the list of Arbitrators. Each Party shall at all times maintain the name of at least one Arbitrator on the list.

2. Subject to paragraph 3 below, an Arbitrator designated by a Party shall remain on the list for a period of five years and shall be eligible for redesignation by that Party for additional five year periods.

3. A Party which designated an Arbitrator may withdraw the name of that Arbitrator from the list. If an Arbitrator dies or if a Party for any reason withdraws from the list the name of an Arbitrator designated by it, the Party which designated the Arbitrator in question shall notify the Secretary promptly. An Arbitrator whose name is withdrawn from the list shall continue to serve on any Arbitral Tribunal to which that Arbitrator has been appointed until the completion of proceedings before the Arbitral Tribunal.

4. The Secretary shall ensure that an up-to-date list is maintained of the Arbitrators designated pursuant to this Article.

Article 3

1. The Arbitral Tribunal shall be composed of three Arbitrators who shall be appointed as follows:
   (a) The party to the dispute commencing the proceedings

shall appoint one Arbitrator, who may be its national, from the list referred to in Article 2. This appointment shall be included in the notification referred to in Article 4.

(b) Within 40 days of the receipt of that notification, the other party to the dispute shall appoint the second Arbitrator, who may be its national, from the list referred to in Article 2.

(c) Within 60 days of the appointment of the second Arbitrator, the parties to the dispute shall appoint by agreement the third Arbitrator from the list referred to in Article 2. The third Arbitrator shall not be either a national of a party to the dispute, or a person designated for the list referred to in Article 2 by a party to the dispute, or of the same nationality as either of the first two Arbitrators. The third Arbitrator shall be the Chairperson of the Arbitral Tribunal.

(d) If the second Arbitrator has not been appointed within the prescribed period, or if the parties to the dispute have not reached agreement within the prescribed period on the appointment of the third Arbitrator, the Arbitrator or Arbitrators shall be appointed, at the request of any party to the dispute and within 30 days of the receipt of such request, by the President of the International Court of Justice from the list referred to in Article 2 and subject to the conditions prescribed in subparagraphs (b) and (c) above. In performing the functions accorded him or her in this subparagraph, the President of the Court shall consult the parties to the dispute.

(e) If the President of the International Court of Justice is unable to perform the functions accorded him or her in subparagraph (d) above or is a national of a party to the dispute, the functions shall be performed by the Vice-President of the Court, except that if the Vice-President is unable to perform the functions or is a national of a party to the dispute the functions shall be performed by the next most senior member of the Court who is available and is not a national of a party to the dispute.

2. Any vacancy shall be filled in the manner prescribed for the initial appointment.
3. In any dispute involving more than two Parties, those Parties having the same interest shall appoint one Arbitrator by agreement within the period specified in paragraph 1(b) above.

Article 4

The party to the dispute commencing proceedings shall so notify the other party or parties to the dispute and the Secretary in writing. Such notification shall include a statement of the claim and the grounds on which it is based. The notification shall be transmitted by the Secretary to all Parties.

Article 5

1. Unless the parties to the dispute agree otherwise, arbitration shall take place at The Hague, where the records of the Arbitral Tribunal shall be kept. The Arbitral Tribunal shall adopt its own rules of procedure. Such rules shall ensure that each party to the dispute has a full opportunity to be heard and to present its case and shall also ensure that the proceedings are conducted expeditiously.
2. The Arbitral Tribunal may hear and decide counter-claims arising out of the dispute.

Article 6

1. The Arbitral Tribunal, where it considers that *prima facie* it has jurisdiction under the Protocol, may:
   (a) at the request of any party to a dispute, indicate such provisional measures as it considers necessary to preserve the respective rights of the parties to the dispute;
   (b) prescribe any provisional measures which it considers appropriate under the circumstances to prevent serious harm to the Antarctic environment or dependent or associated ecosystems.

2. The parties to the dispute shall comply promptly with any provisional measures prescribed under paragraph 1(b) above pending an award under Article 10.

3. Notwithstanding the time period in Article 20 of the Protocol, a party to a dispute may at any time, by notification to the other party or parties to the dispute and to the Secretary in accordance with Article 4, request that the Arbitral Tribunal be constituted as a matter of exceptional urgency to indicate or prescribe emergency provisional measures in accordance with this Article. In such case, the Arbitral Tribunal shall be constituted as soon as possible in accordance with Article 3, except that the time periods in Article 3(1) (b), (c) and (d) shall be reduced to 14 days in each case. The Arbitral Tribunal shall decide upon the request for emergency provisional measures within two months of the appointment of its Chairperson.

4. Following a decision by the Arbitral Tribunal upon a request for emergency provisional measures in accordance with paragraph 3 above, settlement of the dispute shall proceed in accordance with Articles 18,19 and 20 of the Protocol.

Article 7

Any Party which believes it has a legal interest, whether general or individual, which may be substantially affected by the award of an Arbitral Tribunal, may, unless the Arbitral Tribunal decides otherwise, intervene in the proceedings.

Article 8

The parties to the dispute shall facilitate the work of the Arbitral Tribunal and, in particular, in accordance with their law and using all means at their disposal, shall provide it with all relevant documents and information, and enable it, when necessary, to call witnesses or experts and receive their evidence.

Article 9

If one of the parties to the dispute does not appear before the

Arbitral Tribunal or fails to defend its case, any other party to the dispute may request the Arbitral Tribunal to continue the proceedings and make its award.

Article I0

1. The Arbitral Tribunal shall, on the basis of the provisions of the Protocol and other applicable rules and principles of international law that are not incompatible with such provisions, decide such disputes as are submitted to it.
2. The Arbitral Tribunal may decide, *ex aequo et bono*, a dispute submitted to it, if the parties to the dispute so agree.

Article 11

1. Before making its award, the Arbitral Tribunal shall satisfy itself that it has competence in respect of the dispute and that the claim or counterclaim is well founded in fact and law.
2. The award shall be accompanied by a statement of reasons for the decision and shall be communicated to the Secretary who shall transmit it to all Parties.
3. The award shall be final and binding on the parties to the dispute and on any Party which intervened in the proceedings and shall be complied with without delay. The Arbitral Tribunal shall interpret the award at the request of a party to the dispute or of any intervening Party.
4. The award shall have no binding force except in respect of that particular case.
5. Unless the Arbitral Tribunal decides otherwise, the expenses of the Arbitral Tribunal, including the remuneration of the Arbitrators, shall be borne by the parties to the dispute in equal shares.

Article 12

All decisions of the Arbitral Tribunal, including those referred to in Articles 5, 6 and 11, shall be made by a majority of the Arbitrators who may not abstain from voting.

Article 13

1. This Schedule may be amended or modified by a measure
    adopted in accordance with Article IX(1) of the Antarctic
    Treaty. Unless the measure specifies otherwise, the
    amendment or modification shall be deemed to have been
    approved, and shall become effective, one year after the
    close of the Antarctic Treaty Consultative Meeting at which
    it was adopted, unless one or more of the Antarctic Treaty
    Consultative Parties notifies the Depositary, within that
    time period, that it wishes an extension of that period or
    that it is unable to approve the measure.
2. Any amendment or modification of this Schedule which
    becomes effective in accordance with paragraph 1 above
    shall thereafter become effective as to any other Party when
    notice of approval by it has been received by the
    Depositary.

ANNEX I
TO THE PROTOCOL ON ENVIRONMENTAL PROTECTION
TO THE ANTARCTIC TREATY

Environmental Impact Assessment

Article 1: Preliminary Stage

1. The environmental impacts of proposed activities referred
    to in Article 8 of the Protocol shall, before their
    commencement, be considered in accordance with
    appropriate national procedures.
2. If an activity is determined as having less than a minor or
    transitory impact, the activity may proceed forthwith.

Article 2: Initial Environmental Evaluation

1. Unless it has been determined that an activity will have
    less than a minor or transitory impact, or unless a
    Comprehensive Environmental Evaluation is being
    prepared in accordance with Article 3, an Initial
    Environmental Evaluation shall be prepared. It shall

contain sufficient detail to assess whether a proposed activity may have more than a minor or transitory impact and shall include:

(a) a description of the proposed activity, including its purpose, location, duration and intensity; and

(b) consideration of alternatives to the proposed activity and any impacts that the activity may have, including consideration of cumulative impacts in the light of existing and known planned activities.

2. If an Initial Environmental Evaluation indicates that a proposed activity is likely to have no more than a minor or transitory impact, the activity may proceed, provided that appropriate procedures, which may include monitoring, are put in place to assess and verify the impact of the activity.

Article 3: *Comprehensive Environmental Evaluation*

1. If an Initial Environmental Evaluation indicates or if it is otherwise determined that a proposed activity is likely to have more than a minor or transitory impact, a Comprehensive Environmental Evaluation shall be prepared.

2. A Comprehensive Environmental Evaluation shall in

(a) a description of the proposed activity including its purpose, location, duration and intensity, and possible alternatives to the activity, including the alternative of not proceeding, and the consequences of those alternatives;

(b) a description of the initial environmental reference state with which predicted changes are to be compared and a prediction of the future environmental reference state in the absence of the proposed activity;

(c) a description of the methods and data used to forecast the impacts of the proposed activity;

(d) estimation of the nature, extent, duration, and intensity of the likely direct impacts of the proposed activity;

(e) consideration of possible indirect or second order impacts of the proposed activity;

 (f) consideration of cumulative impacts of the proposed activity in the light of existing activities and other known planned activities;

 (g) identification of measures, including monitoring programs, that could be taken to minimise or mitigate impacts of the proposed activity and to detect unforeseen impacts and that could provide early warning of any adverse effects of the activity as well as to deal promptly and effectively with accidents;

 (h) identification of unavoidable impacts of the proposed activity;

 (i) consideration of the effects of the proposed activity on the conduct of scientific research and on other existing uses and values;

 (j) an identification of gaps in knowledge and uncertainties encountered in compiling the information required under this paragraph;

 (k) a non-technical summary of the information provided under this paragraph; and

 (l) the name and address of the person or organisation which prepared the Comprehensive Environmental Evaluation and the address to which comments thereon should be directed.

3. The draft Comprehensive Environmental Evaluation shall be made publicly available and shall be circulated to all Parties, which shall also make it publicly available, for comment. A period of 90 days shall be allowed for the receipt of comments.

4. The draft Comprehensive Environmental Evaluation shall be forwarded to the Committee at the same time as it is circulated to the Parties, and at least 120 days before the next Antarctic Treaty Consultative Meeting, for consideration as appropriate.

5. No final decision shall be taken to proceed with the proposed activity in the Antarctic Treaty area unless there has been an opportunity for consideration of the draft Comprehensive Environmental Evaluation by the Antarctic Treaty Consultative Meeting on the advice of the Committee, provided that no decision to proceed with a proposed activity shall be delayed through the operation

of this paragraph for longer than 15 months from the date of circulation of the draft Comprehensive Environmental Evaluation.

6.   A final Comprehensive Environmental Evaluation shall address and shall include or summarise comments received on the draft Comprehensive Environmental Evaluation. The final Comprehensive Environmental Evaluation, notice of any decisions relating thereto, and any evaluation of the significance of the predicted impacts in relation to the advantages of the proposed activity, shall be circulated to all Parties, which shall also make them publicly available, at least 60 days before the commencement of the proposed activity in the Antarctic Treaty area.

Article 4: Decisions to be Based on Comprehensive Environmental Evaluations

Any decision on whether a proposed activity, to which Article 3 applies, should proceed, and, i f so, whether in its original or in a modified form, shall be based on the Comprehensive Environmental Evaluation as well as other relevant considerations.

Article 5: Monitoring

1.   Procedures shall be put in place, including appropriate monitoring of key environmental indicators, to assess and verify the impact of any activity that proceeds following the completion of a Comprehensive Environmental Evaluation.

2.   The procedures referred to in paragraph 1 above and in Article 2(2) shall be designed to provide a regular and verifiable record of the impacts of the activity in order, *inter alia*, to:
     (a)   enable assessments to be made of the extent to which such impacts are consistent with the Protocol; and
     (b)   provide information useful for minimising or mitigating impacts, and, where appropriate, information on the need for suspension, cancellation or modification of the activity.

Article 6: Circulation of Information

1. The following information shall be circulated to the Parties, forwarded to the Committee and made publicly available:
    (a) a description of the procedures referred to in Article l;
    (b) an annual list of any Initial Environmental Evaluations prepared in accordance with Article 2 and any decisions taken in consequence thereof;
    (c) significant information obtained, and any action taken in consequence thereof, from procedures put in place in accordance with Articles 2(2) and 5; an
    (d) information referred to in Article 3(6).
2. Any Initial Environmental Evaluation prepared in accordance with Article 2 shall be made available on request.

Article 7: Cases of Emergency

1. This Annex shall not apply in cases of emergency relating to the safety of human life or of ships, aircraft or equipment and facilities of high value, or the protection of the environment, which require an activity to be undertaken without completion of the procedures set out in this Annex.
2. Notice of activities undertaken in cases of emergency, which would otherwise have required preparation of a Comprehensive Environmental Evaluation, shall be circulated immediately to all Parties and to the Committee and a full explanation of the activities carried out shall be provided within 90 days of those activities.

Article 8: Amendment or Modification

1. This Annex may be amended or modified by a measure adopted in accordance with Article IX(I) of the Antarctic Treaty. Unless the measure specifies otherwise, the amendment or modification shall be deemed to have been approved, and shall become effective, one year after the close of the Antarctic Treaty Consultative Meeting at which

it was adopted, unless one or more of the Antarctic Treaty Consultative Parties notifies the Depositary, within that period, that it wishes an extension of that period or that it is unable to approve the measure.

2. Any amendment or modification of this Annex which becomes effective in accordance with paragraph 1 above shall thereafter become effective as to any other Party when notice of approval by it has been received by the Depositary.

ANNEX II
TO THE PROTOCOL ON ENVIRONMENTAL PROTECTION
TO THE ANTARCTIC TREATY

Conservation of Antarctic Fauna and Flora

Article 1: Definitions

For the purposes of this Annex:

(a) "native mammal" means any member of any species belonging to the Class Mammalia, indigenous to the Antarctic Treaty area or occurring there seasonally through natural migrations;

(b) "native bird" means any member, at any stage of its life cycle (including eggs), of any species of the Class Aves indigenous to the Antarctic Treaty area or occurring there seasonally through natural migrations;

(c) "native plant" means any terrestrial or freshwater vegetation, including bryophytes, lichens, fungi and algae, at any stage of its life cycle (including seeds, and other propagates), indigenous to the Antarctic Treaty area;

(d) "native invertebrate" means any terrestrial or freshwater invertebrate, at any stage of its life cycle, indigenous to the Antarctic Treaty area;

(e) "appropriate authority" means any person or agency authorised by a Party to issue permits under this Annex;

(f) "permit" means a formal permission in writing issued by an appropriate authority;

(g) "take" or "taking" means to kill, injure, capture, handle or molest, a native mammal or bird, or to remove or damage such quantities of native plants that their local distribution or abundance would be significantly affected;

(h) "harmful interference" means:

    (i) flying or landing helicopters or other aircraft in a manner that disturbs concentrations of birds and seals;

    (ii) using vehicles or vessels, including hovercraft and small boats, in a manner that disturbs concentrations of birds and seals;

    (iii) using explosives or firearms in a manner that disturbs concentrations of birds and seals;

    (iv) willfully disturbing breeding or molting birds or concentrations of birds and seals by persons on foot;

    (v) significantly damaging concentrations of native terrestrial plants by landing aircraft, driving vehicles, or walking on them, or by other means; and

    (vi) any activity that results in the significant adverse modification of habitats of any species or population of native mammal, bird, plant or invertebrate.

(i) "International Convention for the Regulation of Whaling" means the Convention done at Washington on 2 December, 1946.

Article 2: *Cases of Emergency*

1. This Annex shall not apply in cases of emergency relating to the safety of human life or of ships, aircraft, or equipment and facilities of high value, or the protection of the environment.

2. Notice of activities undertaken in cases of emergency shall be circulated immediately to all Parties and to the Committee.

Article 3: *Protection of Native Fauna and Flora*

1. Taking or harmful interference shall be prohibited, except in accordance with a permit.

2. Such permits shall specify the authorised activity, including when, where and by whom it is to be conducted and shall be issued only in the following circumstances:

    (a) to provide specimens for scientific study or scientific information;

    (b) to provide specimens for museums, herbaria, zoological and botanical gardens, or other educational or cultural institutions or uses; and

    (c) to provide for unavoidable consequences of scientific activities not otherwise authorised under sub-paragraphs (a) or (b) above, or of the construction and operation of scientific support facilities.

3. The issue of such permits shall be limited so as to ensure that:

    (a) no more native mammals, birds, or plants are taken than are strictly necessary to meet the purposes set forth in paragraph 2 above;

    (b) only small numbers of native mammals or birds are killed and in no case more native mammals or birds are killed from local populations than can, in combination with other permitted takings, normally be replaced by natural reproduction in the following season; and

    (c) the diversity of species, as well as the habitats essential to their existence, and the balance of the ecological systems existing within the Antarctic Treaty are maintained.

4. Any species of native mammals, birds and plants listed in Appendix A to this Annex shall be designated "Specially Protected Species", and shall be accorded special protection by the Parties.

5. A permit shall not be issued to take a Specially Protected Species unless the taking:

    (a) is for a compelling scientific purpose;

    (b) will not jeopardise the survival or recovery of that species or local population; and

    (c) uses non-lethal techniques where appropriate.

6. All taking of native mammals and birds shall be done in the manner that involves the least degree of pain and suffering practicable.

Article 4: Introduction of Non-native Species, Parasites and Diseases

1. No species of animal or plant not native to the Antarctic

Treaty area shall be introduced onto land or ice shelves, or into water in the Antarctic Treaty area except in accordance with a permit.

2. Dogs shall not be introduced onto land or ice shelves and dogs currently in those areas shall be removed by 1 April, 1994.

3. Permits under paragraph 1 above shall be issued to allow the importation only of the animals and plants listed in Appendix B to this Annex and shall specify the species, numbers and, if appropriate, age and sex and precautions to be taken to prevent escape or contact with native fauna and flora.

4. Any plant or animal for which a permit has been issued in accordance with paragraphs I and 3 above, shall, prior to expiration of the permit, be removed from the Antarctic Treaty area or be disposed of by incineration or equally effective means that eliminates risk to native fauna or flora. The permit shall specify this obligation. Any other plant or animal introduced into the Antarctic Treaty area not native to that area, including any progeny, shall be removed or disposed of, by incineration or by equally effective means, so as to be rendered sterile, unless it is determined that they pose no risk to native flora or fauna.

5. Nothing in this Article shall apply to the importation of food into the Antarctic Treaty area provided that no live animals are imported for this purpose and all plants and animal parts and products are kept under carefully controlled conditions and disposed of in accordance with Annex III to the Protocol and Appendix C to this Annex.

6. Each Party shall require that precautions, including those listed in Appendix C to this Annex, be taken to prevent the introduction of micro-organisms (e.g., viruses, bacteria, parasites, yeasts, fungi) not present in the native fauna and flora.

Article 5: *Information*

Each Party shall prepare and make available information setting forth, in particular, prohibited activities and providing lists of Specially Protected Species and relevant Protected Areas to all those persons present in or intending to enter the Antarctic Treaty area with a view to ensuring that such persons understand and observe the provisions of this Annex.

Article 6: Exchange of Information

1. The Parties shall make arrangements for:
   (a) collecting and exchanging records (including records of permits) and statistics concerning the numbers or quantities of each species of native mammal, bird or plant taken annually in the Antarctic Treaty area;
   (b) obtaining and exchanging information as to the status of native mammals, birds, plants, and invertebrates in the Antarctic Treaty area, and the extent to which any species or population needs protection;
   (c) establishing a common form in which this information shall be submitted by Parties in accordance with paragraph 2 below.
2. Each Party shall inform the other Parties as well as the Committee before the end of November of each year of any step taken pursuant to paragraph 1 above and of the number and nature of permits issued under this Annex in the preceding period of 1 July to 30 June.

Article 7: Relationship with other Agreements outside the Antarctic Treaty System

Nothing in this Annex shall derogate from the rights and obligations of Parties under the International Convention for the Regulation of Whaling.

Article 8: Review

The Parties shall keep under continuing review measures for the conservation of Antarctic fauna and flora, taking into account any recommendations from the Committee.

Article 9: Amendment or Modification

1. This Annex may be amended or modified by a measure

adopted in accordance with Article IX(I) of the Antarctic Treaty. Unless the measure specifies other wise, the amendment or modification shall be deemed o have been approved, and shall become effective, one year after the close of the Antarctic Treaty Consultative Meeting at which it was adopted, unless one or more of the Antarctic Treaty Consultative Parties notifies the Depositary, within that time period, that it wishes an extension of that period or that it is unable to approve the measure.

2. Any amendment or modification of this Annex which becomes effective in accordance with paragraph I above shall thereafter become effective as to any other Party when notice of approval by it has been received by the Depositary.

APPENDICES TO THE ANNEX

Appendix A

Specially Protected Species

All species of the genus *Arctocephalus,* Fur Seals. *Ommatophoca rossii,* Ross Seal.

Appendix B

Importation of Animals and Plants

The following animals and plants may be imported into the Antarctic Treaty area in accordance with permits issued under Article 4 of this Annex:

(a) domestic plants; and
(b) laboratory animals and plants including viruses, bacteria, yeasts and fungi.

Appendix C

Precautions to Prevent Introductions of Micro-organisms

1. Poultry. No live poultry or other living birds shall be

brought into the Antarctic Treaty area'. Before dressed poultry is packaged for shipment to the Antarctic Treaty area, it shall be inspected for evidence of disease, such as Newcastle's Disease, tuberculosis, and yeast infection. Any poultry or parts not consumed shall be removed from the Antarctic Treaty area or disposed of by incineration or equivalent means that eliminates risks to native flora and fauna.

2. The importation of non-sterile soil shall be avoided to the maximum extent practicable.

ANNEX III
TO THE PROTOCOL ON ENVIRONMENTAL PROTECTION
TO THE ANTARCTIC TREATY

Waste Disposal and Waste Management

Article 1: General Obligations

1. This Annex shall apply to activities undertaken in the Antarctic Treaty area pursuant to scientific research programs, tourism and all other governmental and non-governmental activities in the Antarctic Treaty area for which advance notice is required under Article VII(5) of the Antarctic Treaty, including associated logistic support activities.

2. The amount of wastes produced or disposed of in the Antarctic Treaty area shall be reduced as far as practicable so as to minimise impact on the Antarctic environment and to minimise interference with the natural values of Antarctica, with scientific research and with other uses of Antarctica which are consistent with the Antarctic Treaty.

3. Waste storage, disposal and removal from the Antarctic Treaty area, as well as recycling and source reduction, shall be essential considerations in the planning and conduct of activities in the Antarctic Treaty area.

4. Wastes removed from the Antarctic Treaty area shall, to the maximum extent practicable, be returned to the country from which the activities generating the waste were organised or to any other country in which

arrangements have been made for the disposal of such wastes in accordance with relevant international agreements.

5. Past and present waste disposal sites on land and abandoned work sites of Antarctic activities shall be cleaned up by the generator of such wastes and the user of such sites. This obligation shall not be interpreted as requiring:

   (a) the removal of any structure designated as a historic site or monument; or

   (b) the removal of any structure or waste material in circumstances where the removal by any practical option would result in greater adverse environmental impact than leaving the structure or waste material in its existing location.

Article 2: Waste Disposal by Removal from the Antarctic Treaty Area

1. The following wastes, if generated after entry into force of this Annex, shall be removed from the Antarctic Treaty area by the generator of such wastes:

   (a) radio-active materials;

   (b) electrical batteries;

   (c) fuel, both liquid and solid;

   (d) wastes containing harmful levels of heavy metals or acutely toxic or harmful persistent compounds;

   (e) poly-vinyl chloride (PVC), polyurethane foam, polystyrene foam, rubber and lubricating oils, treated timbers and other products which contain additives that could produce harmful emissions if incinerated;

   (f) all other plastic wastes, except low density polyethylene containers (such as bags for storing wastes), provided that such containers shall be incinerated in accordance with Article 3(1);

   (g) fuel drums; and

   (h) other solid, non-combustible wastes; provided that the obligation to remove drums and solid non-combustible wastes contained in subparagraphs (g) and (h) above shall not apply in circumstances where the removal of such wastes by any practical option would result in greater adverse environmental impact than leaving them in their existing locations.

2.   Liquid wastes which are not covered by paragraph 1 above and sewage and domestic liquid wastes, shall, to the maximum extent practicable, be removed from the Antarctic Treaty area by the generator of such wastes.

3.   The following wastes shall be removed from the Antarctic Treaty area by the generator of such wastes, unless incinerated, autoclaved or otherwise treated to be made sterile:

     (a) residues of carcasses of imported animals;
     (b) laboratory culture of micro-organisms and plant pathogens; and
     (c) introduced avian products.

Article 3: Waste Disposal by Incineration

1.   Subject to paragraph 2 below, combustible wastes, other than those referred to in Article 2(1), which are not removed from the Antarctic Treaty area shall be burnt in incinerators which to the maximum extent practicable reduce harmful emissions. Any emission standards and equipment guidelines which may be recommended by, *inter alia*, the Committee and the Scientific Committee on Antarctic Research shall be taken into account. The solid residue of such incineration shall be removed from the Antarctic Treaty area.

2.   All open burning of wastes shall be phased out as soon as practicable, but no later than the end of the 1998/1999 season. Pending the completion of such phase-out, when it is necessary to dispose of wastes by open burning, allowance shall be made for the wind direction and speed and the type of wastes to be burnt to limit particulate deposition and to avoid such deposition over areas of special biological, scientific, historic, aesthetic or wilderness significance including, in particular, areas accorded protection under the Antarctic Treaty.

Article 4: Other Waste Disposal on Land

1.   Wastes not removed or disposed of in accordance with

Articles 2 and 3 shall not be disposed of onto ice-free areas or into fresh water systems.

2. Sewage, domestic liquid wastes and other liquid wastes not removed from the Antarctic Treaty area in accordance with Article 2, shall, to the maximum extent practicable, not be disposed of onto sea ice, ice shelves or the grounded ice-sheet, provided that such wastes which are generated by stations located inland on ice shelves or on the grounded ice-sheet may be disposed of in deep ice pits where such disposal is the only practicable option. Such pits shall not be located on known ice-flow lines which terminate at ice-free areas or in areas of high ablation.

3. Wastes generated at field camps shall, to the maximum extent practicable, be removed by the generator of such wastes to supporting stations or ships for disposal in accordance with this Annex.

Article 5: Disposal of Waste in the Sea

1. Sewage and domestic liquid wastes may be discharged directly into the sea, taking into account the assimilative capacity of the receiving marine environment and provided that:
   (a) such discharge is located, wherever practicable, where conditions exist for initial dilution and rapid dispersal; and
   (b) large quantities of such wastes (generated in a station where the average weekly occupancy over the austral summer is approximately 30 individuals or more) shall be treated at least by maceration.

2. The by-product of sewage treatment by the Rotary Biological Contacter process or similar processes may be disposed of into the sea provided that such disposal does not adversely affect the local environment, and provided also that any such disposal at sea shall be in accordance with Annex IV to the Protocol.

Article 6: Storage of Waste

All wastes to be removed from the Antarctic Treaty area, or

otherwise disposed of, shall be stored in such a way as to prevent their dispersal into the environment.

Article 7: Prohibited Products

No polychlorinated biphenyls (PCBs), non-sterile soil, polystyrene beads, chips or similar forms of packaging, or pesticides (other than those required for scientific, medical or hygiene purposes) shall be introduced onto land or ice shelves or into water in the Antarctic Treaty area.

Article 8: Waste Management Planning

1. Each Party which itself conducts activities in the Antarctic Treaty area shall, in respect of those activities, establish a waste disposal classification system as a basis for recording wastes and to facilitate studies aimed at evaluating the environmental impacts of scientific activity and associated logistic support. To that end, wastes produced shall be classified as:
   (a) sewage and domestic liquid wastes (Group 1);
   (b) other liquid wastes and chemicals, including fuels and lubricants (Group 2);
   (c) solids to be combusted (Group 3);
   (d) other solid wastes (Group 4); and
   (e) radioactive material (Group 5).
2. In order to reduce further the impact of waste on the Antarctic environment, each such Party shall prepare and annually review and update its waste management plans (including waste reduction, storage and disposal), specifying for each fixed site, for field camps generally, and for each ship (other than small boats that are part of the operations of fixed sites or of ships and taking into account existing management plans for ships):
   (a) programs for cleaning up existing waste disposal sites and abandoned work sites;
   (b) current and planned waste management arrangements, including final disposal;
   (c) current and planned arrangements for analysing the environmental effects of waste and waste management; and

(d) other efforts to minimise any environmental effects of wastes and waste management.

3. Each such Party shall, as far as is practicable, also prepare an inventory of locations of past activities (such as traverses, field depots, field bases, crashed aircraft) before the information is lost, so that such locations can be taken into account in planning future scientific programs (such as snow chemistry, pollutants in lichens or ice core drilling).

Article 9: Circulation and Review of Waste Management Plans

1. The waste management plans prepared in accordance with Article 8, reports on their implementation, and the inventories referred to in Article 8(3), shall be included in the annual exchanges of information in accordance with Articles III and VII of the Antarctic Treaty and related Recommendations under Article IX of the Antarctic Treaty.

2. Each Party shall send copies of its waste management plans, and reports on their implementation and review, to the Committee.

3. The Committee may review waste management plans and reports thereon and may offer comments, including suggestions for minimising impacts and modifications and improvement to the plans, for the consideration of the Parties.

4. The Parties may exchange information and provide advice on, *inter alia*, available low waste technologies, reconversion of existing installations, special requirements for effluents, and appropriate disposal and discharge methods.

Article 10: Management Plans

Each Party shall:

(a) designate a waste management official to develop and monitor waste management plans; in the field, this responsibility shall be delegated to an appropriate person at each site;

(b)   ensure that members of its expeditions receive training designed to limit the impact of its operations on the Antarctic environment and to inform them of requirements of this Annex; and

(c)   discourage the use of poly-vinyl chloride (PVC) products and ensure that its expeditions to the Antarctic Treaty are advised of any PVC products they may introduce into that area in order that these products may be removed subsequently in accordance with this Annex.

Article 11: Review

This Annex shall be subject to regular review in order to ensure that it is updated to reflect improvement in waste disposal technology and procedures and to ensure thereby maximum protection of the Antarctic environment.

Article 12: Cases of Emergency

1.   This Annex shall not apply in cases of emergency relating to the safety of human life or of ships, aircraft or equipment and facilities of high value or the protection of the environment.

2.   Notice of activities undertaken in cases of emergency shall be circulated immediately to all Parties and to the Committee.

Article 13: Amendment or Modification

1.   This Annex may be amended or modified by a measure adopted in accordance with Article IX(1) of the Antarctic Treaty. Unless the measure specifies otherwise, the amendment or modification shall be deemed to have been approved, and shall become effective, one year after the close of the Antarctic Treaty Consultative Meeting at which it was adopted, unless one or more of the Antarctic Treaty Consultative Parties notifies the Depositary, within that time period, that it wishes an extension of that period or that it is unable to approve the amendment.

2.   Any amendment or modification of this Annex which

becomes effective in accordance with paragraph 1 above shall thereafter become effective as to any other Party when notice of approval by it has been received by the Depositary.

ANNEX IV
TO THE PROTOCOL ON ENVIRONMENTAL PROTECTION
TO THE ANTARCTIC TREATY

Prevention of Marine Pollution

Article 1: Definitions

For the purpose of this Annex:

(a) "discharge" means any release howsoever caused from a ship and includes any escape, disposal, spilling, leaking, pumping, emitting or emptying;

(b) "garbage" means all kinds of victual, domestic and operational waste excluding fresh fish and parts thereof, generated during the normal operation of the ship, except those substances which are covered by Articles 3 and 4;

(c) "MARPOL 72/78 means the International Convention for the Prevention of Pollution from Ships, 1973, as amended by the Protocol of 1978 relating thereto and by any other amendment in force thereafter;

(d) "noxious liquid substance" means any noxious liquid substance as defined in Annex II of MARPOL 73/78;

(e) "oil" means petroleum in any form including crude oil, fuel oil, sludge, oil refuse and refined oil products (other than petrochemicals which are subject to the provisions of Article 4);

(f) "oily mixture" means a mixture with any oil content; and

(g) ship" means a vessel of any type whatsoever operating in the marine environment and includes hydrofoil boats, air-cushion vehicles, submersibles, floating craft and fixed or floating platforms.

Article 2: Application

This Annex applies, with respect to each Party, to ships entitled to fly its flag and to any other ship engaged in or supporting its Antarctic operations, while operating in the Antarctic Treaty area.

Article 3: Discharge of Oil

1. Any discharge into the sea of oil or oily mixture shall be prohibited, except in cases permitted under Annex I of MARPOL 73/78. While operating in the Antarctic Treaty area, ships shall retain on board all sludge, dirty ballast, tank washing waters and other oily residues and mixtures which may not be discharged into the sea. Ships shall discharge these residues only outside the Antarctic Treaty area, at reception facilities or as otherwise permitted under Annex I of MARPOL 73/78.

2. This Article shall not apply to:
   (a) the discharge into the sea of oil or oily mixture resulting from damage to a ship or its equipment:
       (i) provided that all reasonable precautions have been taken after the occurrence of the damage or discovery of the discharge for the purpose of preventing or minimising the discharge; and
       (ii) except if the owner or the Master acted either with intent to cause damage, or recklessly and with the knowledge that damage would probably result; or
   (b) the discharge into the sea of substances containing oil which are being used for the purpose of combating specific pollution incidents in order to minimise the damage from pollution.

Article 4: Discharge of Noxious Liquid Substances

The discharge into the sea of any noxious liquid substance, and any other chemical or other substances, in quantities or concentrations that are harmful to the marine environment, shall be prohibited.

Article 5: Disposal of Garbage

1. The disposal into the sea of all plastics, including but not

limited to synthetic ropes, synthetic fishing nets, and plastic garbage bags, shall be prohibited.

2. The disposal into the sea of all other garbage, including paper products, rags, glass, metal, bottles, crockery, incineration ash, dunnage, lining and packing materials, shall be prohibited.

3. The disposal into the sea of food wastes may be permitted when they have been passed through a comminuter or grinder, provided that such disposal shall, except in cases permitted under Annex V of MARPOL 73/78, be made as far as practicable from land and ice shelves but in any case not less than 12 nautical miles from the nearest land or ice shelf. Such comminuted or ground food wastes shall be capable of passing through a screen with openings no greater than 25 millimetres.

4. When a substance or material covered by this article is mixed with other such substance or material for discharge or disposal, having different disposal or discharge requirements, the most stringent disposal or discharge requirements shall apply.

5. The provisions of paragraphs 1 and 2 above shall not apply to:
   (a) the escape of garbage resulting from damage to a ship or its equipment provided all reasonable precautions have been taken, before and after the occurrence of the damage, for the purpose of preventing or minimising the escape; or
   (b) the accidental loss of synthetic fishing nets, provided all reasonable precautions have been taken to prevent such loss.

6. The Parties shall, where appropriate, require the use of garbage record books.

Article 6: Discharge of Sewage

1. Except where it would unduly impair Antarctic operations:
   (a) each Party shall eliminate all discharge into the sea of untreated sewage ("sewage" being defined in Annex IV of MARPOL 73/78) within 12 nautical miles of land or ice shelves;

(b) beyond such distance, sewage stored in a holding tank shall not be discharged instantaneously but at a moderate rate and, where practicable, while the ship is en route at a speed of no less than 4 knots.

This paragraph does not apply to ships certified to carry not more than 10 persons.

2. The Parties shall, where appropriate, require the use of sewage record books.

Article 7: Cases of Emergency

1. Articles 3, 4, 5 and 6 of this Annex shall not apply in cases of emergency relating to the safety of a ship and those on board or saving life at sea.
2. Notice of activities undertaken in cases of emergency shall be circulated immediately to all Parties and to the Committee.

Article 8: Effect on Dependent and Associated Ecosystems

In implementing the provisions of this Annex, due consideration shall be given to the need to avoid detrimental effects on dependent and associated ecosystems, outside the Antarctic Treaty area.

Article 9: Ship Retention Capacity and Reception Facilities

1. Each Party shall undertake to ensure that all ships entitled to fly its flag and any other ship engaged in or supporting its Antarctic operations, before entering the Antarctic Treaty area, are fitted with a tank or tanks of sufficient capacity on board for the retention of all sludge, dirty ballast, tank washing water and other oil residues and mixtures, and have sufficient capacity on board for the retention of garbage, while operating in the Antarctic Treaty area and have concluded arrangements to discharge such oily residues and garbage at a reception facility after leaving that area. Ships shall also have sufficient capacity on board for the retention of noxious liquid substances.

2. Each Party at whose ports ships depart en route to or arrive from the Antarctic Treaty area undertakes to ensure that as soon as practicable adequate facilities are provided for the reception of all sludge, dirty ballast, tank washing water, other oily residues and mixtures, and garbage from ships, without causing undue delay, and according to the needs of the ships using them.

3. Parties operating ships which depart to or arrive from the Antarctic Treaty area at ports of other Parties shall consult with those Parties with a view to ensuring that the establishment of port reception facilities does not place an inequitable burden on Parties adjacent to the Antarctic Treaty area.

Article 10: Design, Construction, Manning and Equipment of Ships

In the design, construction, manning and equipment of ships engaged in or supporting Antarctic operations, each Party shall take into account the objectives of this Annex.

Article 11: Sovereign Immunity

1. This Annex shall not apply to any warship, naval auxiliary or other ship owned or operated by a State and used, for the time being, only on government non-commercial service. However, each Party shall ensure by the adoption of appropriate measures not impairing the operations or operational capabilities of such ships owned or operated by it, that such ships act in a manner consistent, so far as is reasonable and practicable, with this Annex.

2. In applying paragraph 1 above, each Party shall take into account the importance of protecting the Antarctic environment.

3. Each Party shall inform the other Parties of how it implements this provision.

4. The dispute settlement procedure set out in Articles 18 to 20 of the Protocol shall not apply to this Article.

Article 12: Preventive Measures and Emergency Preparedness and Response

1. In order to respond more effectively to marine pollution emergencies or the threat thereof in the Antarctic Treaty area, the Parties, in accordance with Article 15 of the Protocol, shall develop contingency plans for marine pollution response in the Antarctic Treaty area, including contingency plans for ships (other than small boats that are part of the operations of fixed sites or of ships) operating in the Antarctic Treaty area, particularly ships carrying oil as cargo, and for oil spills, originating from coastal installations, which enter into the marine environment. To this end they shall:
   (a) co-operate in the formulation and implementation of such plans; and
   (b) draw on the advice of the Committee, the International Maritime Organisation and other international organisations.
2. The Parties shall also establish procedures for cooperative response to pollution emergencies and shall take appropriate response actions in accordance with such procedures.

Article 13: Review

The Parties shall keep under continuous review the provisions of this Annex and other measures to prevent, reduce and respond to pollution of the Antarctic marine environment, including any amendments and new regulations adopted under MARPOL 73/78, with a view to achieving the objectives of this Annex.

Article 14: Relationship with MARPOL 73/78

With respect to those Parties which are also Parties to MARPOL 73/78, nothing in this Annex shall derogate from the specific rights and obligations thereunder.

Article 15: Amendment or Modification

1. This Annex may be amended or modified by a measure

adopted in accordance with Article IX(1) of the Antarctic Treaty. Unless the measure specifies otherwise, the amendment or modification shall be deemed to have been approved, and shall become effective, one year after the close of the Antarctic Treaty Consultative Meeting at which it was adopted, unless one or more of the Antarctic Treaty Consultative Parties notifies the Depositary, within that time period, that it wishes an extension of that period or that it is unable to approve the measure.

2. Any amendment or modification of this Annex which becomes effective in accordance with paragraph 1 above shall thereafter become effective as to any other Party when notice of approval by it has been received by the Depositary.

ANNEX V
TO THE PROTOCOL ON ENVIRONMENTAL PROTECTION TO THE ANTARCTIC TREATY

Area Protection and Management

Article 1: Definitions

For the purposes of this Annex:

(a) "appropriate authority" means any person or agency authorised by a Party to issue permits under this Annex;
(b) "permit" means a formal permission in writing issued by an appropriate authority;
(c) "Management Plan" means a plan to manage the activities and protect the special value or values in an Antarctic Specially Protected Area or an Antarctic Specially Managed Area.

Article 2: Objectives

For the purposes set out in this Annex, any area, including any marine area, may be designated as an Antarctic Specially Protected Area or an Antarctic Specially Managed Area. Activities in those Areas shall be prohibited, restricted or managed in accordance with Management Plans adopted under the provisions of this Annex.

Article 3: Antarctic Specially Protected Areas

1. Any area, including any marine area, may be designated as an Antarctic Specially Protected Area to protect outstanding environmental, scientific, historic, aesthetic or wilderness values, any combination of those values, or ongoing or planned scientific research.

2. Parties shall seek to identify, within a systematic environmental-geographical framework, and to include in the series of Antarctic Specially Protected Areas:

   (a) areas kept inviolate from human interference so that future comparisons may be possible with localities that have been affected by human activities;

   (b) representative examples of major terrestrial, including glacial and aquatic, ecosystems and marine ecosystems;

   (c) areas with important or unusual assemblages of species, including major colonies of breeding native birds or mammals;

   (d) the type locality or only known habitat of any species;

   (e) areas of particular interest to on-going or planned scientific research;

   (f) examples of outstanding geological, glaciological or geomorphological features;

   (g) areas of outstanding aesthetic and wilderness value;

   (h) sites or monuments or recognised historic value; and

   (i) such other areas as may be appropriate to protect the values set out in paragraph 1 above.

3. Specially Protected Areas and Sites of Special Scientific Interest designated as such by past Antarctic Treaty Consultative Meetings are hereby designated as Antarctic Specially Protected Areas and shall be renamed and renumbered accordingly.

4. Entry into an Antarctic Specially Protected Area shall be prohibited except in accordance with a permit issued under Article 7.

Article 4: Antarctic Specially Managed Areas

1. Any area, including any marine area, where activities are being conducted or may in the future be conducted, may be designated as an Antarctic Specially Managed Area to assist in the planning and co-ordination of activities, avoid possible conflicts, improve co-operation between Parties or minimise environmental impacts.

2. Antarctic Specially Managed Areas may include:
   (a) areas where activities pose risks of mutual interference or cumulative environmental impacts; and
   (b) sites or monuments of recognised historic value.

3. Entry into an Antarctic Specially Managed Area shall not require a permit.

4. Notwithstanding paragraph 3 above, an Antarctic Specially Managed Area may contain one or more Antarctic Specially Protected Areas, entry into which shall be prohibited except in accordance with a permit issued under Article 7.

Article 5: Management Plans

1. Any Party, the Committee, the Scientific Committee for Antarctic Research or the Commission for the Conservation of Antarctic Marine Living Resources may propose an area for designation as an Antarctic Specially Protected Area or an Antarctic Specially Managed Area by submitting a proposed Management Plan to the Antarctic Treaty Consultative Meeting.

2. The area proposed for designation shall be of sufficient size to protect the values for which the special protection or management is required.

3. Proposed Management Plans shall include, as appropriate:
   (a) a description of the value or values for which special protection or management is required;
   (b) a statement of the aims and objectives of the Management Plan for the protection or management of those values;
   (c) management activities which are to be undertaken to protect the values for which special protection or management is required;

(d) a period of designation, if any;

(e) a description of the area, including:

    (i) the geographical co-ordinates, boundary markers and natural features that delineate the area;

    (ii) access to the area by land, sea or air including marine approaches and anchorages, pedestrian and vehicular routes within the area, and aircraft routes and landing areas;

    (iii) the location of structures, including scientific stations, research or refuge facilities, both within the area and near to it; and

    (iv) the location in or near the area of other Antarctic Specially Protected Areas or Antarctic Specially Managed Areas designated under this Annex, or other protected areas designated in accordance with measures adopted under other components of the Antarctic Treaty System;

(f) the identification of zones within the area, in which activities are to be prohibited, restricted or managed for the purpose of achieving the aims and objectives referred to in subparagraph b. above;

(g) maps and photographs that show clearly the boundary of the area in relation to surrounding features and key features within the area;

(h) supporting documentation;

(i) in respect of an area proposed for designation as an Antarctic Specially Protected Area, a clear description of the conditions under which permits may be granted by the appropriate authority regarding:

    (i) access to and movement within or over the area;

    (ii) activities which are or may be conducted within the area, including restrictions on time and place;

    (iii) the installation, modification, or removal of structures;

    (iv) the location of field camps;

    (v) restrictions on materials and organisms which may be brought into the area;

    (vi) the taking of or harmful interference with native flora and fauna;

    (vii) the collection or removal of anything not brought

into the area by the permit holder;

(viii) the disposal of waste;

(ix) measures that may be necessary to ensure that the aims and objectives of the Management Plan can continue to be met; and

(x) requirements for reports to be made to the appropriate authority regarding visits to the area;

(j) in respect of an area proposed for designation as an Antarctic Specially Managed Area, a code of conduct regarding:

(i) access to and movement within or over the area;

(ii) activities which are or may be conducted within the area, including restrictions on time and place;

(iii) the installation, modification, or removal of structures;

(iv) the location of field camps;

(v) the taking of or harmful interference with native flora and fauna;

(vi) the collection or removal of anything not brought into the area by the visitor;

(vii) the disposal of waste; and

(viii) any requirements for reports to be made to the appropriate authority regarding visits to the area; and

(k) provisions relating to the circumstances in which Parties should seek to exchange information in advance of activities which they propose to conduct.

Article 6: Designation Procedures

1. Proposed Management Plans shall be forwarded to the Committee, the Scientific Committee on Antarctic Research and, as appropriate, to the Commission for the Conservation of Antarctic Marine Living Resources. In formulating its advice to the Antarctic Treaty Consultative Meeting, the Committee shall take into account any comments provided by the Scientific Committee on Antarctic Research and, as appropriate, by the Commission for the Conservation of Antarctic Marine Living Resources. Thereafter, Management Plans may be approved by the Antarctic Treaty Consultative Parties by a measure adopted at an Antarctic Treaty Consultative

Meeting in accordance with Article IX(1) of the Antarctic Treaty. Unless the measure specifies otherwise, the Plan shall be deemed to have been approved 90 days after the close of the Antarctic Treaty Consultative Meeting at which it was adopted, unless one or more of the Consultative Parties notifies the Depositary, within that time period, that it wishes an extension of that period or is unable to approve the measure.

2. Having regard to the provisions of Articles 4 and 5 of the Protocol, no marine area shall be designated as an Antarctic Specially Protected Area or an Antarctic Specially Managed Area without the prior approval of the Commission for the Conservation of Antarctic Marine Living Resources.

3. Designation of an Antarctic Specially Protected Area or an Antarctic Specially Managed Area shall be for an indefinite period unless the Management Plan provides otherwise. A review of a Management Plan shall be initiated at least every five years. The Plan shall be updated as necessary.

4. Management Plans may be amended or revoked in accordance with paragraph 1 above.

5. Upon approval Management Plans shall be circulated promptly by the Depositary to all Parties. The Depositary shall maintain a record of all currently approved Management Plans.

Article 7: Permits

1. Each Party shall appoint an appropriate authority to issue permits to enter and engage in activities within an Antarctic Specially Protected Area in accordance with the requirements of the Management Plan relating to that Area. The permit shall be accompanied by the relevant sections of the Management Plan and shall specify the extent and location of the Area, the authorised activities and when, where and by whom the activities are authorised and any other conditions imposed by the Management Plan.

2. In the case of a Specially Protected Area designated as

such by past Antarctic Treaty Consultative Meeting which does not have a Management Plan, the appropriate authority may issue a permit for a compelling scientific purpose which cannot be served elsewhere and which will not jeopardise the natural ecological system in that Area.

3. Each Party shall require a permit-holder to carry a copy of the permit while in the Antarctic Specially Protected Area concerned.

Article 8: Historic Sites and Monuments

1. Sites or monuments of recognised historic value which have been designated as Antarctic Specially Protected Areas or Antarctic Specially Managed Areas, or which are located within such Areas, shall be listed as Historic Sites and Monuments.

2. Any Party may propose a site or monument of recognised historic value which has not been designated as an Antarctic Specially Protected Area or an Antarctic Specially Managed Area, or which is not located within such an Area, for listing as a Historic Site or Monument. The proposal for listing may be approved by the Antarctic Treaty Consultative Parties by a measure adopted at an Antarctic Treaty Consultative Meeting in accordance with Article IX(1) of the Antarctic Treaty. Unless the measure specifies otherwise, the proposal shall be deemed to have been approved 90 days after the close of the Antarctic Treaty Consultative Meeting at which it was adopted, unless one or more of the Consultative Parties notifies the Depositary, within that time period, that it wishes an extension of that period or is unable to approve the measure.

3. Existing Historic Sites and Monuments which have been listed as such by previous Antarctic Treaty Consultative Meetings shall be included in the list of Historic Sites and Monuments under this Article.

4. Listed Historic Sites and Monuments shall not be damaged, removed or destroyed.

5. The list of Historic Sites and Monuments may be amended in accordance with paragraph 2 above. The Depositary

shall maintain a list of current Historic Sites and Monuments.

Article 9: Information and Publicity

1. With a view to ensuring that all persons visiting or proposing to visit Antarctica understand and observe the provisions of this Annex, each Party shall make available information setting forth, in particular:
    (a) the location of Antarctic Specially Protected Areas and Antarctic Specially Managed Areas;
    (b) listing and maps of those Areas;
    (c) the Management Plans, including listings of prohibitions relevant to each Area;
    (d) the location of Historic Sites and Monuments and any relevant prohibition or restriction.
2. Each Party shall ensure that the location and, if possible, the limits of Antarctic Specially Protected Areas, Antarctic Specially Managed Areas and Historic Sites and Monuments are shown on its topographic maps, hydrographic charts and in other relevant publications.
3. Parties shall co-operate to ensure that, where appropriate, the boundaries of Antarctic Specially Protected Areas, Antarctic Specially Managed Areas and Historic Sites and Monuments are suitably marked on the site.

Article 10: Exchange of Information

1. The Parties shall make arrangements for:
    (a) collecting and exchanging records, including records of permits and reports of visits, including inspection visits, to Antarctic Specially Protected Areas and reports of inspection visits to Antarctic Specially Managed Areas;
    (b) obtaining and exchanging information on any significant change or damage to any Antarctic Specially Managed Area, Antarctic Specially Protected Area or Historic Site or Monument; and
    (c) establishing common forms in which records and information shall be submitted by Parties in accordance with paragraph 2 below.

2. Each Party shall inform the other Parties and the Committee before the end of November of each year of the number and nature of permits issued under this Annex in the preceding period of 1 July to 30 June.

3. Each Party conducting, funding or authorising research or other activities in Antarctic Specially Protected Areas or Antarctic Specially Managed Areas shall maintain a record of such activities and in the annual exchange of information in accordance with the Antarctic Treaty shall provide summary descriptions of the activities conducted by persons subject to its jurisdiction in such areas in the preceding year.

4. Each Party shall inform the other Parties and the Committee before the end of November each year of measures it has taken to implement this Annex, including any site inspections and any steps it has taken to address instances of activities in contravention of the provisions of the approved Management Plan for an Antarctic Specially Protected Area or Antarctic Specially Managed Area.

Article 11: Cases of Emergency

1. The restrictions laid down and authorised by this Annex shall not apply in cases of emergency involving safety of human life or of ships, aircraft, or equipment and facilities of high value or the protection of the environment.

2. Notice of activities undertaken in cases of emergency shall be circulated immediately to all Parties and to the Committee.

Article 12: Amendment or Modification

1. This Annex may be amended or modified by a measure adopted in accordance with Article IX(1) of the Antarctic Treaty. Unless the measure specifies otherwise, the amendment or modification shall be deemed to have been approved, and shall, become effective, one year after the close of the Antarctic Treaty Consultative Meeting at which it was adopted, unless one or more of the Antarctic Treaty

Consultative Parties notifies the Depositary, within that time period, that it wishes an extension of that period or that it is unable to approve the measure.

2. Any amendment or modification of this Annex which becomes effective in accordance with paragraph 1 above shall thereafter become effective as to any other Party when notice of approval by it has been received by the Depositary.

ANNEX VI
TO THE PROTOCOL ON ENVIRONMENTAL PROTECTION
TO THE ANTARCTIC TREATY

Liability Arising from Environmental Emergencies

Article 1: Scope

This Annex shall apply to environmental emergencies in the Antarctic Treaty area which relate to scientific research programmes, tourism and all other governmental and non-governmental activities in the Antarctic Treaty area for which advance notice is required under Article VII(5) of the Antarctic Treaty, including associated logistic support activities. Measures and plans for preventing and responding to such emergencies are also included in this Annex. It shall apply to all tourist vessels that enter the Antarctic Treaty area. It shall also apply to environmental emergencies in the Antarctic Treaty area which relate to other vessels and activities as may be decided in accordance with Article 13.

Article 2: Definitions

For the purposes of this Annex:

(a) "Decision" means a Decision adopted pursuant to the Rules of Procedure of Antarctic Treaty Consultative Meetings and referred to in Decision 1 (1995) of the XIXth Antarctic Treaty Consultative Meeting;

(b) "Environmental emergency" means any accidental event that has occurred, having taken place after the entry into force of this Annex, and that results in, or imminently threatens to result in, any significant and harmful impact on the Antarctic environment;

(c) "Operator" means any natural or juridical person, whether governmental or non-governmental, which organises activities to be carried out in the Antarctic Treaty area. An operator does not include a natural person who is an employee, contractor, subcontractor, or agent of, or who is in the service of, a natural or juridical person, whether governmental or non-governmental, which organises activities to be carried out in the Antarctic Treaty area, and does not include a juridical person that is a contractor or subcontractor acting on behalf of a State operator;

(d) "Operator of the Party" means an operator that organises, in that Party's territory, activities to be carried out in the Antarctic Treaty area, and:

    (i) those activities are subject to authorisation by that Party for the Antarctic Treaty area; or

    (ii) in the case of a Party which does not formally authorise activities for the Antarctic Treaty area, those activities are subject to a comparable regulatory process by that Party.

    The terms "its operator", "Party of the operator", and "Party of that operator" shall be interpreted in accordance with this definition;

(e) "Reasonable", as applied to preventative measures and response action, means measures or actions which are appropriate, practicable, proportionate and based on the availability of objective criteria and information, including:

    (i) risks to the Antarctic environment, and the rate of its natural recovery;

    (ii) risks to human life and safety; and

    (iii) technological and economic feasibility;

(f) "Response action" means reasonable measures taken after an environmental emergency has occurred to avoid, minimise or contain the impact of that environmental emergency, which to that end may include clean-up in appropriate circumstances, and includes determining the extent of that emergency and its impact;

(g) "The Parties" means the States for which this Annex has

become effective in accordance with Article 9 of the Protocol.

Article 3: Preventative Measures

1. Each Party shall require its operators to undertake reasonable preventative measures that are designed to reduce the risk of environmental emergencies and their potential adverse impact.
2. Preventative measures may include:
    (a) specialised structures or equipment incorporated into the design and construction of facilities and means of transportation;
    (b) specialised procedures incorporated into the operation or maintenance of facilities and means of transportation; and
    (c) specialised training of personnel.

Article 4: Contingency Plans

1. Each Party shall require its operators to:
    (a) establish contingency plans for responses to incidents with potential adverse impacts on the Antarctic environment or dependent and associated ecosystems; and
    (b) co-operate in the formulation and implementation of such contingency plans.
2. Contingency plans shall include, when appropriate, the following components:
    (a) procedures for conducting an assessment of the nature of the incident;
    (b) notification procedures;
    (c) identification and mobilisation of resources;
    (d) response plans;
    (e) training;
    (f) record keeping; and
    (g) demobilisation.
3. Each Party shall establish and implement procedures for immediate notification of, and co-operative responses to, environmental emergencies, and shall promote the use of

notification procedures and co-operative response procedures by its operators that cause environmental emergencies.

Article 5: Response Action

1. Each Party shall require each of its operators to take prompt and effective response action to environmental emergencies arising from the activities of that operator.

2. In the event that an operator does not take prompt and effective response action, the Party of that operator and other Parties are encouraged to take such action, including through their agents and operators specifically authorised by them to take such action on their behalf.

3. (a) Other Parties wishing to take response action to an environmental emergency pursuant to paragraph 2 above shall notify their intention to the Party of the operator and the Secretariat of the Antarctic Treaty beforehand with a view to the Party of the operator taking response action itself, except where a threat of significant and harmful impact to the Antarctic environment is imminent and it would be reasonable in all the circumstances to take immediate response action, in which case they shall notify the Party of the operator and the Secretariat of the Antarctic Treaty as soon as possible.

   (b) Such other Parties shall not take response action to an environmental emergency pursuant to paragraph 2 above, unless a threat of significant and harmful impact to the Antarctic environment is imminent and it would be reasonable in all the circumstances to take immediate response action, or the Party of the operator has failed within a reasonable time to notify the Secretariat of the Antarctic Treaty that it will take the response action itself, or where that response action has not been taken within a reasonable time after such notification.

   (c) In the case that the Party of the operator takes response action itself, but is willing to be assisted by another Party or Parties, the Party of the operator shall coordinate the response action.

4. However, where it is unclear which, if any, Party is the Party of the operator or it appears that there may be more than one such Party, any Party taking response action shall make best endeavours to consult as appropriate and shall, where practicable, notify the Secretariat of the Antarctic Treaty of the circumstances.

5. Parties taking response action shall consult and coordinate their action with all other Parties taking response action, carrying out activities in the vicinity of the environmental emergency, or otherwise impacted by the environmental emergency, and shall, where practicable, take into account all relevant expert guidance which has been provided by permanent observer delegations to the Antarctic Treaty Consultative Meeting, by other organisations, or by other relevant experts.

Article 6: Liability

1. An operator that fails to take prompt and effective response action to environmental emergencies arising from its activities shall be liable to pay the costs of response action taken by Parties pursuant to Article 5(2) to such Parties.

2. (a) When a State operator should have taken prompt and effective response action but did not, and no response action was taken by any Party, the State operator shall be liable to pay the costs of the response action which should have been undertaken, into the fund referred to in Article 12.

   (b) When a non-State operator should have taken prompt and effective response action but did not, and no response action was taken by any Party, the non-State operator shall be liable to pay an amount of money that reflects as much as possible the costs of the response action that should have been taken. Such money is to be paid directly to the fund referred to in Article 12, to the Party of that operator or to the Party that enforces the mechanism referred to in Article 7(3). A Party receiving such money shall make best efforts to make a contribution to the fund referred to in Article

12 which at least equals the money received from the operator.

3. Liability shall be strict.

4. When an environmental emergency arises from the activities of two or more operators, they shall be jointly and severally liable, except that an operator which establishes that only part of the environmental emergency results from its activities shall be liable in respect of that part only.

5. Notwithstanding that a Party is liable under this Article for its failure to provide for prompt and effective response action to environmental emergencies caused by its warships, naval auxiliaries, or other ships or aircraft owned or operated by it and used, for the time being, only on government non-commercial service, nothing in this Annex is intended to affect the sovereign immunity under international law of such warships, naval auxiliaries, or other ships or aircraft.

Article 7: Actions

1. Only a Party that has taken response action pursuant to Article 5(2) may bring an action against a non-State operator for liability pursuant to Article 6(1) and such action may be brought in the courts of not more than one Party where the operator is incorporated or has its principal place of business or his or her habitual place of residence. However, should the operator not be incorporated in a Party or have its principal place of business or his or her habitual place of residence in a Party, the action may be brought in the courts of the Party of the operator within the meaning of Article 2(d). Such actions for compensation shall be brought within three years of the commencement of the response action or within three years of the date on which the Party bringing the action knew or ought reasonably to have known the identity of the operator, whichever is later. In no event shall an action against a non-State operator be commenced later than 15 years after the commencement of the response action.

2. Each Party shall ensure that its courts possess the necessary

jurisdiction to entertain actions under paragraph 1 above.

3. Each Party shall ensure that there is a mechanism in place under its domestic law for the enforcement of Article 6(2)(b) with respect to any of its non-State operators within the meaning of Article 2(d), as well as where possible with respect to any non-State operator that is incorporated or has its principal place of business or his or her habitual place of residence in that Party. Each Party shall inform all other Parties of this mechanism in accordance with Article 13(3) of the Protocol. Where there are multiple Parties that are capable of enforcing Article 6(2)(b) against any given non-State operator under this paragraph, such Parties should consult amongst themselves as to which Party should take enforcement action. The mechanism referred to in this paragraph shall not be invoked later than 15 years after the date the Party seeking to invoke the mechanism became aware of the environmental emergency.

4. The liability of a Party as a State operator under Article 6(1) shall be resolved only in accordance with any enquiry procedure which may be established by the Parties, the provisions of Articles 18, 19 and 20 of the Protocol and, as applicable, the Schedule to the Protocol on Arbitration.

5. (a) The liability of a Party as a State operator under Article 6(2)(a) shall be resolved only by the Antarctic Treaty Consultative Meeting and, should the question remain unresolved, only in accordance with any enquiry procedure which may be established by the Parties, the provisions of Articles 18, 19 and 20 of the Protocol and, as applicable, the Schedule to the Protocol on Arbitration.

    (b) The costs of the response action which should have been undertaken and was not, to be paid by a State operator into the fund referred to in Article 12, shall be approved by means of a Decision. The Antarctic Treaty Consultative Meeting should seek the advice of the Committee on Environmental Protection as appropriate.

6. Under this Annex, the provisions of Articles 19(4), 19(5), and 20(1) of the Protocol, and, as applicable, the Schedule to the Protocol on arbitration, are only applicable to

liability of a Party as a State operator for compensation for response action that has been undertaken to an environmental emergency or for payment into the fund.

Article 8: Exemptions from Liability

1. An operator shall not be liable pursuant to Article 6 if it proves that the environmental emergency was caused by:
   (a) an act or omission necessary to protect human life or safety;
   (b) an event constituting in the circumstances of Antarctica a natural disaster of an exceptional character, which could not have been reasonably foreseen, either generally or in the particular case, provided all reasonable preventative measures have been taken that are designed to reduce the risk of environmental emergencies and their potential adverse impact;
   (c) an act of terrorism; or
   (d) an act of belligerency against the activities of the operator.
2. A Party, or its agents or operators specifically authorised by it to take such action on its behalf, shall not be liable for an environmental emergency resulting from response action taken by it pursuant to Article 5(2) to the extent that such response action was reasonable in all the circumstances.

Article 9: Limits of Liability

1. The maximum amount for which each operator may be liable under Article 6(1) or Article 6(2), in respect of each environmental emergency, shall be as follows:
   (a) for an environmental emergency arising from an event involving a ship:
      (i) one million SDR for a ship with a tonnage not exceeding 2,000 tons;
      (ii) for a ship with a tonnage in excess thereof, the following amount in addition to that referred to in (i) above:

    — for each ton from 2,001 to 30,000 tons, 400 SDR;

    — for each ton from 30,001 to 70,000 tons, 300 SDR; and

    — for each ton in excess of 70,000 tons, 200 SDR;

(b) for an environmental emergency arising from an event which does not involve a ship, three million SDR.

2. (a) Notwithstanding paragraph 1(a) above, this Annex shall not affect:

    (i) the liability or right to limit liability under any applicable international limitation of liability treaty; or

    (ii) the application of a reservation made under any such treaty to exclude the application of the limits therein for certain claims; provided that the applicable limits are at least as high as the following: for a ship with a tonnage not exceeding 2,000 tons, one million SDR; and for a ship with a tonnage in excess thereof, in addition, for a ship with a tonnage between 2,001 and 30,000 tons, 400 SDR for each ton; for a ship with a tonnage from 30,001 to 70,000 tons, 300 SDR for each ton; and for each ton in excess of 70,000 tons, 200 SDR for each ton.

(b) Nothing in subparagraph (a) above shall affect either the limits of liability set out in paragraph 1(a) above that apply to a Party as a State operator, or the rights and obligations of Parties that are not parties to any such treaty as mentioned above, or the application of Article 7(1) and Article 7(2).

3. Liability shall not be limited if it is proved that the environmental emergency resulted from an act or omission of the operator, committed with the intent to cause such emergency, or recklessly and with knowledge that such emergency would probably result.

4. The Antarctic Treaty Consultative Meeting shall review the limits in paragraphs 1(a) and 1(b) above every three years, or sooner at the request of any Party. Any amendments to these limits, which shall be determined after consultation amongst the Parties and on the basis of

advice including scientific and technical advice, shall be made under the procedure set out in Article 13(2).

5. For the purpose of this Article:
   (a) "ship" means a vessel of any type whatsoever operating in the marine environment and includes hydrofoil boats, air-cushion vehicles, submersibles, floating craft and fixed or floating platforms;
   (b) "SDR" means the Special Drawing Rights as defined by the International Monetary Fund;
   (c) a ship's tonnage shall be the gross tonnage calculated in accordance with the tonnage measurement rules contained in Annex I of the International Convention on Tonnage Measurement of Ships, 1969.

Article 10: State Liability

A Party shall not be liable for the failure of an operator, other than its State operators, to take response action to the extent that that Party took appropriate measures within its competence, including the adoption of laws and regulations, administrative actions and enforcement measures, to ensure compliance with this Annex.

Article 11: Insurance and Other Financial Security

1. Each Party shall require its operators to maintain adequate insurance or other financial security, such as the guarantee of a bank or similar financial institution, to cover liability under Article 6(1) up to the applicable limits set out in Article 9(1) and Article 9(2).

2. Each Party may require its operators to maintain adequate insurance or other financial security, such as the guarantee of a bank or similar financial institution, to cover liability under Article 6(2) up to the applicable limits set out in Article 9(1) and Article 9(2).

3. Notwithstanding paragraphs 1 and 2 above, a Party may maintain self-insurance in respect of its State operators, including those carrying out activities in the furtherance of scientific research.

Article 12: The Fund

1. The Secretariat of the Antarctic Treaty shall maintain and administer a fund, in accordance with Decisions including terms of reference to be adopted by the Parties, to provide, inter alia, for the reimbursement of the reasonable and justified costs incurred by a Party or Parties in taking response action pursuant to Article 5(2).

2. Any Party or Parties may make a proposal to the Antarctic Treaty Consultative Meeting for reimbursement to be paid from the fund. Such a proposal may be approved by the Antarctic Treaty Consultative Meeting, in which case it shall be approved by way of a Decision. The Antarctic Treaty Consultative Meeting may seek the advice of the Committee of Environmental Protection on such a proposal, as appropriate.

3. Special circumstances and criteria, such as: the fact that the responsible operator was an operator of the Party seeking reimbursement; the identity of the responsible operator remaining unknown or not subject to the provisions of this Annex; the unforeseen failure of the relevant insurance company or financial institution; or an exemption in Article 8 applying, shall be duly taken into account by the Antarctic Treaty Consultative Meeting under paragraph 2 above.

4. Any State or person may make voluntary contributions to the fund.

Article 13: Amendment or Modification

1. This Annex may be amended or modified by a Measure adopted in accordance with Article IX(1) of the Antarctic Treaty.

2. In the case of a Measure pursuant to Article 9(4), and in any other case unless the Measure in question specifies otherwise, the amendment or modification shall be deemed to have been approved, and shall become effective, one year after the close of the Antarctic Treaty Consultative Meeting at which it was adopted, unless one or more Antarctic Treaty Consultative Parties notifies the

Depositary, within that time period, that it wishes any extension of that period or that it is unable to approve the Measure.

3. Any amendment or modification of this Annex which becomes effective in accordance with paragraph 1 or 2 above shall thereafter become effective as to any other Party when notice of approval by it has been received by the Depositary.

THE ANTARCTIC TREATY SYSTEM

Nobody lives permanently in Antarctica, owing to its extreme cold, severe storms, and frozen ocean. It is so dangerous and remote that it wasn't discovered until 1820. Although tourism is increasing on the continent, its only long-term human residents are scientists and support personnel living on seasonal or year-round national bases. Whether they are public or private, all of these expeditions come from just a handful of the world's countries. Therefore, the laws that govern Antarctica are the agreements negotiated by nations capable of maintaining a presence on the southern continent.

Collectively, these negotiated agreements are called the Antarctic Treaty System (ATS). The foundation for this system is the Antarctic Treaty, which became effective in 1961. Under the ATS, select members, called the "Consultative Parties," set policy by adopting recommendations at annual meetings. For instance, the CPs adopted the "Agreed Measures for the Conservation of Antarctic Fauna and Flora" as Recommendations III-8 of 1964. Additionally, these ATS nations have since ratified three complementary treaties. The three are:

1. the Convention for the Conservation of Antarctic Seals (CCAS);
2. the Convention on the Conservation of Antarctic Marine Living Resources (CCAMLR);
3. and the Protocol on Environmental Protection to the Antarctic Treaty (Protocol).

To understand the legal structure of the ATS, we might say

that the Antarctic Treaty is like the U.S. Constitution, and the complementary treaties are like its Amendments. Each expands or refines the Antarctic Treaty without impeding or overlapping the original compact. Of course there are some problems with this analogy. For instance, CCAMLR (above) has slightly different national membership than the original Antarctic Treaty, and it governs an enlarged geographic area without increasing the jurisdiction of the original.

There is no international organization to enforce the ATS. Instead, each signatory nation must write and enforce its own laws to implement these treaties.

The Antarctic Treaty originated in an extraordinary moment of Cold War-era cooperation. In the mid-nineteen-fifties, a group of scientists convinced the U.N. to institute an event to promote cooperation in the sciences. To this end, the U.N. designated 1 July, 1957, to 31 December, 1958, the "International Geophysical Year (IGY)." During the eighteen-month IGY, scientists from twelve nations worked together in Antarctica, where they all agreed that the idea had been a complete success. The momentum of this symbolic event carried into the writing of the Antarctic Treaty in Washington in 1959. (For more on the history of the Treaty, see the "additional readings.")

SCAR AND
INTERNATIONAL POLAR YEAR (2007-2008)

Welcome to the Home Page of the Scientific Committee on Antarctic Research (SCAR), an inter-disciplinary committee of the International Council for Science (ICSU). SCAR is charged with the initiating, developing and coordinating high quality international scientific research in the Antarctic region, and on the role of the Antarctic region in the Earth system. The scientific business of SCAR is conducted by its Standing Scientific Groups which represent the scientific disciplines active in Antarctic research and report to SCAR.

In addition to carrying out its primary scientific role, SCAR also provides objective and independent scientific advice to the Antarctic Treaty Consultative Meetings and other organizations on issues of science and conservation affecting the management of Antarctica and the Southern Ocean. In that role, SCAR has made numerous recommendations on a variety of matters, most of which have been incorporated into Antarctic Treaty instruments. Foremost amongst these have been the advice provided for the many international agreements which provide protection for the ecology and environment of the Antarctic.

SCAR meets every two years to conduct its administrative business at the SCAR Delegates Meeting. At these meetings the members of SCAR, through their appointed Delegates, are responsible for approving SCAR finances, and formulating SCAR policy and strategy. They also elect an Executive Committee from among themselves which is responsible for the day-to-day administration of SCAR though its Secretariat at the Scott Polar Research Institute in Cambridge, England. The Executive Committee comprises the President and four Vice-Presidents. The SCAR Secretariat is staffed by the Executive Director, Executive Officer and an Administrative Assistant.

SCAR also holds, prior to the Delegates Meeting a major Open Science Conference to draw attention to Antarctic issues, along with meetings of the Standing Scientific Groups that are designed to finalise the Science Programmes for eventual approval by the Delegates.

Press Release
Embargoed for release until Wednesday, 19 October, 2005 at 12:01 am GMT

International Polar Year 2007-2008, an Endeavor of Historical Proportions: with Environmental Changes at Poles Driving Planetary Transformation, Scientists Energized by Opportunity to "Make a Difference"

Suzhou, China—Sparking a sense of urgency, enthusiasm and unity of purpose in the scientific community reminiscent of galvanizing endeavors such as man's ventures into space and the Human Genome Project, the International Council for Science (ICSU) today formally launched an ambitious global programme for polar research that already has attracted more than 1000 research proposals submitted by scientists from around the world.

The International Polar Year (IPY) 2007-2008—which is being

co-sponsored by the World Meteorological Organization—was officially adopted by ICSU members at their 28th General Assembly in Suzhou, China. Yet the planning for IPY was already well underway. For more than a year ICSU and WMO have been assembling what is expected to be a burst of internationally coordinated research that will focus on dramatic and disturbing changes occurring in the polar regions and analyze their broader environmental and economic importance for the planet.

"We've seen scientists from a wide range of disciplines immediately drawn to this endeavor because they seem to share a sense that if we don't pay considerable attention to the poles now, we will have missed a major opportunity and avoided our responsibilities as explorers of the planet," said Dr. David J. Carlson, director of the IPY International Programme Office established by ICSU and WMO and based at the British Antarctic Survey. "I think intellectually, and perhaps even emotionally, scientists want to be part of something that will make a difference, and polar research, given how it can help us understand such pressing matters as global climate change, certainly affords that opportunity."

The ICSU commitment to the IPY plan comes as polar research is increasingly capturing the attention of not only scientists but policy makers and the general public as well. Just a few weeks ago scientists at the US National Snow and Ice Data Center generated headlines with their alarming findings that over the past century

International Polar Year 2007-08

IPY Proposals Approved in April, 2006

- Next steps in the evolving shape of the programme-November, 2005
- List of approved Antarctic or Bipolar proposals-updated April, 2006
- Honeycomb chart of accepted proposals
- Proposed Activities

Press Release

- International Council for Science Launches International

Polar Year 2007-2008, an Endeavor of Historical Proportions

Director of the International Polar Year 2007-2008 Programme Office

- In May 2005 Dr. David Carlson began as the Director of the IPY International Programme Office located in Cambridge, UK

SCAR News on the IPY

- Launch of the International Polar Year (IPY), 2007-2008: It's official: The International Polar Year 2007-2008 will be launched on 1 March, 2007 at the "Palais de la Découverte", a famous science museum in central Paris. A press conference is being organized for the event by IPY's co-sponsors, ICSU and the World Meteorological Organization (WMO), and the IPY Programme Office in Cambridge. The event will take place in conjunction with the IPY Joint-Committee meeting being held on 28 February and 2 March. More than a dozen countries are also planning national launch events on or around 1 March and an international IPY group is working hard to stimulate activities in schools and science centres around the globe.
- The Chilean Antarctic Institute (INACH) has designed a web page with information and media news about IPY in Spanish (IPY=API in Spanish: Año Polar Internacional): http://www.inach.cl/api/medios.htm
- Report from the IPY Consultative Forum in Hobart, Tasmania, 8 July, 2006
- In association with the XXIX SCAR meeting in Hobart, on 8 July the International Polar Year Steering Committee held an IPY Consultative Forum to introduce the wider community to the goals and activities of the IPY and the progress being made, and to give the community an opportunity to ask questions about plans and progress and involvement.
- Hydrographers make plea for IPY scientists to collect more

detailed bathymetric information, especially around the Antarctic Peninsula and South Shetlands to improve the safety of navigation.

- Progress Report for SCAR
- SCAR nominated to participate on new International Polar Year Joint Committee for planning and coordination of the International Polar Year
- Call for Expression of Intent for the IPY

Example of National Approaches

- Unites States National Committee Vision Report
- Unites States National Committee Report Summary

2

International Gene Pool as Global Commons

PORTO ALEGRE TREATY

"PRESS RELEASE"
Embargo Date: 1 February, 2002

Hundreds of NGOs from More than 50 Nations Announce Support of a Treaty to Establish the Gene Pool as a Global Commons

Biotech Activists to Challenge Government and Corporate Claims on Patents on Life
Treaty to Be Centerpiece of International Campaigns Around the World

(Porto Alegre) 1 February, 2002—Biotech activists from more than 50 nations announce today their support for a treaty which would establish the earth's gene pool as a global commons. Non-Governmental Organizations' (NGOs) leaders say they will challeng e government and corporate claims on patents on life in every country. The treaty is the first globally coordinated campaign among biotech activists, and already has the support of over 250 organizations.

Activists will be working with political parties to introduce the Treaty Initiative in parliaments around the world over the next year. In September, 2002, activists will demand that governmental delegates to the Rio +10 Conference in South Africa endorse the Treaty to Share the Genetic Commons and make it the centerpiece of future biodiversity efforts.

Jeremy Rifkin, President of the Foundation on Economic Trends in Washington, DC, says, "The gene pool should not be allowed to be claimed as commercially negotiable genetic information or intellectual property by governments, commercial enterprises, other institutions or individuals. The global gene pool is a shared legacy and, therefore, a collective responsibility." Mr. Rifkin added, "A global treaty to share the gene pool is the most important task ahead of us as we make the transition into the Age of Biology."

The Treaty Initiative to Share the Genetic Commons, which aims to prohibit all patents on plant, microorganism, animal, and human life, will be

(Contd.)

(Contd.)

launched at a press conference hosted by NGO leaders on 1 February, 2002, during the greatly anticipated World Social Forum in Porto Alegre. The press conference will be held at 10:00 am (local time) at the Catholic University (PUC), Av. Ipiranga 6681, Bairro Paternon, Porto Alegre, Rio Grande do Sul.

The official workshop, "The Launch of the Porto Alegre Treaty to Share the Genetic Commons" will take place during the World Social Forum on Saturday, 2 February, 2002 at 16h00 in the Catholic University/Predio 11/Sala 603.

"Currently, under the protection of the WTO, multinational corporations are exploiting critical genetic resources for private gain," says Mark Ritchie, President of the Institute for Agriculture and Trade Policy. "This ground-breaking global initiative represents a major new effort by NGOs to work within the existing global system to change international law so that it works for all people."

"Our initiative improves upon other international agreements dealing with this issue in one very fundamental aspect," says Vandana Shiva, Director of the Research Foundation for Science, Technology, and Ecology in India, "unlike other initiatives, we oppose the extension of intellectual property rights to any living thing as well as the components of the living things."

Eighteen organizations, including the Foundation on Economic Trends and the International Forum on Globalization in the US, Centro de Educacion y Tecnología in Chile, Comitato Scientifico Antivivisezionista in Italy, the Indigenous Peoples' Biodiversity Network in Peru, Southeast Asia Regional Institute for Community Education (SEARICE) in the Philippines, the Community Technology Development Trust in Zimbabwe, and Via Campesina have formed an international committee working to create a civil society process which would lead to the presentation of the Treaty to governments at the Rio+10 Conference in South Africa in the fall.

"We believe that our evolutionary heritage is not a commodity to be bought or sold," adds Maude Barlow, National chairperson of the Council of Canadians. "All of the current arrangements and consultative initiatives based on the principle of selling prospecting rights to genetic information and extending intellectual property protection to life are unacceptable mechanisms for governing the gene pool."

"This treaty is designed to ensure that governments and Indigenous Peoples are the caretakers of their part of the genetic commons and to establish the appropriate statutory mechanisms needed to ensure both sovereignty and open access to the worlds genetic diversity," says Pat Mooney, Executive Director of ETC Group (formerly RAFI).

For more information:

Alexia Robinson, Foundation on Economic Trends, ph: (202) 466-2823

Chela Vazquez, Institute for Agriculture and Trade Policy
ph: (612) 203-5633

Jennifer Story, Council of Canadians, ph: (613) 233-4487, ext. 234

Visit: http://www.tradeobservatory.org/ or http://www.iatp.org/

Treaty to Share the Genetic Commons

We proclaim these truths to be universal and indivisible;

That the intrinsic value of the Earth's gene pool, in all of its biological forms and manifestations, precedes its utility and commercial value, and therefore must be respected and safeguarded by all political, commercial and social institutions,

That the Earth's gene pool, in all of its biological forms and manifestations, exists in nature and, therefore, must not be claimed as intellectual property even if purified and synthesized in the laboratory,

That the global gene pool, in all of its biological forms and manifestations, is a shared legacy and, therefore, a collective responsibility, and,

Whereas, our increasing knowledge of biology confers a special obligation to serve as a steward on behalf of the preservation and well being of our species as well as all of our other fellow creatures,

Therefore, the nations of the world declare the Earth's gene pool, in all of its biological forms and manifestations, to be a global commons, to be protected and nurtured by all peoples and further declare that genes and the products they code for, in their natural, purified or synthesized form as well as chromosomes, cells, tissue, organs and organisms, including cloned, transgenic and chimeric organisms, will not be allowed to be claimed as commercially negotiable genetic information or intellectual property by governments, commercial enterprises, other institutions or individuals.

The Parties to the treaty-to include signatory nation states and Indigenous Peoples-further agree to administer the gene pool as a trust. The signatories acknowledge the sovereign right and responsibility of every nation and homeland to oversee the biological resources within their borders and determine how they are managed and shared. However, because the gene pool, in all of its biological forms and manifestations, is a global commons, it cannot be sold by any institution or individual as genetic information. Nor can any institution or individual, in turn, lay claim to the genetic information as intellectual property.

NGOs Support a Treaty to Establish the Gene Pool as a Global Commons

Biotech activists from more than 50 nations announced their support for a treaty which would establish the earth's gene pool as a global commons. Non-Governmental Organizations' (NGOs) leaders say they will challenge government and corporate claims on patents on life in every country. The treaty is the first globally coordinated campaign among biotech activists, and already has the support of over 250 organizations.

The Treaty Initiative was announced simultaneously in New York at the United Nations preparatory meetings for the Rio+10 meeting, and in Porto Alegre, Brazil at the World Social Forum.

Activists will be working with political parties to introduce the Treaty Initiative in parliaments around the world over the next year. In September, 2002, activists will demand that governmental delegates to the Rio+10 Conference in South Africa endorse the Treaty to Share the Genetic Commons and make it the centerpiece of future biodiversity efforts.

Jeremy Rifkin, President of the Foundation on Economic Trends in Washington, DC, says, "The gene pool should not be allowed to be claimed as commercially negotiable genetic information or intellectual property by governments, commercial enterprises, other institutions or individuals. The global gene pool is a shared legacy and, therefore, a collective responsibility." Mr Rifkin added, "A global treaty to share the gene pool is the most important task ahead of us as we make the transition into the Age of Biology."

The Treaty Initiative to Share the Genetic Commons aims to prohibit all patents on plant, microorganism, animal, and human life.

The Treaty Initiative to Share the Genetic Commons aims to prohibit all patents on plant, microorganism, animal, and human life. "Currently, under the protection of the WTO, multinational corporations are exploiting critical genetic resources for private gain," says Kristin Dawkins, Vice President of Global Programs at the Institute for Agriculture and Trade Policy. "This ground-breaking global initiative represents a major new effort by NGOs to work within the existing global system to change international law so that it works for all people."

"Biodiversity has been the base of agriculture and food security for 10,000 years," says Elizabeth Brazo, of Accion Eco Log Ica (Ecuador). "The use of intellectual property rights has prevented this generation of new biodiversity. In fact, we are losing genetic diversity every day."

"The exploitation of genetic material that permits human life would change forever the potential of mankind," said Bill Christison, President of the National Family Farm Coalition which is the US member of Via Campesina. "A major theme supported by farmers and peasants in Via Campesina is that the world is not for sale and certainly this includes the gene pools of the people of the world."

Eighteen organizations, including the Foundation on Economic Trends, the International Forum on Globalization, and the National Family Farm Coalition in the US, Centro de Educacion y Tecnología in Chile, Comitato Scientifico Antivivisezionista in Italy, the Indigenous Peoples' Biodiversity Network in Peru, Southeast Asia Regional Institute for Community Education (SEARICE) in the Philippines, the Community Technology Development Trust in Zimbabwe, and Via Campesina have formed an international committee working to create a civil society process which would lead to the presentation of the Treaty to governments at the Rio+10 Conference in South Africa in the fall.

"This treaty is designed to ensure that governments and Indigenous Peoples are the caretakers of their part of the genetic commons and to establish the appropriate statutory mechanisms needed to ensure both sovereignty and open access to the worlds genetic diversity," says Hope Shand of ETC Group (formerly RAFI).

3

Outer Space, Moon and Other Celestial Bodies

BANNING NUCLEAR WEAPON TESTS IN ATMOSPHERE, OUTER SPACE AND UNDER WATER

Entered Into Force: 10 October, 1963

The Governments of the United States of America, the United Kingdom of Great Britain and Northern Ireland, and the Union of Soviet Socialist Republics, hereinafter referred to as the "Original Parties",

Proclaiming as their principal aim the speediest possible achievement of an agreement on general and complete disarmament under strict international control in accordance with the objectives of the United Nations which would put an end to the armaments race and eliminate the incentive to the production and testing of all kinds of weapons, including nuclear weapons,

Seeking to achieve the discontinuance of all test explosions of nuclear weapons for all time, determined to continue negotiations to this end, and desiring to put an end to the contamination of man's environment by radioactive substances,

Have agreed as follows:

Article I

1. Each of the Parties to this Treaty undertakes to prohibit, to prevent, and not to carry out any nuclear weapon test explosion, or any other nuclear explosion, at any place under its jurisdiction or control:

(a) in the atmosphere; beyond its limits, including outer space;

or under water, including territorial waters or high seas; or
(b) in any other environment if such explosion causes radioactive debris to be present outside the territorial limits of the State under whose jurisdiction or control such explosion is conducted. It is understood in this connection that the provisions of this subparagraph are without prejudice to the conclusion of a treaty resulting in the permanent banning of all nuclear test explosions, including all such explosions underground, the conclusion of which, as the Parties have stated in the Preamble to this Treaty, they seek to achieve.

2. Each of the Parties to this Treaty undertakes furthermore to refrain from causing, encouraging, or in any way participating in, the carrying out of any nuclear weapon test explosion, or any other nuclear explosion, anywhere which would take place in any of the environments described, or have the effect referred to, in paragraph 1 of this Article.

Article II

1. Any Party may propose amendments to this Treaty. The text of any proposed amendment shall be submitted to the Depositary Governments which shall circulate it to all Parties to this Treaty. Thereafter, if requested to do so by one-third or more of the Parties, the Depositary Governments shall convene a conference, to which they shall invite all the Parties, to consider such amendment.

2. Any amendment to this Treaty must be approved by a majority of the votes of all the Parties to this Treaty, including the votes of all of the Original Parties. The amendment shall enter into force for all Parties upon the deposit of instruments of ratification by a majority of all the Parties, including the instruments of ratification of all of the Original Parties.

Article III

1. This Treaty shall be open to all States for signature. Any State which does not sign this Treaty before its entry into

　　force in accordance with paragraph 3 of this Article may accede to it at any time.

2. This Treaty shall be subject to ratification by signatory States. Instruments of ratification and instruments of accession shall be deposited with the Governmen's of the Original Parties—the United States of America, the United Kingdom of Great Britain and Northern Ireland, and the Union of Soviet Socialist Republics—which are hereby designated the Depositary Governments.

3. This Treaty shall enter into force after its ratification by all the Original Parties and the deposit of their instruments of ratification.

4. For States whose instruments of ratification or accession are deposited subsequent to the entry into force of this Treaty, it shall enter into force on the date of the deposit of their instruments of ratification or accession.

5. The Depositary Governments shall promptly inform all signatory and acceding States of the date of each signature, the date of deposit of each instrument of ratification of and accession to this Treaty, the date of its entry into force, and the date of receipt of any requests for conferences or other notices.

6. This Treaty shall be registered by the Depositary Governments pursuant to Article 102 of the Charter of the United Nations.

Article IV

This Treaty shall be of unlimited duration.

　　Each Party shall in exercising its national sovereignty have the right to withdraw from the Treaty if it decides that extraordinary events, related to the subject matter of this Treaty, have jeopardized the supreme interests of its country. It shall give notice of such withdrawal to all other Parties to the Treaty three months in advance.

Article V

This Treaty, of which the English and Russian texts are equally authentic, shall be deposited in the archives of the Depositary

Governments. Duly certified copies of this Treaty shall be transmitted by the Depositary Governments to the Governments of the signatory and acceding States.

In Witness Whereof the undersigned, duly authorized, have signed this Treaty.

Done in triplicate at the city of Moscow the fifth day of August, one thousand nine hundred and sixty-three.

PRINCIPLES GOVERNING THE ACTIVITIES IN
THE EXPLORATION AND USE OF OUTER SPACE
(OUTER SPACE TREATY)

Bureau of Verification, Compliance, and Implementation
**Signed at Washington, London, Moscow, 27 January, 1967
Entered into force 10 October, 1967**

Narrative

The Outer Space Treaty, as it is known, was the second of the so-called "non-armament" treaties; its concepts and some of its provisions were modeled on its predecessor, the Antarctic Treaty. Like that Treaty it sought to prevent "a new form of colonial competition" and the possible damage that self-seeking exploitation might cause.

In early 1957, even before the launching of Sputnik in October, developments in rocketry led the United States to propose international verification of the testing of space objects. The development of an inspection system for outer space was part of a Western proposal for partial disarmament put forward in August, 1957. The Soviet Union, however, which was in the midst of testing its first ICBM and was about to orbit its first Earth satellite, did not accept these proposals.

Between 1959 and 1962 the Western powers made a series of proposals to bar the use of outer space for military purposes. Their successive plans for general and complete disarmament included provisions to ban the orbiting and stationing in outer space of weapons of mass destruction. Addressing the General Assembly on 22 September, 1960, President Eisenhower proposed that the principles of the Antarctic Treaty be applied to outer space and celestial bodies.

Soviet plans for general and complete disarmament between 1960 and 1962 included provisions for ensuring the peaceful use of outer space. The Soviet Union, however, would not separate outer space from other disarmament issues, nor would it agree to restrict outer space to peaceful uses unless U.S. foreign bases at which short-range and medium-range missiles were stationed were eliminated also.

The Western powers declined to accept the Soviet approach; the linkage, they held, would upset the military balance and weaken the security of the West.

After the signing of the Limited Test Ban Treaty, the Soviet Unions position changed. It ceased to link an agreement on outer space with the question of foreign bases. On 19 September, 1963, Foreign Minister Gromyko told the General Assembly that the Soviet Union wished to conclude an agreement banning the orbiting of objects carrying nuclear weapons. Ambassador Stevenson stated that the United States had no intention of orbiting weapons of mass destruction, installing them on celestial bodies or stationing them in outer space. The General Assembly unanimously adopted a resolution on 17 October, 1963, welcoming the Soviet and U.S. statements and calling upon all states to refrain from introducing weapons of mass destruction into outer space.

The United States supported the resolution, despite the absence of any provisions for verification; the capabilities of its space-tracking systems, it was estimated, were adequate for detecting launchings and devices in orbit.

Seeking to sustain the momentum for arms control agreements, the United States in 1965 and 1966 pressed for a Treaty that would give further substance to the U.N. resolution.

On 16 June, 1966, both the United States and the Soviet Union submitted draft treaties. The U.S. draft dealt only with celestial bodies; the Soviet draft covered the whole outer space environment. The United States accepted the Soviet position on the scope of the Treaty, and by September agreement had been reached in discussions at Geneva on most Treaty provisions. Differences on the few remaining issues — chiefly involving access to facilities on celestial bodies, reporting on space activities, and the use of military equipment and personnel in space exploration — were satisfactorily resolved in private consultations during the General Assembly session by December.

On the 19th of that month the General Assembly approved by acclamation a resolution commending the Treaty. It was opened for signature at Washington, London, and Moscow on 27 January, 1967. On 25 April the Senate gave unanimous consent to its ratification, and the Treaty entered into force on 10 October, 1967.

The substance of the arms control provisions is in Article IV. This article restricts activities in two ways:

First, it contains an undertaking not to place in orbit around the Earth, install on the moon or any other celestial body, or otherwise station in outer space, nuclear or any other weapons of mass destruction.

Second, it limits the use of the moon and other celestial bodies exclusively to peaceful purposes and expressly prohibits their use for establishing military bases, installation, or fortifications; testing weapons of any kind; or conducting military maneuvers.

After the Treaty entered into force, the United States and the Soviet Union collaborated in jointly planned and manned space enterprises.

Treaty Text

Treaty on Principles Governing the Activities of States in the Exploration and Use of Outer Space, Including the Moon and Other Celestial Bodies

Signed at Washington, London, Moscow, 27 January, 1967
Ratification advised by U.S. Senate 25 April, 1967
Ratified by U.S. President 24 May, 1967
U.S. ratification deposited at Washington, London, and Moscow 10 October, 1967
Proclaimed by U.S. President 10 October, 1967
Entered into force 10 October, 1967

The States Parties to this Treaty,

Inspired by the great prospects opening up before mankind as a result of mans entry into outer space,

Recognizing the common interest of all mankind in the progress of the exploration and use of outer space for peaceful purposes,

Believing that the exploration and use of outer space should be carried on for the benefit of all peoples irrespective of the degree of their economic or scientific development,

Desiring to contribute to broad international co-operation in the scientific as well as the legal aspects of the exploration and use of outer space for peaceful purposes,

Believing that such co-operation will contribute to the development of mutual understanding and to the strengthening of friendly relations between States and peoples,

Recalling resolution 1962 (XVIII), entitled "Declaration of Legal Principles Governing the Activities of States in the Exploration and Use of Outer Space," which was adopted unanimously by the United Nations General Assembly on 13 December 1963,

Recalling resolution 1884 (XVIII), calling upon States to refrain from placing in orbit around the Earth any objects carrying nuclear weapons or any other kinds of weapons of mass destruction or from installing such weapons on celestial bodies, which was adopted unanimously by the United Nations General Assembly on 17 October, 1963,

Taking account of United Nations General Assembly resolution 110 (II) of 3 November, 1947, which condemned propaganda designed or likely to provoke or encourage any threat to the peace, breach of the peace or act of aggression, and considering that the aforementioned resolution is applicable to outer space,

Convinced that a Treaty on Principles Governing the Activities of States in the Exploration and Use of Outer Space, including the Moon and Other Celestial Bodies, will further the Purposes and Principles of the Charter of the United Nations,

Have agreed on the following:

Article I

The exploration and use of outer space, including the moon and other celestial bodies, shall be carried out for the benefit and in the interests of all countries, irrespective of their degree of economic or scientific development, and shall be the province of all mankind.

Outer space, including the moon and other celestial bodies, shall be free for exploration and use by all States without discrimination of any kind, on a basis of equality and in accordance with international law, and there shall be free access to all areas of celestial bodies.

There shall be freedom of scientific investigation in outer space, including the moon and other celestial bodies, and States shall facilitate and encourage international co-operation in such investigation.

Article II

Outer space, including the moon and other celestial bodies, is not subject to national appropriation by claim of sovereignty, by means of use or occupation, or by any other means.

Article III

States Parties to the Treaty shall carry on activities in the exploration and use of outer space, including the moon and other celestial bodies, in accordance with international law, including the Charter of the United Nations, in the interest of maintaining international peace and security and promoting international co-operation and understanding.

Article IV

States Parties to the Treaty undertake not to place in orbit around the Earth any objects carrying nuclear weapons or any other kinds of weapons of mass destruction, install such weapons on celestial bodies, or station such weapons in outer space in any other manner.

The Moon and other celestial bodies shall be used by all States Parties to the Treaty exclusively for peaceful purposes. The establishment of military bases, installations and fortifications, the testing of any type of weapons and the conduct of military maneuvers on celestial bodies shall be forbidden. The use of military personnel for scientific research or for any other peaceful purposes shall not be prohibited. The use of any equipment or facility necessary for peaceful exploration of the Moon and other celestial bodies shall also not be prohibited.

Article V

States Parties to the Treaty shall regard astronauts as envoys of mankind in outer space and shall render to them all possible assistance in the event of accident, distress, or emergency landing on the territory of another State Party or on the high seas. When astronauts make such a landing, they shall be safely and promptly returned to the State of registry of their space vehicle.

In carrying on activities in outer space and on celestial bodies, the astronauts of one State Party shall render all possible assistance to the astronauts of other States Parties.

States Parties to the Treaty shall immediately inform the other States Parties to the Treaty or the Secretary-General of the United Nations of any phenomena they discover in outer space, including the Moon and other celestial bodies, which could constitute a danger to the life or health of astronauts.

Article VI

States Parties to the Treaty shall bear international responsibility for national activities in outer space, including the Moon and other celestial bodies, whether such activities are carried on by governmental agencies or by non-governmental entities, and for assuring that national activities are carried out in conformity with the provisions set forth in the present Treaty. The activities of non-governmental entities in outer space, including the Moon and other celestial bodies, shall require authorization and continuing supervision by the appropriate State Party to the Treaty. When activities are carried on in outer space, including the Moon and other celestial bodies, by an international organization, responsibility for compliance with this Treaty shall be borne both by the international organization and by the States Parties to the Treaty participating in such organization.

Article VII

Each State Party to the Treaty that launches or procures the launching of an object into outer space, including the Moon and other celestial bodies, and each State Party from whose territory or facility an object is launched, is internationally liable for damage to another State Party to the Treaty or to its natural or juridical persons by such object or its component parts on the Earth, in air space or in outer space, including the Moon and other celestial bodies.

Article VIII

A State Party to the Treaty on whose registry an object launched into outer space is carried shall retain jurisdiction and control over such object, and over any personnel thereof, while in outer space or on a celestial body. Ownership of objects launched into outer space, including objects landed or constructed on a celestial body, and of their component parts, is not affected by their presence in outer space or on a celestial body or by their return to the Earth. Such objects or component parts found beyond the limits of the State Party to the Treaty on whose registry they are carried shall be returned to that State Party, which shall, upon request, furnish identifying data prior to their return.

Article IX

In the exploration and use of outer space, including the Moon and other celestial bodies, States Parties to the Treaty shall be guided by the principle of co-operation and mutual assistance and shall conduct all their activities in outer space, including the Moon and other celestial bodies, with due regard to the corresponding interests of all other States Parties to the Treaty. States Parties to the Treaty shall pursue studies of outer space, including the Moon and other celestial bodies, and conduct exploration of them so as to avoid their harmful contamination and also adverse changes in the environment of the Earth resulting from the introduction of extraterrestrial matter and, where necessary, shall adopt appropriate measures for this purpose. If a State Party to the Treaty has reason to believe that an activity or experiment planned by it or its nationals in outer space, including the Moon and other celestial bodies, would cause potentially harmful interference with activities of other States Parties in the peaceful exploration and use of outer space, including the Moon and other celestial bodies, it shall undertake appropriate international consultations before proceeding with any such activity or experiment. A State Party to the Treaty which has reason to believe that an activity or experiment planned by another State Party in outer space, including the Moon and other celestial bodies, would cause potentially harmful interference with activities in the peaceful exploration and use of outer space, including the Moon and other celestial bodies, may request consultation concerning the activity or experiment.

Article X

In order to promote international co-operation in the exploration and use of outer space, including the Moon and other celestial bodies, in conformity with the purposes of this Treaty, the States Parties to the Treaty shall consider on a basis of equality any requests by other States Parties to the Treaty to be afforded an opportunity to observe the flight of space objects launched by those States.

The nature of such an opportunity for observation and the conditions under which it could be afforded shall be determined by agreement between the States concerned.

Article XI

In order to promote international co-operation in the peaceful exploration and use of outer space, States Parties to the Treaty conducting activities in outer space, including the Moon and other celestial bodies, agree to inform the Secretary-General of the United Nations as well as the public and the international scientific community, to the greatest extent feasible and practicable, of the nature, conduct, locations and results of such activities. On receiving the said information, the Secretary-General of the United Nations should be prepared to disseminate it immediately and effectively.

Article XII

All stations, installations, equipment and space vehicles on the Moon and other celestial bodies shall be open to representatives of other States Parties to the Treaty on a basis of reciprocity. Such representatives shall give reasonable advance notice of a projected visit, in order that appropriate consultations may be held and that maximum precautions may be taken to assure safety and to avoid interference with normal operations in the facility to be visited.

Article XIII

The provisions of this Treaty shall apply to the activities of States Parties to the Treaty in the exploration and use of outer space, including the Moon and other celestial bodies, whether such activities are carried on by a single State Party to the Treaty or jointly with other States, including cases where they are carried on within the framework of international intergovernmental organizations.

Any practical questions arising in connection with activities carried on by international inter-governmental organizations in the exploration and use of outer space, including the Moon and other celestial bodies, shall be resolved by the States Parties to the Treaty either with the appropriate international organization or with one or more States members of that international organization, which are Parties to this Treaty.

Article XIV

1. This Treaty shall be open to all States for signature. Any State which does not sign this Treaty before its entry into force in accordance with paragraph 3 of this article may accede to it at any time.
2. This Treaty shall be subject to ratification by signatory States. Instruments of ratification and instruments of accession shall be deposited with the Governments of the United States of America, the United Kingdom of Great Britain and Northern Ireland and the Union of Soviet Socialist Republics, which are hereby designated the Depositary Governments.
3. This Treaty shall enter into force upon the deposit of instruments of ratification by five Governments including the Governments designated as Depositary Governments under this Treaty.
4. For States whose instruments of ratification or accession are deposited subsequent to the entry into force of this

Treaty, it shall enter into force on the date of the deposit of their instruments of ratification or accession.

5. The Depositary Governments shall promptly inform all signatory and acceding States of the date of each signature, the date of deposit of each instrument of ratification of and accession to this Treaty, the date of its entry into force and other notices.

6. This Treaty shall be registered by the Depositary Governments pursuant to Article 102 of the Charter of the United Nations.

Article XV

Any State Party to the Treaty may propose amendments to this Treaty. Amendments shall enter into force for each State Party to the Treaty accepting the amendments upon their acceptance by a majority of the States Parties to the Treaty and thereafter for each remaining State Party to the Treaty on the date of acceptance by it.

Article XVI

Any State Party to the Treaty may give notice of its withdrawal from the Treaty one year after its entry into force by written notification to the Depositary Governments. Such withdrawal shall take effect one year from the date of receipt of this notification.

Article XVII

This Treaty, of which the English, Russian, French, Spanish and Chinese texts are equally authentic, shall be deposited in the archives of the Depositary Governments. Duly certified copies of this Treaty shall be transmitted by the Depositary Governments to the Governments of the signatory and acceding States.

In Witness Whereof the undersigned, duly authorized, have signed this Treaty.

Done in triplicate, at the cities of Washington, London and Moscow, this twenty-seventh day of January one thousand nine hundred sixty-seven.

Outer Space Treaty

Country	Date[1] of Signature	Date of Deposit[1] of Ratification	Date of Deposit[1] of Accession
Afghanistan	01/27/67	03/21/88	
Antigua and Barbuda			01/01/81
Argentina	01/27/67	03/26/69	
Australia	01/27/67	10/10/67	
Austria	02/20/67	02/26/68	
Bahamas, The			08/11/76
Bangladesh			01/17/86
Barbados			09/12/68
Belgium	01/27/67	03/30/73	
Benin			06/19/86
Bolivia	01/27/67		
Botswana	01/27/67		
Brazil	01/30/67	03/05/69	
Brunei			01/18/84
Bulgaria	01/27/67		03/28/67
Burkina Faso	03/03/67	06/18/68	
Burma	05/22/67	03/18/70	
Burundi	01/27/67		
Byelorussian S.S.R.[2]	02/10/67	10/31/67	
Cameroon	01/27/67		
Canada	01/27/67	10/10/67	
Central African Republic	01/27/67		
Chile	01/27/67	10/08/81	
China, People's Republic of			12/30/83
China (Taiwan)[4]	01/27/67	07/24/70	
Colombia	01/27/67		
Cuba			06/03/77
Cyprus	01/27/67	07/05/72	
Czechoslovakia	01/27/67	05/11/67	
Denmark	01/27/67	10/10/67	
Dominica			11/08/78
Dominican Republic	01/27/67	11/21/68	
Ecuador	01/27/67	03/07/69	
Egypt	01/27/67	10/10/67	
El Salvador	01/27/67	01/15/69	
Ethiopia	01/27/67		
Fiji			07/14/72
Finland	01/27/67	07/12/67	
France	09/25/67	08/05/70	
Gambia, The	06/02/67		
German Democratic Republic	01/27/67	02/02/67	
Germany, Federal Republic of	01/27/67	02/10/71	

(Contd.)

(*Contd.*)

Country	Date[1] of Signature	Date of Deposit[1] of Ratification	Date of Deposit[1] of Accession
Ghana	01/27/67		
Greece	01/27/67	01/19/71	
Grenada			02/07/74
Guinea-Bissau			08/20/76
Guyana	02/03/67		
Haiti	01/27/67		
Holy See	04/05/67		
Honduras	01/27/67		
Hungary	01/27/67	06/26/67	
Iceland	01/27/67	02/05/68	
India	03/03/67	01/18/82	
Indonesia	01/27/67		
Iran	01/27/67		
Iraq	02/27/67	12/04/68	
Ireland	01/27/67	07/17/68	
Israel	01/27/67	02/18/77	
Italy	01/27/67	05/04/72	
Jamaica	06/29/67	08/06/70	
Japan	01/27/67	10/10/67	
Jordan	02/02/67		
Kenya			01/19/84
Korea, Republic of	01/27/67	10/13/67	
Kuwait			06/07/72
Laos	01/27/67	11/27/72	
Lebanon	02/23/67	03/31/69	
Lesotho	01/27/67		
Libya			7/03/68
Luxembourg	01/27/67		
Madagascar			08/22/68
Malaysia	02/20/67		
Mali			06/11/68
Mauritius			04/07/69
Mexico	01/27/67	01/31/68	
Mongolia	01/27/67	10/10/67	
Morocco			12/21/67
Nepal	02/03/67	10/10/67	
Netherlands	02/10/67	10/10/69	
New Zealand	01/27/67	05/31/68	
Nicaragua	01/27/67		
Niger	02/01/67	04/17/67	
Nigeria			11/14/67
Norway	02/03/67	07/01/69	
Pakistan	09/12/67	04/08/68	
Panama	01/27/67		
Papua New Guinea			10/27/80
Peru	06/30/67	02/28/79	

(*Contd.*)

(Contd.)

Country	Date[1] of Signature	Date of Deposit[1] of Ratification	Date of Deposit[1] of Accession
Philippines	01/27/67		
Poland	01/27/67	01/30/68	
Romania	01/27/67	04/09/68	
Rwanda	01/27/67		
Saint Christopher-Nevis			09/19/83
Saint Lucia			02/22/79
San Marino	04/21/67	10/29/68	
Saudi Arabia			12/17/76
Seychelles			01/05/78
Sierra Leone	01/27/67	07/13/67	
Singapore			09/10/76
Solomon Islands			07/07/78
Somalia	02/02/67		
South Africa	03/01/67	09/30/68	
Spain			11/27/68
Sri Lanka	03/10/69	11/18/86	
Swaziland			10/22/68
Sweden	01/27/67	10/11/67	
Switzerland	01/27/67	12/18/69	
Syria			11/19/68
Thailand	01/27/67	09/05/68	
Togo	01/27/67		
Tonga			06/22/71
Trinidad and Tobago	07/24/67		
Tunisia	01/27/67	03/28/68	
Turkey	01/27/67	03/27/68	
Uganda			04/24/68
Ukrainian S.S.R.[2]	02/10/67	10/31/67	
Union of Soviet Socialist Republics	01/27/67	10/10/67	
United Kingdom	01/27/67	10/10/67	
United States	01/27/67	10/10/67	
Uruguay	01/27/67	08/31/70	
Venezuela	01/27/67	03/03/70	
Vietnam			06/20/80
Yemen, People's Democratic Republic of (Aden)			06/01/79
Yugoslavia	01/27/67		
Zaire	01/27/67		
Zambia			08/20/73
Total[3]	91	62	36

Notes:

1. Dates given are the earliest dates on which countries signed the agreements or deposited their ratifications or accessions—

whether in Washington, London, Moscow, or New York. In the case of a country that was a dependent territory which became a party through succession, the date given is the date on which the country gave notice that it would continue to be bound by the terms of the agreement.

2. The United States regards the signature and ratification by the Byelorussian S.S.R. and the Ukrainian S.S.R. as already included under the signature and ratification of the Union of Soviet Socialist Republics.

3. This total does not include actions by the Byelorussian S.S.R. and the Ukrainian S.S.R. (See footnote 2.)

4. Effective 1 January, 1979, the United States recognized the Government of the People's Republic of China as the sole government of China.

RESCUE AND RETURN OF ASTRONAUTS AND OBJECTS LAUNCHED INTO OUTER SPACE

Entered into Force: 3 December, 1968

The Contracting Parties,

Noting the great importance of the Treaty on Principles Governing the Activities of States in the Exploration and Use of Outer Space, including the Moon and Other Celestial Bodies, which calls for the rendering of all possible assistance to astronauts in the event of accident, distress or emergency landing, the prompt and safe return of astronauts, and the return of objects launched into outer space,

Desiring to develop and give further concrete expression to these duties,

Wishing to promote international co-operation in the peaceful exploration and use of outer space,

Prompted by sentiments of humanity,

Have agreed on the following:

Article 1

Each Contracting Party which receives information or discovers that the personnel of a spacecraft have suffered accident or are experiencing conditions of distress or have made an emergency or unintended landing in territory under its jurisdiction or on the high seas or in any other place not under the jurisdiction of any State shall immediately:

(a) notify the launching authority or, if it cannot identify and immediately communicate with the launching authority, immediately make a public announcement by all appropriate means of communication at its disposal;

(b) notify the Secretary-General of the United Nations, who should disseminate the information without delay by all appropriate means of communication at his disposal.

Article 2

If, owing to accident, distress, emergency or unintended landing, the personnel of a spacecraft land in territory under the jurisdiction of a Contracting Party, it shall immediately take all possible steps to rescue them and render them all necessary assistance. It shall inform the launching authority and also the Secretary-General of the United Nations of the steps it is taking and of their progress. If assistance by the launching authority would help to effect a prompt rescue or would contribute substantially to the effectiveness of search and rescue operations, the launching authority shall co-operate with the Contracting Party with a view to the effective conduct of search and rescue operations. Such operations shall be subject to the direction and control of the Contracting Party, which shall act in close and continuing consultation with the launching authority.

Article 3

If information is received or it is discovered that the personnel of a spacecraft have alighted on the high seas or in any other place not under the jurisdiction of any State, those Contracting Parties which are in a position to do so shall, if necessary, extend assistance in search and rescue operations for such personnel to assure their speedy rescue. They shall inform the launching authority and the Secretary-General of the United Nations of the steps they are taking and of their progress.

Article 4

If, owing to accident, distress, emergency or unintended landing, the personnel of a spacecraft land in territory under the jurisdiction of a Contracting Party or have been found on the high seas or in any other place not under the jurisdiction of any State, they shall be safely and promptly returned to representatives of the launching authority.

Article 5

1. Each Contracting Party which receives information or discovers that a space object or its component parts has returned to Earth in territory under its jurisdiction or on the high seas or in any other place not under the jurisdiction of any State, shall notify the launching authority and the Secretary-General of the United Nations.

2. Each Contracting Party having jurisdiction over the territory on which a space object or its component parts has been discovered shall, upon the request of the launching authority and with assistance from that authority if requested, take such steps as it finds practicable to recover the object or component parts.

3. Upon request of the launching authority, objects launched into outer space or their component parts found beyond the territorial limits of the launching authority shall be returned to or held at the disposal of representatives of the launching authority, which shall, upon request, furnish identifying data prior to their return.

4. Notwithstanding paragraphs 2 and 3 of this Article, a Contracting Party which has reason to believe that a space object or its component parts discovered in territory under its jurisdiction, or recovered by it elsewhere, is of a hazardous or deleterious nature may so notify the launching authority, which shall immediately take effective steps, under the direction and control of the said Contracting Party, to eliminate possible danger of harm.

5. Expenses incurred in fulfilling obligations to recover and return a space object or its component parts under paragraphs 2 and 3 of this Article shall be borne by the launching authority.

Article 6

For the purposes of this Agreement, the term "launching authority" shall refer to the State responsible for launching, or, where an international intergovernmental organization is responsible for launching, that organization, provided that that organization declares its acceptance of the rights and obligations provided for in this Agreement and a majority of the States members of that organization are Contracting Parties to this Agreement and to the Treaty on Principles Governing the Activities of States in the Exploration and Use of Outer Space, including the Moon and Other Celestial Bodies.

Article 7

1. This Agreement shall be open to all States for signature. Any State which does not sign this Agreement before its entry into force in accordance with paragraph 3 of this Article may accede to it at any time.
2. This Agreement shall be subject to ratification by signatory States. Instruments of ratification and instruments of accession shall be deposited with the Governments of the United Kingdom of Great Britain and Northern Ireland, the Union of Soviet Socialist Republics and the United States of America, which are hereby designated the Depositary Governments.
3. This Agreement shall enter into force upon the deposit of instruments of ratification by five Governments including the Governments designated as Depositary Governments under this Agreement.
4. For States whose instruments of ratification or accession are deposited subsequent to the entry into force of this Agreement, it shall enter into force on the date of the deposit of their instruments of ratification or accession.
5. The Depositary Governments shall promptly inform all signatory and acceding States of the date of each signature, the date of deposit of each instrument of ratification of and accession to this Agreement, the date of its entry into force and other notices.
6. This Agreement shall be registered by the Depositary

Governments pursuant to Article 102 of the Charter of the United Nations.

Article 8

Any State Party to the Agreement may propose amendments to this Agreement. Amendments shall enter into force for each State Party to the Agreement accepting the amendments upon their acceptance by a majority of the States Parties to the Agreement and thereafter for each remaining State Party to the Agreement on the date of acceptance by it.

Article 9

Any State Party to the Agreement may give notice of its withdrawal from the Agreement one year after its entry into force by written notification to the Depositary Governments. Such withdrawal shall take effect one year from the date of receipt of this notification.

Article 10

This Agreement, of which the English, Russian, French, Spanish and Chinese texts are equally authentic, shall be deposited in the archives of the Depositary Governments. Duly certified copies of this Agreement shall be transmitted by the Depositary Governments to the Governments of the signatory and acceding States.

In witness whereof the undersigned, duly authorised, have signed this Agreement.

Done in triplicate, at the cities of London, Moscow and Washington, the twenty-second day of April, one thousand nine hundred and sixty-eight.

INTELSAT AND INMARSAT

Agreement Relating to the International Telecommunications Satellite Organization "Intelsat" (with Annexes and Operating Agreement) (1971)

Entered into Force: 12 February, 1973

Preamble

The States Parties to this Agreement,

Considering the principle set forth in Resolution 1721 (XVI) of the General Assembly of the United Nations that communication by means of satellites should be available to the nations of the world as soon as practicable on a global and nondiscriminatory basis,

Considering the relevant provisions of the Treaty on Principles Governing the Activities of States in the Exploration and Use of Outer Space, Including the Moon and Other Celestial Bodies, and in particular Article I, which states that outer space shall be used for the benefit and in the interests of all countries,

Noting that pursuant to the Agreement Establishing Interim Arrangements for a Global Commercial Communications Satellite System and the related Special Agreement, a global commercial telecommunications satellite system has been established,

Desiring to continue the development of this telecommunications satellite system with the aim of achieving a single global commercial telecommunications satellite system as part of an improved global telecommunications network which will provide expanded telecommunications services to all areas of the world and which will contribute to world peace and understanding,

Determined, to this end, to provide, for the benefit of all mankind, through the most advanced technology available, the most efficient and economic facilities possible consistent with the best and most equitable use of the radio frequency spectrum and of orbital space,

Believing that satellite telecommunications should be organized in such a way as to permit all peoples to have access to the global satellite system and those States members of the International Telecommunication Union so wishing to invest in the system with consequent participation in the design, development, construction, including the provision of equipment, establishment, operation, maintenance and ownership of the system,

Pursuant to the Agreement Establishing Interim Arrangements for a Global Commercial Communications Satellite System,

Agree as follows:

Article I: Definitions

For the purposes of this Agreement:

(a) "Agreement" means the present agreement, including its Annexes but excluding all titles of Articles, opened for signature by Governments at Washington on 20 August, 1971, by which the international telecommunications satellite organization "INTELSAT" is established;

(b) "Operating Agreement" means the agreement, including its Annex but excluding all titles of Articles, opened for signature at Washington on 20 August, 1971,' by Governments or telecommunications entities designated by Governments in accordance with the provisions of this Agreement;

(c) "Interim Agreement" means the Agreement Establishing Interim Arrangements for a Global Commercial Communications Satellite System signed by Governments at Washington on 20 August, 1964;

(d) "Special Agreement" means the agreement signed on 20 August, 1964, by Governments or telecommunications entities designated by Governments, pursuant to the provisions of the Interim Agreement;

(e) "Interim Communications Satellite Committee" means the Committee established by Article IV of the Interim Agreement;

(f) "Party" means a State for which the Agreement has entered into force or been provisionally applied;

(g) "Signatory" means a Party, or the telecommunications entity designated by a Party, which has signed the Operating Agreement and for which it has entered into force or been provisionally applied;

(h) "Space segment" means the telecommunications satellites, and the tracking, telemetry, command, control, monitoring and related facilities and equipment required to support the operation of these satellites;

(i) "INTELSAT space segment" means the space segment owned by INTELSAT;

(j) "Telecommunications" means any transmission, emission or reception of signs, signals, writing, images and sounds or intelligence of any nature, by wire, radio, optical or other electromagnetic systems;

(k) "Public telecommunications services" means fixed or mobile telecommunications services which can be provided by satellite and which are available for use by the public, such as telephony, telegraphy, telex, facsimile, data transmission, transmission of radio and television programs between approved earth stations having access to the INTELSAT space segment for further transmission to the public, and leased circuits for any of these purposes; but excluding those mobile services of a type not provided under the Interim Agreement and the Special Agreement prior to the opening for signature of this Agreement, which are provided through mobile stations operating directly to a satellite which is designed, in whole or in part to provide services relating to the safety or flight control of aircraft or to aviation or maritime radio navigation;

(l) "Specialized telecommunications services" means telecommunications services which can be provided by satellite, other than those defined in paragraph (k) of this Article, including, but not limited to, radio navigation services, broadcasting satellite services for reception by the general public, space research services, meteorological services, and earth resources services;

(m) "Property" includes every subject of whatever nature to which a right of ownership can attach, as well as contractual rights; and

(n) "Design" and "development" include research directly related to the purposes of INTELSAT.

Article II: Establishment of INTELSAT

(a) With full regard for the principles set forth in the Preamble to this Agreement, the Parties hereby establish the international telecommunications satellite organization "INTELSAT", the main purpose of which is to continue and carry forward on a definitive basis the design, development, construction, establishment, operation and maintenance of the space segment of the global commercial telecommunications satellite system as established under the provisions of the Interim Agreement and the Special Agreement.

(b) Each State Party shall sign, or shall designate a telecommunications entity, public or private, to sign, the Operating Agreement which shall be concluded in conformity with the provisions of this Agreement and which shall be opened for signature at the same time as this Agreement. Relations between any telecommunications entity, acting as Signatory, and the Party which has designated it shall be governed by applicable domestic law.

(c) Telecommunications administrations and entities may, subject to applicable domestic law, negotiate and enter directly into appropriate traffic agreements with respect to their use of channels of telecommunications provided pursuant to this Agreement and the Operating Agreement, as well as services to be furnished to the public, facilities, divisions of revenue and related business arrangements.

Article III: (Scope of Intelsat Activities)

(a) In continuing and carrying forward on a definitive basis activities concerning the space segment of the global commercial telecommunications satellite system referred to in paragraph(a) of Article II of this Agreement, INTELSAT shall have as its prime objective the provision, on a commercial basis, of the space segment required for international public telecommunications services of high quality and reliability to be available on a non-discriminatory basis to all areas of the world.

(b) The following shall be considered on the same basis as international public telecommunications services:

(i) Domestic public telecommunications services between areas separated by areas not under the jurisdiction of the State concerned, or between areas separated by the high seas; and

(ii) Domestic public telecommunications services between areas which are not linked by any terrestrial wideband facilities and which are separated by natural barriers of such an exceptional nature that they impede the viable establishment of terrestrial wideband facilities between such areas, provided that the Meeting of Signatories, having regard to advice tendered by the Board of Governors, has given the appropriate approval in advance.

(c) The INTELSAT space segment established to meet the prime objective shall also be made available for other domestic public telecommunications services on a non-discriminatory basis to the extent that the ability of INTELSAT to achieve its prime objective is not impaired.

(d) The INTELSAT space segment may also, on request and under appropriate terms and conditions, be utilized for the purpose of specialized telecommunications services, either international or domestic, other than for military purposes, provided that:

    (i) The provision of public telecommunications services is not unfavorably affected thereby; and

    (ii) The arrangements are otherwise acceptable from a technical and economic point of view.

(e) INTELSAT may, on request and under appropriate terms and conditions, provide satellites or associated facilities separate from the INTELSAT space segment for:

    (i) Domestic public telecommunications services in territories under the jurisdiction of one or more Parties;

    (ii) International public telecommunications services between or among territories under the jurisdiction of two or more Parties;

    (iii) Specialized telecommunications services, other than for military purposes; provided that the efficient and economic operation of the INTELSAT space segment is not unfavorably affected in any way.

(f) The utilization of the INTELSAT space segment for specialized telecommunications services pursuant to paragraph(d) of this Article, and the provision of satellites or associated facilities separate from the INTELSAT space segment pursuant to paragraph(e) of this Article, shall be covered by contracts entered into between INTELSAT and the applicants concerned. The utilization of INTELSAT space segment facilities for specialized telecommunications services pursuant to paragraph (d) of this Article, and the provision of satellites or associated facilities separate from the INTELSAT space segment for specialized telecommunications services pursuant to subparagraph (e) (iii) of this Article, shall be in accordance with appropriate authorizations, at the planning stage, of the Assembly of Parties pursuant to subparagraph (c) (iv) of Article VII of this Agreement. Where the utilization of INTELSAT space segment facilities for specialized telecommunications services would involve additional costs which result from required modifications to existing or planned INTELSAT space segment facilities, or where the provision of satellites or associated facilities separate from the INTELSAT space segment is sought for specialized telecommunications services as provided for in subparagraph (e) (iii) of this Article, authorization pursuant to subparagraph (c) (iv) of Article VII of this Agreement shall be sought from the Assembly of Parties as soon as the Board of Governors is in a position to advise the Assembly of Parties in detail regarding the estimated cost of the proposal, the benefits to be derived, the technical or other problems involved and the probable effects on present or foreseeable INTELSAT services. Such authorization shall be obtained before the procurement process for the facility or facilities involved is initiated. Before making such authorizations, the Assembly of Parties, in appropriate cases, shall consult or ensure that there has been consultation by INTELSAT with Specialized Agencies of the United Nations directly concerned with the provision of the specialized telecommunications services in question.

Article IV: Juridical Personality

(a) INTELSAT shall possess juridical personality. It shall enjoy the full capacity necessary for the exercise of its functions and the achievement of its purposes, including the capacity to:

   (i) Conclude agreements with States or international organizations;

(ii) Contract;

(iii) Acquire and dispose of property; and

(iv) Be a party to legal proceedings.

(b) Each Party shall take such action as is necessary within its jurisdiction for the purpose of making effective in terms of its own law the provisions of this Article.

Article V: Financial Principles

(a) INTELSAT shall be the owner of the INTELSAT space segment and of all other property acquired by INTELSAT. The financial interest in INTELSAT of each Signatory shall be equal to the amount arrived at by the application of its investment share to the valuation effected pursuant to Article 7 of the Operating Agreement.

(b) Each Signatory shall have an investment share corresponding to its percentage of all utilization of the INTELSAT space segment by all Signatories as determined in accordance with the provisions of the Operating Agreement. However, no Signatory, even if its utilization of the INTELSAT space segment is nil, shall have an investment share less than the minimum established in the Operating Agreement.

(c) Each Signatory shall contribute to the capital requirements of INTELSAT, and shall receive capital repayment and compensation for use of capital in accordance with the provisions of the Operating Agreement.

(d) All users of the INTELSAT space segment shall pay utilization charges determined in accordance with the provisions of this Agreement and the Operating Agreement. The rates of space segment utilization charge for each type of utilization shall be the same for all applicants for space segment capacity for that type of utilization.

(e) The separate satellites and associated facilities referred to in paragraph (e) of Article III of this Agreement may be financed and owned by INTELSAT as part of the INTELSAT space segment upon the unanimous approval of all the Signatories. If such approval is withheld, they shall be separate from the INTELSAT space segment and shall be financed and owned by those requesting them. In this case the financial terms and conditions set by INTELSAT shall be such as to cover fully the costs directly resulting from the design, development, construction and provision of such separate satellites and associated facilities as well as an adequate part of the general and administrative costs of INTELSAT.

Article VI: Structure of Intelsat

  (a) INTELSAT shall have the following organs:
    (i) The Assembly of Parties;
    (ii) The Meeting of Signatories;
    (iii) The Board of Governors; and
    (iv) An executive organ, responsible to the Board of Governors.

  (b) Except to the extent that this Agreement or the Operating Agreement specifically provides otherwise, no organ shall make determinations or otherwise act in such a way as to alter, nullify, delay or in any other manner interfere with the exercise of a power or the discharge of a responsibility or a function attributed to another organ by this Agreement or the Operating Agreement.

  (c) Subject to paragraph (b) of this Article, the Assembly of Parties, the Meeting of Signatories and the Board of Governors shall each take note of and give due and proper consideration to any resolution, recommendation or view made or expressed by another of these organs acting in the exercise of the responsibilities and functions attributed to it by this Agreement or the Operating Agreement.

Article VII: Assembly of Parties

  (a) The Assembly of Parties shall be composed of all the Parties and shall be the principal organ of INTELSAT.

  (b) The Assembly of Parties shall give consideration to those aspects of INTELSAT which are primarily of interest to the Parties as sovereign States. It shall have the power to give consideration to general policy and long-term objectives of INTELSAT consistent with the principles, purposes and scope of activities of INTELSAT, as provided for in this Agreement. In accordance with paragraphs (b) and (c) of Article VI of this Agreement, the Assembly of Parties shall give due and proper consideration to resolutions, recommendations and views addressed to it by the Meeting of Signatories or the Board of Governors.

(c) The Assembly of Parties shall have the following functions and powers:

   (i) In the exercise of its power of considering general policy and long-term objectives of INTELSAT, to formulate its views or make recommendations, as it may deem appropriate, to the other organs of INTELSAT;

   (ii) To determine that measures should be taken to prevent the activities of INTELSAT from conflicting with any general multilateral convention which is consistent with this Agreement and which is adhered to by at least two-thirds of the Parties;

   (iii) To consider and take decisions on proposals for amending this Agreement in accordance with Article XVII of this Agreement and to propose, express its views and make recommendations on amendments to the Operating Agreement;

   (iv) To authorize, through general rules or by specific determinations, the utilization of the INTELSAT space segment and the provision of satellites and associated facilities separate from the INTELSAT space segment for specialized telecommunications services within the scope of activities referred to in paragraph (d) and subparagraph (e) (iii) of Article III of this Agreement;

   (v) To review, in order to ensure the application of the principle of non-discrimination, the general rules established pursuant to subparagraph (b) (v) of Article VIII of this Agreement;

   (vi) To consider and express its views on the reports presented by the Meeting of Signatories and the Board of Governors concerning the implementation of general policies, the activities and the long-term program of INTELSAT;

   (vii) To express, pursuant to Article XIV of this Agreement, its findings in the form of recommendations, with respect to the intended establishment, acquisition or utilization of space segment facilities separate from the INTELSAT space segment facilities;

(viii) To take decisions, pursuant to subparagraph (b) (i) of Article XVI of this Agreement, in connection with the withdrawal of a Party from INTELSAT;

(ix) To decide upon questions concerning formal relationships between INTELSAT and States, whether Parties or not, or international organizations;

(x) To consider complaints submitted to it by Parties;

(xi) To select the legal experts referred to in Article 3 of Annex C to this Agreement;

(xii) To act upon the appointment of the Director General in accordance with Articles XI and XII of this Agreement;

(xiii) Pursuant to Article XII of this Agreement, to adopt the organizational structure of the executive organ; and

(xiv) To exercise any other powers coming within the purview of the Assembly of Parties according to the provisions of this Agreement.

(d) The first ordinary meeting of the Assembly of Parties shall be convened by the Secretary General within one year following the date on which this Agreement enters into force. Ordinary meetings shall thereafter be scheduled to be held every two years. The Assembly of Parties, however, may decide otherwise from meeting to meeting.

(e) (i) In addition to the ordinary meetings provided for in paragraph (d) of this Article, the Assembly of Parties may meet in extraordinary meetings, which may be convened either upon request of the Board of Governors acting pursuant to the provisions of Article XIV or XVI of this Agreement, or upon the request of one or more Parties which receives the support of at least one-third of the Parties including the requesting Party or Parties.

(ii) Requests for extraordinary meetings shall state the purpose of the meeting and shall be addressed in writing to the Secretary General or the Director General, who shall arrange for the meeting to be held

as soon as possible and in accordance with the rules
of procedure of the Assembly of Parties for convening
such meetings.

(f) A quorum for any meeting of the Assembly of Parties shall
consist of representatives of a majority of the Parties. Each
Party shall have one vote. Decisions on matters of
substance shall be taken by an affirmative vote cast by at
least two-thirds of the Parties whose representatives are
present and voting. Decisions on procedural matters shall
be taken by an affirmative vote cast by a simple majority
of the Parties whose representatives are present and
voting. Disputes whether a specific matter is procedural
or substantive shall be decided by a vote cast by a simple
majority of the Parties whose representatives are present
and voting.

(g) The Assembly of Parties shall adopt its own rules of
procedure, which shall include provision for the election
of a Chairman and other officers.

(h) Each Party shall meet its own costs of representation at a
meeting of the Assembly of Parties. Expenses of meetings
of the Assembly of Parties shall be regarded as an
administrative cost of INTELSAT for the purpose of Article
8 of the Operating Agreement.

Article VIII: Meeting of Signatories

(a) The Meeting of Signatories shall be composed of all the
Signatories. In accordance with paragraphs (b) and (c) of
Article VI of this Agreement, the Meeting of Signatories
shall give due and proper consideration to resolutions,
recommendations and views addressed to it by the
Assembly of Parties or the Board of Governors.

(b) The Meeting of Signatories shall have the following
functions and powers:

(i) To consider and express its views to the Board of
Governors on the annual report and annual financial
statements submitted to it by the Board of Governors;

(ii) To express its views and make recommendations on
proposed amendments to this Agreement pursuant
to Article XVII of this Agreement and to consider and

take decisions, in accordance with Article 22 of the Operating Agreement and taking into account any views and recommendations received from the Assembly of Parties or the Board of Governors, on proposed amendments to the Operating Agreement which are consistent with this Agreement;

(iii) To consider and express its views regarding reports on future programs, including the estimated financial implications of such programs, submitted by the Board of Governors;

(iv) To consider and decide on any recommendation made by the Board of Governors concerning an increase in the ceiling provided for in Article 5 of the Operating Agreement;

(v) To establish general rules, upon the recommendation of and for the guidance of the Board of Governors, concerning:

  (a) The approval of earth stations for access to the INTELSAT space segment,

  (b) The allotment of INTELSAT space segment capacity, and

  (c) The establishment and adjustment of the rates of charge for utilization of the INTELSAT space segment on a non-discriminatory basis;

(vi) To take decisions pursuant to Article XVI of this Agreement in connection with the withdrawal of a Signatory from INTELSAT;

(vii) To consider and express its views on complaints submitted to it by Signatories directly or through the Board of Governors or submitted to it through the Board of Governors by users of the INTELSAT space segment who are not Signatories;

(viii) To prepare and present to the Assembly of Parties, and to the Parties, reports concerning the implementation of general policies, the activities and the long-term program of INTELSAT;

(ix) To take decisions concerning the approval referred to in subparagraph (b) (ii) of Article III of this Agreement;

(x) To consider and express its views on the report on permanent management arrangements submitted by the Board of Governors to the Assembly of Parties pursuant to paragraph (g) of Article XII of this Agreement;

(xi) To make annual determinations for the purpose of representation on the Board of Governors in accordance with Article IX of this Agreement; and

(xii) To exercise any other powers coming within the purview of the Meeting of Signatories according to the provisions of this Agreement or the Operating Agreement.

(c) The first ordinary meeting of the Meeting of Signatories shall be convened by the Secretary General at the request of the Board of Governors within nine months after the entry into force of this Agreement. Thereafter an ordinary meeting shall be held in every calendar year.

(d) (i) In addition to the ordinary meetings provided for in paragraph (c) of this Article, the Meeting of Signatories may hold extraordinary meetings, which may be convened either upon the request of the Board of Governors or upon the request of one or more Signatories which receives the support of at least one-third of the Signatories including the requesting Signatory or Signatories.

(ii) Requests for extraordinary meetings shall state the purpose for which the meeting is required and shall be addressed in writing to the Secretary General or the Director General, who shall arrange for the meeting to be held as soon as possible and in accordance with the rules of procedure of the Meeting of Signatories for convening such meetings. The agenda for an extraordinary meeting shall be restricted to the purpose or purposes for which the meeting was convened.

(e) A quorum for any meeting of the Meeting of Signatories shall consist of representatives of a majority of the Signatories. Each Signatory shall have one vote. Decisions on matters of substance shall be taken by an affirmative vote cast by at least two-thirds of the Signatories whose representatives are present and voting. Decisions on procedural matters shall be taken by an affirmative vote cast by a simple majority of the Signatories whose representatives are present and voting. Disputes whether a specific matter is procedural or substantive shall be decided by a vote cast by a simple majority of the Signatories whose representatives are present and voting.

(f)   The Meeting of Signatories shall adopt its own rules of procedure, which shall include provision for the election of a Chairman and other officers.

(g)   Each Signatory shall meet its own costs of representation at meetings of the Meeting of Signatories. Expenses of meetings of the Meeting of Signatories shall be regarded as an administrative cost of INTELSAT for the purpose of Article 8 of the Operating Agreement.

Article IX: Board of Governors: Composition and Voting

(a)   The Board of Governors shall be composed of:

   (i)   One Governor representing each Signatory whose investment share is not less than the minimum investment share as determined in accordance with paragraph (b) of this Article;

   (ii) One Governor representing each group of any two or more Signatories not represented pursuant to subparagraph (i) of this paragraph whose combined investment share is not less than the minimum investment share as determined in accordance with paragraph (b) of this Article and which have agreed to be so represented;

   (iii) One Governor representing any group of at least five Signatories not represented pursuant to subparagraph (i) or (ii) of this paragraph from any one of the regions defined by the Plenipotentiary Conference of the International Telecommunication Union, held at Montreux in 1965, regardless of the total investment shares held by the Signatories comprising the group. However, the number of Governors under this category shall not exceed two for any region defined by the Union or five for all such regions.

(b)   (i) During the period between the entry into force of this Agreement and the first meeting of the Meeting of Signatories, the minimum investment share that will entitle a Signatory or group of Signatories to be represented on the Board of Governors shall be equal to the investment share of the Signatory holding position thirteen in the list of the descending order of size of initial investment shares of all the Signatories.

(ii) Subsequent to the period mentioned in subparagraph (i) of this paragraph, the Meeting of Signatories shall determine annually the minimum investment share that will entitle a Signatory or group of Signatories to be represented on the Board of Governors. For this purpose, the Meeting of Signatories shall be guided by the desirability of the number of Governors being approximately twenty, excluding any selected pursuant to subparagraph (a) (iii) of this Article.

(iii) For the purpose of making the determinations referred to in subparagraph (ii) of this paragraph, the Meeting of Signatories shall fix a minimum investment share according to the following provisions:

(a) If the Board of Governors, at the time the determination is made, is composed of twenty, twenty-one or twenty-two Governors, the Meeting of Signatories shall fix a minimum investment share equal to the investment share of the Signatory which, in the list in effect at that time, holds the same position held in the list in effect when the previous determination was made, by the Signatory selected on that occasion,

(b) If the Board of Governors, at the time the determination is made, is composed of more than twenty-two Governors, the Meeting of Signatories shall fix a minimum investment share equal to the investment share of a Signatory which, in the list in effect at that time, holds a position above the one held in the list in effect when the previous determination was made, by the Signatory selected on that occasion,

(c) If the Board of Governors, at the time the determination is made, is composed of less than twenty Governors, the Meeting of Signatories shall fix a minimum investment share equal to the investment share of a Signatory which, in the list in effect at that time, holds a position below the one held in the list in effect when the previous determination was made, by the Signatory selected on that occasion.

(iv) If, by applying the ranking method set forth in subparagraph (iii) (B)   of this paragraph, the number of Governors would be less than twenty, or, by applying that set forth in subparagraph (iii) (C) of this paragraph, would be more than twenty-two, the Meeting of Signatories shall determine a minimum investment share that will better ensure that there will be twenty Governors.

(v) For the purpose of the provisions of subparagraphs (iii) and (iv) of this paragraph, the Governors selected in accordance with subparagraph (a) (iii) of this Article shall not be taken into consideration.

(vi) For the purpose of the provisions of this paragraph, investment shares determined pursuant to subparagraph (c) (ii) of Article 6 of the Operating Agreement shall take effect from the first day of the ordinary meeting of the Meeting of Signatories following such determination.

(c) Whenever a Signatory or group of Signatories fulfills the requirements for representation pursuant to subparagraph (a) (i), (ii) or (iii) of this Article, it shall be entitled to be represented on the Board of Governors. In the case of any group of Signatories referred to in subparagraph (a) (iii) of this Article, such entitlement shall become effective upon receipt by the executive organ of a written request from such group, provided, however, that the number of such groups represented on the Board of Governors has not, at the time of receipt of any such written request, reached the applicable limitations prescribed in subparagraph (a) (iii) of this Article. If at the time of receipt of any such written request representation on the Board of Governors pursuant to subparagraph (a) (iii) of this Article has reached the applicable limitations prescribed therein, the group of Signatories may submit its request to the next ordinary meeting of the Meeting of Signatories for a determination pursuant to paragraph (d) of this Article.

(d) Upon the request of any group or groups of Signatories referred to in subparagraph (a) (iii) of this Article, the Meeting of Signatories shall annually determine which of these groups shall be or continue to be represented on the Board of Governors. For this purpose, if such groups exceed two for any one region defined by the International Telecommunication Union, or five for all such regions, the Meeting of Signatories shall first select the group which has the highest combined investment share from each such region from which there has been submitted a written request pursuant to paragraph (c) of this Article. If the number of groups so selected is less than five, the remaining groups which are to be represented shall be selected in decreasing order of the combined investment shares of each group, without exceeding the applicable limitations prescribed in subparagraph (a) (iii) of this Article.

(e) In order to ensure continuity within the Board of Governors, every Signatory or group of Signatories represented pursuant to subparagraph (a) (i), (ii) or (iii) of this Article shall remain represented, either individually or as part of such group, until the next determination made in accordance with paragraph (b) or (d) of this Article, regardless of the changes that may occur in its or their investment shares as the result of any adjustment of investment shares. However, representation as part of a group constituted pursuant to subparagraph (a) (ii) or (iii) of this Article shall cease if the withdrawal from the group of one or more Signatories would make the group ineligible to be represented on the Board of Governors pursuant to this Article.

(f) Subject to the provisions of paragraph (g) of this Article, each Governor shall have a voting participation equal to that part of the investment share of the Signatory, or group of Signatories, he represents, which is derived from the utilization of the INTELSAT space segment for services of the following types:

(i) International public telecommunications services;

(ii) Domestic public telecommunications services between areas separated by areas not under the jurisdiction of the State concerned, or between areas separated by the high seas; and

(iii) Domestic public telecommunications services between areas which are not linked by any terrestrial wide-band facilities and which are separated by natural barriers of such an exceptional nature that they impede the viable establishment of terrestrial wide-band facilities between such areas, provided that the Meeting of Signatories has given in advance the appropriate approval required by subparagraph (b) (ii) of Article III of this Agreement.

(g) For the purposes of paragraph (f) of this Article, the following arrangements shall apply:

(i) In the case of a Signatory which is granted a lesser investment share in accordance with the provisions of paragraph (d) of Article 6 of the Operating Agreement, the reduction shall apply proportionately to all types of its utilization;

(ii) In the case of a Signatory which is granted a greater investment share in accordance with the provisions of paragraph (d) of Article 6 of the Operating Agreement, the increase shall apply proportionately to all types of its utilization;

(iii) In the case of a Signatory which has an investment share of 0.05 per cent in accordance with the provisions of paragraph (h) of Article 6 of the Operating Agreement and which forms part of a group for the purpose of representation in the Board of Governors pursuant to the provisions of subparagraph (a) (ii) or (a) (iii) of this Article, its investment share shall be regarded as being derived from utilization of the INTELSAT space segment for services of the types listed in paragraph Ct~ of this Article; and

(iv) No Governor may cast more than forty per cent of the total voting participation of all Signatories and groups of Signatories represented on the Board of Governors. To the extent that the voting participation of any Governor exceeds forty per cent of such total voting

participation, the excess shall be distributed equally
to the other Governors on the Board of Governors.

(h) For the purposes of composition of the Board of Governors
and calculation of the voting participation of Governors,
the investment shares determined pursuant to
subparagraph (c) (ii) of Article 6 of the Operating Agreement
shall take effect from the first day of the ordinary meeting
of the Meeting of Signatories following such determination.

(i) A quorum for any meeting of the Board of Governors shall
consist of either a majority of the Board of Governors,
which majority shall have at least two-thirds of the total
voting participation of all Signatories and groups of
Signatories represented on the Board of Governors, or else
the total number constituting the Board of Governors
minus three, regardless of the amount of voting
participation they represent.

(j) The Board of Governors shall endeavor to take decisions
unanimously. However, if it fails to reach unanimous
agreement, it shall take decisions:

(i) On all substantive questions, either by an affirmative
vote cast by at least four Governors having at least
two-thirds of the total voting participation of all
Signatories and groups of Signatories represented on
the Board of Governors taking into account the
distribution of the excess referred to in subparagraph
(g) (iv) of this Article, or else by an affirmative vote
cast by at least the total number constituting the Board
of Governors minus three, regardless of the amount
of voting participation they represent;

(ii) On all procedural questions, by an affirmative vote
representing a simple majority of Governors present
and voting, each having one vote.

(k) Disputes whether a specific question is procedural or
substantive shall be decided by the Chairman of the Board
of Governors. The decision of the Chairman may be
overruled by a two-thirds majority of the Governors
present and voting, each having one vote.

(l) The Board of Governors, if it deems appropriate, may
create advisory committees to assist it in the performance
of its responsibilities.

(m) The Board of Governors shall adopt its own rules of procedure, which shall include the method of election of a Chairman and such other officers as may be required. Notwithstanding the provisions of paragraph (j) of this Article, such rules may provide for any method of voting in the election of officers which the Board of Governors deems appropriate.

(n) The first meeting of the Board of Governors shall be convened in accordance with paragraph 2 of the Annex to the Operating Agreement. The Board of Governors shall meet as often as is necessary but at least four times a year.

Article X: Board of Governors: Functions

(a) The Board of Governors shall have the responsibility for the design, development, construction, establishment, operation and maintenance of the INTELSAT space segment and, pursuant to this Agreement, the Operating Agreement and such determinations that in this respect may have been made by the Assembly of Parties pursuant to Article VII of this Agreement, for carrying out any other activities which are undertaken by INTELSAT. To discharge the foregoing responsibilities, the Board of Governors shall have the powers and shall exercise the functions coming within its purview according to the provisions of this Agreement and the Operating Agreement, including:

   (i) Adoption of policies, plans and programs in connection with the design, development, construction, establishment, operation and maintenance of the INTELSAT space segment and, as appropriate, in connection with any other activities which INTELSAT is authorized to undertake;

   (ii) Adoption of procurement procedures, regulations, terms and conditions, consistent with Article XIII of this Agreement, and approval of procurement contracts;

   (iii) Adoption of financial policies and annual financial statements, and approval of budgets;

   (iv) Adoption of policies and procedures for the acquisition, protection and distribution of rights in

inventions and technical information, consistent with
Article 17 of the Operating Agreement;

(v) Formulation of recommendations to the Meeting of
Signatories in relation to the establishment of the
general rules referred to in subparagraph (b) (v) of
Article VIII of this Agreement;

(vi) Adoption of criteria and procedures, in accordance
with such general rules as may have been established
by the Meeting of Signatories, for approval of earth
stations for access to the INTELSAT space segment,
for verification and monitoring of performance
characteristics of earth stations having access, and for
coordination of earth station access to and utilization
of the INTELSAT space segment;

(vii) Adoption of terms and conditions governing the
allotment of INTELSAT space segment capacity, in
accordance with such general rules as may have been
established by the Meeting of Signatories;

(viii) Periodic establishment of the rates of charge for
utilization of the INTELSAT space segment, in
accordance with such general rules as may have been
established by the Meeting of Signatories;

(ix) Action as may be appropriate, in accordance with the
provisions of Article 5 of the Operating Agreement,
with respect to an increase in the ceiling provided for
in that Article;

(x) Direction of the negotiation with the Party in whose
territory the headquarters of INTELSAT is situated,
and submission to the Assembly of Parties for decision
thereon, of the Headquarters Agreement covering
privileges, exemptions and immunities, referred to in
paragraph (c) of Article XV of this Agreement;

(xi) Approval of non-standard earth stations for access to
the INTELSAT space segment in accordance with the
general rules which may have been established by the
Meeting of Signatories;

(xii) Establishment of terms and conditions for access to
the INTELSAT space segment by telecommunications
entities which are not under the jurisdiction of a Party,
in accordance with the general rules established by

the Meeting of Signatories pursuant to subparagraph (b) (v) of Article VIII of this Agreement and consistent with the provisions of paragraph (d) of Article V of this Agreement;

(xiii) Decisions on the making of arrangements for overdrafts and the raising of loans in accordance with Article 10 of the Operating Agreement;

(xiv) Submission to the Meeting of Signatories of an annual report on the activities of INTELSAT and of annual financial statements;

(xv) Submission to the Meeting of Signatories of reports on future programs including the estimated financial implications of such programs;

(xvi) Submission to the Meeting of Signatories of reports and recommendations on any other matter which the Board of Governors deems appropriate for consideration by the Meeting of Signatories;

(xvii) Provision of such information as may be required by any Party or Signatory to enable that Party or Signatory to discharge its obligations under this Agreement or the Operating Agreement;

(xviii) Appointment and removal from office of the Secretary General pursuant to Article XII, and of the Director General pursuant to Articles VII, XI and XII, of this Agreement;

(xix) Designation of a senior officer of the executive organ to serve as Acting Secretary General pursuant to subparagraph (d) (i) of Article XII and designation of a senior officer of the executive organ to serve as Acting Director General pursuant to subparagraph (d) (i) of Article XI of this Agreement;

(xx) Determination of the number, status and terms and conditions of employment of all posts on the executive organ upon the recommendation of the Secretary General or the Director General;

(xxi) Approval of the appointment by the Secretary General or the Director General of senior officers reporting directly to him;

(xxii) Arrangement of contracts in accordance with subparagraph (c) (ii) of Article XI of this Agreement;

(xxiii) Establishment of general internal rules, and adoption of decisions in each instance, concerning notification to the International Telecommunication Union in accordance with its rules of procedure of the frequencies to be used for the INTELSAT space segment;

(xxiv) Tendering to the Meeting of Signatories the advice referred to in subparagraph (b) (ii) of Article III of this Agreement;

(xxv) Expression, pursuant to paragraph (c) of Article XIV of this Agreement, of its findings in the form of recommendations, and the tendering of advice to the Assembly of Parties, pursuant to paragraph (d) or (e) of Article XIV of this Agreement, with respect to the intended establishment, acquisition or utilization of space segment facilities separate from the INTELSAT space segment facilities;

(xxvi) Action in accordance with Article XVI of this Agreement and Article 21 of the Operating Agreement in connection with the withdrawal of a Signatory from INTELSAT; and

(xxvii) Expression of its views and recommendations on proposed amendments to this Agreement pursuant to paragraph (b) of Article XVII of this Agreement, the proposal of amendments to the Operating Agreement pursuant to paragraph (a) of Article 22 of the Operating Agreement, and the expression of its views and recommendations on proposed amendments to the Operating Agreement pursuant to paragraph (b) of Article 22 of the Operating Agreement.

(b) In accordance with the provisions of paragraphs (b) and (c) of Article VI of this Agreement, the Board of Governors shall:

(i) Give due and proper consideration to resolutions, recommendations and views addressed to it by the Assembly of Parties or the Meeting of Signatories; and

(ii) Include in its reports to the Assembly of Parties and to the Meeting of Signatories information on actions or decisions taken with respect to such resolutions, recommendations and views, and its reasons for such actions or decisions.

Article XI: Director General

(a) The executive organ shall be headed by the Director General and shall have its organizational structure implemented not later than six years after the entry into force of this Agreement.

(b) (i) The Director General shall be the chief executive and the legal representative of INTELSAT and shall be directly responsible to the Board of Governors for the performance of all management functions.

(ii) The Director General shall act in accordance with the policies and directives of the Board of Governors.

(iii) The Director General shall be appointed by the Board of Governors, subject to confirmation by the Assembly of Parties. The Director General may be removed from office for cause by the Board of Governors on its own authority.

(iv) The paramount consideration in the appointment of the Director General and in the selection of other personnel of the executive organ shall be the necessity of ensuring the highest standards of integrity, competency and efficiency. The Director General and the personnel of the executive organ shall refrain from any action incompatible with their responsibilities to INTELSAT.

(c) (i) The permanent management arrangements shall be consistent with the basic aims and purposes of INTELSAT, its international character and its obligation to provide on a commercial basis telecommunications facilities of high quality and reliability.

(ii) The Director General, on behalf of INTELSAT, shall contract out, to one or more competent entities, technical and operational functions to the maximum extent practicable with due regard to cost and consistent with competence, effectiveness and efficiency. Such entities may be of various nationalities or may be an international corporation owned and controlled by INTELSAT. Such contracts shall be negotiated, executed and administered by the Director General.

(d) (i) The Board of Governors shall designate a senior officer of the executive organ to serve as the Acting Director General whenever the Director General is absent or is unable to discharge his duties, or if the office of Director General should become vacant. The Acting Director General shall have the capacity to exercise all the powers of the Director General pursuant to this Agreement and the Operating Agreement. In the event of a vacancy, the Acting Director General shall serve in that capacity until the assumption of office by a Director General appointed and confirmed, as expeditiously as possible, in accordance with subparagraph (b) (iii) of this Article.

   (ii) The Director General may delegate such of his powers to other officers in the executive organ as may be necessary to meet appropriate requirements.

Article XII: Transitional Management and Secretary General

(a) As a matter of priority after entry into force of this Agreement, the Board of Governors shall:
   (i) Appoint the Secretary General and authorize the necessary support staff;
   (ii) Arrange the management services contract in accordance with paragraph (e) of this Article; and
   (iii) Initiate the study concerning permanent management arrangements in accordance with paragraph (f) of this Article.

(b) The Secretary General shall be the legal representative of INTELSAT until the first Director General shall have assumed office. In accordance with the policies and directives of the Board of Governors, the Secretary General shall be responsible for the performance of all management services other than those which are to be provided under the terms of the management services contract concluded pursuant to paragraph (e) of this Article including those specified in Annex A to this Agreement. The Secretary General shall keep the Board of Governors fully and currently informed on the performance of the management services contractor under its contract. To the extent practicable, the Secretary General shall be present at or represented at and observe, but not participate in, major contract negotiations conducted by the management services contractor on behalf of INTELSAT. For this purpose the Board of Governors may authorize the appointment to the executive organ of a small number of technically qualified personnel to assist the Secretary General. The Secretary General shall not be interposed between the Board of Governors and the management services contractor nor shall he exercise a supervisory role over the said contractor.

(c) The paramount consideration in the appointment of the Secretary General and in the selection of other personnel of the executive organ shall be the necessity of ensuring the highest standards of integrity, competency and efficiency. The Secretary General and the personnel of the executive organ shall refrain from any action incompatible with their responsibilities to INTELSAT. The Secretary General may be removed from office for cause by the Board of Governors. The office of Secretary General shall cease to exist on the assumption of office by the first Director General.

(d)(i) The Board of Governors shall designate a senior officer of the executive organ to serve as the Acting Secretary General whenever the Secretary General is absent or is unable to discharge his duties, or if the office of Secretary General should become vacant. The Acting Secretary General shall have the capacity to exercise all the powers of the Secretary General pursuant to this Agreement and the Operating Agreement. In the event of a vacancy, the Acting Secretary General shall serve in that capacity until the assumption of office by a Secretary General, who shall be appointed by the Board of Governors as expeditiously as possible.

(ii) The Secretary General may delegate such of his powers to other officers in the executive organ as may be necessary to meet appropriate requirements.

(e) The contract referred to in subparagraph (a) (ii) of this

Article shall be between the Communications Satellite Corporation, referred to in this Agreement as "the management services contractor", and INTELSAT, and shall be for the performance of technical and operational management services for INTELSAT, as specified in Annex B to this Agreement and in accordance with the guidelines set out therein, for a period terminating at the end of the sixth year after the date of entry into force of this Agreement. The contract shall contain provisions for the management services contractor:

  (i) To act pursuant to relevant policies and directives of the Board of Governors;

  (ii) To be responsible directly to the Board of Governors until the assumption of office by the first Director General and thereafter through the Director General; and

  (iii) To furnish the Secretary General with all the information necessary for the Secretary General to keep the Board of Governors informed on the performance under the management services contract and for the Secretary General to be present at or represented at and observe, but not participate in, major contract negotiations conducted by the management services contractor on behalf of INTELSAT.

The management services contractor shall negotiate, place, amend and administer contracts on behalf of INTELSAT within the area of its responsibilities under the management services contract and as otherwise authorized by the Board of Governors. Pursuant to authorization under the management services contract, or as otherwise authorized by the Board of Governors, the management services contractor shall sign contracts on behalf of INTELSAT in the area of its responsibilities. All other contracts shall be signed by the Secretary General.

  (f) The study referred to in subparagraph (a) (iii) of this Article shall be commenced as soon as possible and, in any event, within one year after entry into force of this Agreement. It shall be conducted by the Board of

Governors and shall be designed to provide the information necessary for the determination of the most efficient and effective permanent management arrangements consistent with the provisions of Article XI of this Agreement. The study shall, among other matters, give due regard to:

(i) The principles set forth in subparagraph (c) (i) of Article XI and the policy expressed in subparagraph (c) (ii) of Article XI, of this Agreement;

(ii) Experience gained during the period of the Interim Agreement and of the transitional management arrangements provided for in this Article;

(iii) The organization and procedures adopted by telecommunications entities throughout the world, with particular reference to the integration of policy and management and to management efficiency;

(iv) Information, similar to that referred to in subparagraph (iii) of this paragraph, in respect of multinational ventures for implementing advanced technologies; and

(v) Reports commissioned from not less than three professional management consultants from various parts of the world.

(g) Not later than four years after the entry into force of this Agreement, the Board of Governors shall submit to the Assembly of Parties a comprehensive report, which incorporates the results of the study referred to in subparagraph (a) (iii) of this Article, and which includes the recommendations of the Board of Governors for the organizational structure of the executive organ. It shall also transmit copies of this report to the Meeting of Signatories and to all Parties and Signatories as soon as it is available.

(h) By not later than five years after entry into force of this Agreement, the Assembly of Parties, after having considered the report of the Board of Governors referred to in paragraph (g) of this Article and any views which may have been expressed by the Meeting of Signatories thereon, shall adopt the organizational structure of the executive organ which shall be consistent with the provisions of Article XI of this Agreement.

(i) The Director General shall assume office one year before the end of the management services contract referred to in subparagraph (a) (ii) of this Article or by 31 December, 1976, whichever is earlier. The Board of Governors shall appoint the Director General, and the Assembly of Parties shall act upon the confirmation of the appointment, in time to enable the Director General to assume office in accordance with this paragraph. Upon his assumption of office, the Director General shall be responsible for all management services, including the performance of the functions performed by the Secretary General up to that time, and for the supervision of the performance of the management services contractor.

(j) The Director General, acting under relevant policies and directives of the Board of Governors, shall take all necessary steps to ensure that the permanent management arrangements are fully implemented not later than the end of the sixth year after the date of entry into force of this Agreement.

Article XIII: Procurement

(a) Subject to this Article, procurement of goods and services required by INTELSAT shall be effected by the award of contracts, based on responses to open international invitations to tender, to bidders offering the best combination of quality, price and the most favorable delivery time. The services to which this Article refers are those provided by juridical persons.

(b) If there is more than one bid offering such a combination, the contract shall be awarded so as to stimulate, in the interests of INTELSAT, world-wide competition.

(c) The requirement of open international invitations to tender may be dispensed with in those cases specifically referred to in Article 16 of the Operating Agreement.

Article XIV: Rights and Obligations of Members

(a) The Parties and Signatories shall exercise their rights and meet their obligations under this Agreement in a manner fully consistent with and in furtherance of the principles stated in the Preamble and other provisions of this Agreement.

(b) All Parties and all Signatories shall be allowed to attend and participate in all conferences and meetings, in which they are entitled to be represented in accordance with any provisions of this Agreement or the Operating Agreement, as well as in any other meeting called by or held under the auspices of INTELSAT, in accordance with the arrangements made by INTELSAT for such meetings regardless of where they may take place. The executive organ shall ensure that arrangements with the host Party or Signatory for each such conference or meeting shall include a provision for the admission to the host country and sojourn for the duration of such conference or meeting, of representatives of all Parties and all Signatories entitled to attend.

(c) To the extent that any Party or Signatory or person within the jurisdiction of a Party intends to establish, acquire or utilize space segment facilities separate from the INTELSAT space segment facilities to meet its domestic public telecommunications services requirements, such Party or Signatory, prior to the establishment, acquisition or utilization of such facilities, shall consult the Board of Governors, which shall express, in the form of recommendations, its findings regarding the technical compatibility of such facilities and their operation with the use of the radio frequency spectrum and orbital space by the existing or planned INTELSAT space segment.

(d) To the extent that any Party or Signatory or person within the jurisdiction of a Party intends individually or jointly to establish, acquire or utilize space segment facilities separate from the INTELSAT space segment facilities to meet its international public telecommunications services requirements, such Party or Signatory, prior to the establishment, acquisition or utilization of such facilities, shall furnish all relevant information to and shall consult with the Assembly of Parties, through the Board of Governors, to ensure technical compatibility of such facilities and their operation with the use of the radio frequency spectrum and orbital space by the existing or planned INTELSAT space segment and to avoid significant economic harm to the global system of INTELSAT. Upon such consultation, the Assembly of Parties, taking into account the advice of the Board of Governors, shall express, in the form of recommendations, its findings regarding the considerations set out in this paragraph, and further regarding the assurance that the provision or utilization of such facilities shall not prejudice the establishment of direct telecommunication links through the INTELSAT space segment among all the participants.

(e) To the extent that any Party or Signatory or person within the jurisdiction of a party intends to establish, acquire or utilize space segment facilities separate from the INTELSAT space segment facilities to meet its specialized telecommunications services requirements, domestic or international, such Party or Signatory, prior to the establishment, acquisition or utilization of such facilities, shall furnish all relevant information to the Assembly of Parties, through the Board of Governors. The Assembly of Parties, taking into account the advice of the Board of Governors, shall express, in the form of recommendations, its findings regarding the technical compatibility of such facilities and their operation with the use of the radio frequency spectrum and orbital space by the existing or planned INTELSAT space segment.

(f) Recommendations by the Assembly of Parties or the Board of Governors pursuant to this Article shall be made within a period of six months from the date of commencing the procedures provided for in the foregoing paragraphs. An extraordinary meeting of the Assembly of Parties may be convened for this purpose.

(g) This Agreement shall not apply to the establishment, acquisition or utilization of space segment facilities separate from the INTELSAT space segment facilities solely for national security purposes.

Article XV: Intelsat Headquarters, Privileges, Exemptions, Immunities

(a) The headquarters of INTELSAT shall be in Washington.

(b) Within the scope of activities authorized by this Agreement, INTELSAT and its property shall be exempt in all States Party to this Agreement from all national income and direct national property taxation and from customs duties on communications satellites and components and parts for such satellites to be launched for use in the global system. Each Party undertakes to use its best endeavors to bring about, in accordance with the applicable domestic procedure, such further exemption of INTELSAT and its property from income and direct property taxation, and customs duties, as is desirable, bearing in mind the particular nature of INTELSAT.

(c) Each Party other than the Party in whose territory the headquarters of INTELSAT is located shall grant in accordance with the Protocol referred to in this paragraph, and the Party in whose territory the headquarters of INTELSAT is located shall grant in accordance with the Headquarters Agreement referred to in this paragraph, the appropriate privileges, exemptions and immunities to INTELSAT, to its officers, and to those categories of its employees specified in such Protocol and Headquarters Agreement, to Parties and representatives of Parties, to Signatories and representatives of Signatories and to persons participating in arbitration proceedings. In particular, each Party shall grant to these individuals immunity from legal process in respect of acts done or words written or spoken in the exercise of their functions and within the limits of their duties, to the extent and in the cases to be provided for in the Headquarters Agreement and Protocol referred to in this paragraph. The Party in whose territory the headquarters of INTELSAT is located shall, as soon as possible, conclude a Headquarters Agreement with INTELSAT covering privileges, exemptions and immunities. The Headquarters Agreement shall include a provision that all Signatories acting in their capacity as such, except the Signatory designated by the Party in whose territory the headquarters is located, shall be exempt from national taxation on income earned from INTELSAT in the territory of such Party. The other Parties shall also as soon as possible conclude a Protocol covering privileges, exemptions and immunities. The Headquarters Agreement and the Protocol shall be independent of this Agreement and each shall prescribe the conditions of its termination.

Article XVI: Withdrawal

(a) (i) Any Party or Signatory may withdraw voluntarily from INTELSAT. A Party shall give written notice to the Depositary of its decision to withdraw. The decision of a Signatory to withdraw shall be notified in writing to the executive organ by the Party which has designated it and such notification shall signify the acceptance by the Party of such notification of decision to withdraw.

(ii) Voluntary withdrawal shall become effective and this Agreement and the Operating Agreement shall cease to be in force for a Party or Signatory three months after the date of receipt of the notice referred to in subparagraph (i) of this paragraph or, if the notice so states, on the date of the next determination of investment shares pursuant to subparagraph (c) (ii) of Article 6 of the Operating Agreement following the expiration of such three months.

(b) (i) If a Party appears to have failed to comply with any obligation under this Agreement, the Assembly of Parties, having received notice to that effect or acting on its own initiative, and having considered any representations made by the Party, may decide, if it finds that the failure to comply has in fact occurred, that the Party be deemed to have withdrawn from INTELSAT. This Agreement shall cease to be in force for the Party as of the date of such decision. An extraordinary meeting of the Assembly of Parties may be convened for this purpose.

(ii) If any Signatory, in its capacity as such, appears to have failed to comply with any obligation under this

Agreement or the Operating Agreement, other than obligations under paragraph (a) of Article 4 of the Operating Agreement and the failure to comply shall not have been remedied within three months after the Signatory has been notified in writing by the executive organ of a resolution of the Board of Governors taking note of the failure to comply, the Board of Governors may, after considering any representations made by the Signatory or the Party which designated it, suspend the rights of the Signatory, and may recommend to the Meeting of Signatories that the Signatory be deemed to have withdrawn from INTELSAT. If the Meeting of Signatories, after consideration of any representations made by the Signatory or by the Party which designated it, approves the recommendation of the Board of Governors, the withdrawal of the Signatory shall become effective upon the date of the approval, and this Agreement and the Operating Agreement shall cease to be in force for the Signatory as of that date.

(c) If any Signatory fails to pay any amount due from it pursuant to paragraph (a) of Article 4 of the Operating Agreement within three months after the payment has become due, the rights of the Signatory under this Agreement and the Operating Agreement shall be automatically suspended. If within three months after the suspension the Signatory has not paid all sums due or the Party which has designated the Signatory has not made a substitution pursuant to paragraph o of this Article, the Board of Governors, after considering any representations made by the Signatory or by the Party which has designated it, may recommend to the Meeting of Signatories that the Signatory be deemed to have withdrawn from INTELSAT. The Meeting of Signatories, after considering any representations made by the Signatory, may decide that the Signatory be deemed to have withdrawn from INTELSAT and, from the date of the decision, this Agreement and the Operating Agreement shall cease to be in force for the Signatory.

(d) Withdrawal of a Party, in its capacity as such, shall entail the simultaneous withdrawal of the Signatory designated by the Party or of the Party in its capacity as Signatory, as the case may be, and this Agreement and the Operating Agreement shall cease to be in force for the Signatory on the same date on which this Agreement ceases to be in force for the Party which has designated it.

(e) In all cases of withdrawal of a Signatory from INTELSAT, the Party which designated the Signatory shall assume the capacity of a Signatory, or shall designate a new Signatory effective as of the date of such withdrawal, or shall withdraw from INTELSAT.

(f) If for any reason a Party desires to substitute itself for its designated Signatory or to designate a new Signatory, it shall give written notice thereof to the Depositary, and upon assumption by the new Signatory of all the outstanding obligations of the previously designated Signatory and upon signature of the Operating Agreement, this Agreement and the Operating Agreement shall enter into force for the new Signatory and thereupon shall cease to be in force for such previously designated Signatory.

(g) Upon the receipt by the Depositary or the executive organ, as the case may be, of notice of decision to withdraw pursuant to subparagraph (a) (i) of this Article, the Party giving notice and its designated Signatory, or the Signatory in respect of which notice has been given, as the case may be, shall cease to have any rights of representation and any voting rights in any organ of INTELSAT, and shall incur no obligation or liability after the receipt of the notice, except that the Signatory, unless the Board of Governors decides otherwise pursuant to paragraph (d) of Article 21 of the Operating Agreement, shall be responsible for contributing its share of the capital contributions necessary to meet both contractual commitments specifically authorized before such receipt and liabilities arising from acts or omissions before such receipt.

(h) During the period of suspension of the rights of a Signatory pursuant to subparagraph (b) (ii) or paragraph (c) of this Article, the Signatory shall continue to have all the obligations and liabilities of a Signatory under this

Agreement and the Operating Agreement.

(i) If the Meeting of Signatories, pursuant to subparagraph (b) (ii) or paragraph (c) of this Article, decides not to approve the recommendation of the Board of Governors that the Signatory be deemed to have withdrawn from INTELSAT, as of the date of that decision the suspension shall be lifted and the Signatory shall thereafter have all rights under this Agreement and the Operating Agreement, provided that where a Signatory is suspended pursuant to paragraph (c) of this Article the suspension shall not be lifted until the Signatory has paid the amounts due from it pursuant to paragraph (a) of Article 4 of the Operating Agreement.

(j) If the Meeting of Signatories approves the recommendation of the Board of Governors pursuant to subparagraph (b) (ii) or paragraph (c) of this Article that a Signatory be deemed to have withdrawn from INTELSAT, that Signatory shall incur no obligation or liability after such approval, except that the Signatory, unless the Board of Governors decides otherwise pursuant to paragraph (d) of Article 21 of the Operating Agreement, shall be responsible for contributing its share of the capital contributions necessary to meet both contractual commitments specifically authorized before such approval and liabilities arising from acts or omissions before such approval.

(k) If the Assembly of Parties decides pursuant to subparagraph (b) (i) of this Article that a Party be deemed to have withdrawn from INTELSAT, the Party, in its capacity as Signatory or its designated Signatory, as the case may be, shall incur no obligation or liability after such decision, except that the Party, in its capacity as Signatory or its designated Signatory, as the case may be, unless the Board of Governors decides otherwise pursuant to paragraph (d) of Article 21 of the Operating Agreement, shall be responsible for contributing its share of the capital contributions necessary to meet both contractual commitments specifically authorized before such decision and liabilities arising from acts or omissions before such decision.

(l) Settlement between INTELSAT and a Signatory for which this Agreement and the Operating Agreement have ceased to be in force, other than in the case of substitution pursuant to paragraph (f) of this Article, shall be accomplished as provided in Article 21 of the Operating Agreement.

(m) (i) Notification of the decision of a Party to withdraw pursuant to subparagraph (a) (i) of this Article shall be transmitted by the Depositary to all Parties and to the executive organ, and the latter shall transmit the notification to all Signatories.

(ii) If the Assembly of Parties decides that a Party shall be deemed to have withdrawn from INTELSAT pursuant to subparagraph (b) (i) of this Article, the executive organ shall notify all Signatories and the Depositary, and the latter shall transmit the notification to all Parties.

(iii) Notification of the decision of a Signatory to withdraw pursuant to subparagraph (a) (i) of this Article or of the withdrawal of a Signatory pursuant to subparagraph (b) (ii) or paragraph (c) or (d) of this Article, shall be transmitted by the executive organ to all Signatories and to the Depositary, and the latter shall transmit the notification to all Parties.

(iv) The suspension of a Signatory pursuant to subparagraph (b) (ii) or paragraph (c) of this Article shall be notified by the executive organ to all Signatories and to the Depositary, and the latter shall transmit the notification to all Parties.

(v) The substitution of a Signatory pursuant to paragraph (f) of this Article shall be notified by the Depositary to all Parties and to the executive organ, and the latter shall transmit the notification to all Signatories.

(n) No Party or its designated Signatory shall be required to withdraw from INTELSAT as a direct result of any change in the status of that Party with regard to the International Telecommunication Union.

Article XVII: Amendment

(a) Any Party may propose amendments to this Agreement.

Proposed amendments shall be submitted to the executive organ, which shall distribute them promptly to all Parties and Signatories.

(b) The Assembly of Parties shall consider each proposed amendment at its first ordinary meeting following its distribution by the executive organ, or at an earlier extraordinary meeting convened in accordance with the provisions of Article VII of this Agreement, provided that the proposed amendment has been distributed by the executive organ at least ninety days before the opening date of the meeting. The Assembly of Parties shall consider any views and recommendations which it receives from the Meeting of Signatories or the Board of Governors with respect to a proposed amendment.

(c) The Assembly of Parties shall take decisions on each proposed amendment in accordance with the provisions relating to quorum and voting contained in Article VII of this Agreement. It may modify any proposed amendment, distributed in accordance with paragraph (b) of this Article, and may also take decisions on any amendment not so distributed but directly consequential to a proposed or modified amendment.

(d) An amendment which has been approved by the Assembly of Parties shall enter into force in accordance with paragraph (e) of this Article after the Depositary has received notice of approval, acceptance or ratification of the amendment from either:

(i) Two-thirds of the States which were Parties as of the date upon which the amendment was approved by the Assembly of Parties, provided that such two-thirds include Parties which then held, or whose designated Signatories then held, at least two-thirds of the total investment shares; or

(ii) A number of States equal to or exceeding eighty-five per cent of the total number of States which were Parties as of the date upon which the amendment was approved by the Assembly of Parties, regardless of the amount of investment shares such Parties or their designated Signatories then held.

(e) The Depositary shall notify all the Parties as soon as it has received the acceptances, approvals or ratifications required by paragraph (d) of this Article for the entry into force of an amendment. Ninety days after the date of issue of this notification, the amendment shall enter into force for all Parties, including those that have not yet accepted, approved, or ratified it and have not withdrawn from INTELSAT.

(f) Notwithstanding the provisions of paragraphs (d) and (e) of this Article, an amendment shall not enter into force less than eight months or more than eighteen months after the date it has been approved by the Assembly of Parties.

Article XVIII: Settlement of Disputes

(a) All legal disputes arising in connection with the rights and obligations under this Agreement or in connection with obligations undertaken by Parties pursuant to paragraph (c) of Article 14 or paragraph (c) of Article 15 of the Operating Agreement, between Parties with respect to each other, or between INTELSAT and one or more Parties, if not otherwise settled within a reasonable time, shall be submitted to arbitration in accordance with the provisions of Annex C to this Agreement. Any legal dispute arising in connection with the rights and obligations under this Agreement or the Operating Agreement between one or more Parties and one or more Signatories may be submitted to arbitration in accordance with the provisions of Annex C to this Agreement, provided that the Party or Parties and the Signatory or Signatories involved agree to such arbitration.

(b) All legal disputes arising in connection with the rights and obligations under this Agreement, or in connection with the obligations undertaken by Parties pursuant to paragraph (c) of Article 14 or paragraph (c) of Article 15 of the Operating Agreement, between a Party and a State which has ceased to be a Party or between INTELSAT and a State which has ceased to be a Party, and which arise after the State ceased to be a Party, if not otherwise settled within a reasonable time, shall be submitted to arbitration. Such arbitration shall be in accordance with the provisions of Annex C to this Agreement, provided that the State which has ceased to be a Party so agrees. If a State ceases to be a Party, or if a State or a telecommunications entity ceases to be a Signatory, after a dispute in which it is a disputant has been submitted to arbitration pursuant to paragraph (a) of this Article, the arbitration shall be continued and concluded.

(c) All legal disputes arising as a result of agreements between INTELSAT and any Party shall be subject to the provisions on settlement of disputes contained in such agreements. In the absence of such provisions, such disputes, if not otherwise settled, may be submitted to arbitration in accordance with the provisions of Annex C to this Agreement if the disputants so agree.

Article XIX: Signature

(a) This Agreement shall be open for signature at Washington from 20 August, 1971 until it enters into force, or until a period of nine months has elapsed, whichever occurs first:
  (i) By the Government of any State party to the Interim Agreement;
  (ii) By the Government of any other State member of the International Telecommunication Union.

(b) Any Government signing this Agreement may do so without its signature being subject to ratification, acceptance or approval or with a declaration accompanying its signature that it is subject to ratification, acceptance or approval.

(c) Any State referred to in paragraph (a) of this Article may accede to this Agreement after it is closed for signature.

(d) No reservation may be made to this Agreement.

Article XX: Entry into Force

(a) This Agreement shall enter into force sixty days after the date on which it has been signed not subject to ratification, acceptance or approval, or has been ratified, accepted, approved or acceded to, by two-thirds of the States which were parties to the Interim Agreement as of the date upon which this Agreement is opened for signature, provided that:

(i) Such two-thirds include parties to the Interim Agreement which then held, or whose signatories to the Special Agreement then held, at least two-thirds of the quotas under the Special Agreement; and

(ii) Such parties or their designated telecommunications entities have signed the Operating Agreement.

Upon the commencement of such sixty days, the provisions of paragraph 2 of the Annex to the Operating Agreement shall enter into force for the purposes stated in that paragraph. Notwithstanding the foregoing provisions, this Agreement shall not enter into force less than eight months or more than eighteen months after the date it is opened for signature.

(b) For a State whose instrument of ratification, acceptance, approval or accession is deposited after the date this Agreement enters into force pursuant to paragraph (a) of this Article, this Agreement shall enter into force on the date of such deposit.

(c) Upon entry into force of this Agreement pursuant to paragraph (a) of this Article, it may be applied provisionally with respect to any State whose Government signed it subject to ratification, acceptance or approval if that Government so requests at the time of signature or at any time thereafter prior to the entry into force of this Agreement. Provisional application shall terminate:

(i) Upon deposit of an instrument of ratification, acceptance or approval of this Agreement by that Government;

(ii) Upon expiration of two years from the date on which this Agreement enters in to force without having been ratified, accepted or approved by that Government; or

(iii) Upon notification by that Government, before expiration of the period mentioned in subparagraph (ii) of this paragraph, of its decision not to ratify, accept or approve this Agreement.

If provisional application terminates pursuant to

subparagraph (ii) or (iii) of this paragraph, the provisions of paragraphs (g) and (l) of Article XVI of this Agreement shall govern the rights and obligations of the Party and of its designated Signatory.

(d) Notwithstanding the provisions of this Article, this Agreement shall neither enter into force for any State nor be applied provisionally with respect to any State until the Government of that State or the telecommunications entity designated pursuant to this Agreement shall have signed the Operating Agreement.

(e) Upon entry into force, this Agreement shall replace and terminate the Interim Agreement.

Article XXI: Miscellaneous Provisions

(a) The official and working languages of INTELSAT shall be English, French and Spanish.

(b) Internal regulations for the executive organ shall provide for the prompt distribution to all Parties and Signatories of copies of any INTELSAT document in accordance with their requests.

(c) Consistent with the provisions of Resolution 1721 (XVI) of the General Assembly of the United Nations, the executive organ shall send to the Secretary General of the United Nations, and to the Specialized Agencies concerned, for their information, an annual report on the activities of INTELSAT.

Article XXII: Depositary

(a) The Government of the United States of America shall be the Depositary for this Agreement, with which shall be deposited declarations made pursuant to paragraph (b) of Article XIX of this Agreement, instruments of ratification, acceptance, approval or accession, requests for provisional application, and notifications of ratification, acceptance or approval of amendments, of decisions to withdraw from INTELSAT, or of termination of the provisional application of this Agreement.

(b) This Agreement, of which the English, French and Spanish texts are equally authentic, shall be deposited in the archives of the Depositary. The Depositary shall transmit certified copies of the text of this Agreement to all Governments that have signed it or deposited instruments of accession to it, and to the International Telecommunication Union, and shall notify those Governments, and the International Telecommunication Union, of signatures, of declarations made pursuant to paragraph (b) of Article XIX of this Agreement, of the deposit of instruments of ratification, acceptance, approval or accession, of requests for provisional application, of commencement of the sixty-day period referred to in paragraph (a) of Article XX of this Agreement, of the entry into force of this Agreement, of notifications of ratification, acceptance or approval of amendments, of the entry into force of amendments, of decisions to withdraw from INTELSAT of withdrawals and of terminations of provisional application of this Agreement. Notice of the commencement of the sixty-day period shall be issued on the first day of that period.

(c) Upon entry into force of this Agreement, the Depositary shall register it with the Secretariat of the United Nations in accordance with Article 102 of the Charter of the United Nations.

In Witness Whereof the Plenipotentiaries gathered together in the city of Washington, who have submitted their full powers, found to be in good and due form, have signed this Agreement.

Done at Washington, on the 20th day of August, one thousand nine hundred and seventy one.

ANNEX A
FUNCTIONS OF THE SECRETARY GENERAL

The functions of the Secretary General referred to in paragraph (b) of Article XII of this Agreement include the following:

1. Maintain the INTELSAT traffic data projections and, for this purpose, convene periodic regional meetings in order to estimate traffic demands;

2. Approve applications for access to the INTELSAT space segment by standard earth stations, report to the Board of Governors on applications for access by non-standard earth stations, and maintain records on dates of availability of existing and proposed earth stations;

3. Maintain records based on reports submitted by Signatories, other earth station owners and the management services contractor, on the technical and operational capabilities and limitations of all existing and proposed earth stations;

4. Maintain an office of record of the assignment of frequencies to users and arrange for the notification of frequencies to the International Telecommunication Union;

5. Based on planning assumptions approved by the Board of Governors, prepare capital and operating budgets and estimates of revenue requirements;

6. Recommend INTELSAT space segment utilization charges to the Board of Governors;

7. Recommend accounting policies to the Board of Governors;

8. Maintain books of account and make them available for audit as required by the Board of Governors, and prepare monthly and annual financial statements;

9. Calculate the investment shares of Signatories, render accounts to Signatories for capital contributions and to allottees for INTELSAT space segment utilization charges, receive cash payments on behalf of INTELSAT, and make revenue distributions and other cash disbursements to Signatories on behalf of INTELSAT;

10. Advise the Board of Governors of Signatories in default of capital contributions, and of allottees in default of payments for INTELSAT space segment utilization charges;

11. Approve and pay invoices submitted to INTELSAT with respect to authorized purchases and contracts made by the executive organ, and reimburse the management services contractor for expenditures incurred in connection with purchases and contracts made on behalf of INTELSAT and authorized by the Board of Governors;

12. Administer INTELSAT personnel benefit programs and pay salaries and authorized expenses of INTELSAT personnel;

13. Invest or deposit funds on hand, and draw upon such investments or deposits as necessary to meet INTELSAT obligations;

14. Maintain INTELSAT property and depreciation accounts, and arrange with the management services contractor and the appropriate Signatories for the necessary inventories of INTELSAT property;

15. Recommend terms and conditions of allotment agreements for utilization of the INTELSAT space segment;

16. Recommend insurance programs for protection of INTELSAT property and, as authorized by the Board of Governors, arrange for necessary coverage;

17. For the purpose of paragraph (d) of Article XIV of this Agreement, analyze and report to the Board of Governors on the estimated economic effects to INTELSAT of any proposed space segment facilities separate from the INTELSAT space segment facilities;

18. Prepare the tentative agenda for meetings of the Assembly of Parties, the Meeting of Signatories and the Board of Governors and their advisory committees, and the provisional summary records of such meetings, and assist the chairmen of advisory committees in preparation of their agenda, records and reports to the Assembly of Parties, the Meeting of Signatories and the Board of Governors;

19. Arrange for interpretation services, for the translation, reproduction, and distribution of documents, and for the preparation of verbatim records of meetings, as necessary;

20. Provide the history of the decisions taken by the Assembly of Parties, the Meeting of Signatories and the Board of Governors, and prepare reports and correspondence relating to decisions taken during their meetings;

21. Assist in the interpretation of the rules of procedure of the Assembly of Parties, the Meeting of Signatories and the Board of Governors, and the terms of reference for their advisory committees;

22. Make arrangements for any meetings of the Assembly of Parties, the Meeting of Signatories and the Board of Governors and of their advisory committees;
23. Recommend procedures and regulations for contracts and purchases made on behalf of INTELSAT;
24. Keep the Board of Governors informed on the performance of the obligations of contractors, including the management services contractor;
25. Compile and maintain a world-wide list of bidders for all INTELSAT procurement;
26. Negotiate, place and administer contracts necessary to enable the Secretary General to perform his assigned functions, including contracts for obtaining assistance from other entities to perform such functions;
27. Provide or arrange for the provision of legal advice to INTELSAT, as required in connection with the functions of the Secretary General;
28. Provide appropriate public information services; and
29. Arrange and convene conferences for negotiation of the Protocol covering privileges, exemptions and immunities, referred to in paragraph (c) of Article XV of this Agreement.

ANNEX B
FUNCTIONS OF
THE MANAGEMENT SERVICES CONTRACTOR AND
GUIDELINES OF
THE MANAGEMENT SERVICES CONTRACT

1. Pursuant to Article XII of this Agreement, the management services contractor shall perform the following functions:
   (a) Recommend to the Board of Governors research and development programs directly related to the purposes of INTELSAT;
   (b) As authorized by the Board of Governors:
       (i) Conduct studies and research and development, directly or under contract with other entities or persons,
       (ii) Conduct system studies in the fields of engineering, economics and cost effectiveness,

    (iii) Perform system simulation tests and evaluations, and

    (iv) Study and forecast potential demands for new telecommunications satellite services;

(c) Advise the Board of Governors on the need to procure space segment facilities for the INTELSAT space segment;

(d) As authorized by the Board of Governors, prepare and distribute requests for proposals, including specifications, for procurement of space segment facilities;

(e) Evaluate all proposals submitted in response to requests for proposals and make recommendations to the Board of Governors on such proposals;

(f) Pursuant to procurement regulations and in accordance with decisions of the Board of Governors:

    (i) Negotiate, place, amend and administer all contracts on behalf of INTELSAT for space segments,

    (ii) Make arrangements for launch services and necessary supporting activities, and cooperate in launches,

    (iii) Arrange insurance coverage to protect the INTELSAT space segment as well as equipment designated for launch or launch services,

    (iv) Provide or arrange for the provision of services for tracking, telemetry, command and control of the telecommunications satellites, including coordination of the efforts of Signatories and other owners of earth stations participating in the provision of these services, to perform satellite positioning, maneuvers, and tests, and

    (v) Provide or arrange for the provision of services for monitoring satellite performance characteristics, outages, and effectiveness, and the satellite power and frequencies used by the earth stations, including coordination of the efforts of Signatories and other owners of earth stations participating in the provision of these services;

(g) Recommend to the Board of Governors frequencies

for use by the INTELSAT space segment and location
plans for telecommunications satellites;

(h) Operate the INTELSAT Operations Center and the
Spacecraft Technical Control Center;

(i) Recommend to the Board of Governors standard earth
station performance characteristics, both mandatory
and non-mandatory;

(j) Evaluate applications for access to the INTELSAT
space segment by non-standard earth stations;

(k) Allot units of INTELSAT space segment capacity, as
determined by the Board of Governors;

(l) Prepare and coordinate system operations plans
(including network configuration studies and
contingency plans), procedures, guides, practices and
standards, for adoption by the Board of Governors;

(m) Prepare, coordinate and distribute frequency plans for
assignment to earth stations having access to the
INTELSAT space segment;

(n) Prepare and distribute system status reports, to
include actual and projected system utilization;

(o) Distribute information to Signatories and other users
on new telecommunications services and methods;

(p) For the purpose of paragraph (d) of Article XIV of this
Agreement, analyze and report to the Board of
Governors on the estimated technical and operational
effect on INTELSAT of any proposed space segment
facilities separate from the INTELSAT space segment
facilities, including.he effect on the frequency and
location plans of INTELSAT;

(q) Provide the Secretary General with the information
necessary for the performance of his responsibility to
the Board of Governors pursuant to paragraph 24 of
Annex A to this Agreement;

(r) Make recommendations relating to the acquisition,
disclosure, distribution and protection of rights in
inventions and technical information in accordance
with Article 17 of the Operating Agreement;

(s) Pursuant to decisions of the Board of Governors,
arrange to make available to Signatories and others
the rights of INTELSAT in inventions and technical

information in accordance with Article 17 of the Operating Agreement, and enter into licensing agreements on behalf of INTELSAT; and

(t) Take all operational, technical, financial, procurement, administrative and supporting actions necessary to carry out the above listed functions.

2. The management services contract shall include appropriate terms to implement the relevant provisions of Article XII of this Agreement and to provide for:

(a) Reimbursement by INTELSAT in US dollars of all direct and indirect costs documented and identified, properly incurred by the management services contractor under the contract;

(b) Payment to the management services contractor of a fixed fee at an annual rate in US dollars to be negotiated between the Board of Governors and the contractor;

(c) Periodic review by the Board of Governors in consultation with the management services contractor of the costs under subparagraph (a) of this paragraph;

(d) Compliance with procurement policies and procedures of INTELSAT, consistent with the relevant provisions of this Agreement and the Operating Agreement, in the solicitation and negotiation of contracts on behalf of INTELSAT;

(e) Provisions with respect to inventions and technical information which are consistent with Article 17 of the Operating Agreement;

(f) Technical personnel selected by the Board of Governors, with the concurrence of the management services contractor, from among persons nominated by Signatories, to participate in the assessment of designs and of specifications for equipment for the space segment;

(g) Disputes or disagreements between INTELSAT and the management services contractor which may arise under the management services contract to be settled in accordance with the Rules of Conciliation and Arbitration of the International Chamber of Commerce; and (h) The furnishing by the management services contractor to the Board of Governors of such information as may be required by any Governor to enable him to discharge his responsibilities as a Governor.

ANNEX C
PROVISIONS ON PROCEDURES RELATING TO SETTLEMENT OF DISPUTES REFERRED TO IN ARTICLE XVIII OF THIS AGREEMENT AND ARTICLE 20 OF THE OPERATING AGREEMENT

Article 1

The only disputants in arbitration proceedings instituted in accordance with this Annex shall be those referred to in Article XVIII of this Agreement, and Article 20 of, and the Annex to, the Operating Agreement.

Article 2

An arbitral tribunal of three members duly constituted in accordance with the provisions of this Annex shall be competent to give a decision in any dispute cognizable pursuant to Article XVIII of this Agreement, and Article 20 of, and the Annex to, the Operating Agreement.

Article 3

(a) Not later than sixty days before the opening date of the first and each subsequent ordinary meeting of the Assembly of Parties, each Party may submit to the executive organ the names of not more than two legal experts who will be available for the period from the end of such meeting until the end of the next ordinary meeting of the Assembly of Parties to serve as presidents or members of tribunals constituted in accordance with this Annex. From such nominees the executive organ shall prepare a list of all the persons thus nominated and shall attach to this list any biographical particulars submitted by the nominating Party, and shall distribute such list to all Parties not later than thirty days before the opening date of the meeting in question. If for any reason a nominee becomes unavailable for selection to the panel during the sixty-day period before the opening date of the meeting of the Assembly of Parties, the nominating Party may, not later than fourteen days before the opening date of the meeting of the Assembly of Parties, substitute the name of another legal expert.

(b) From the list mentioned in paragraph (a) of this Article, the Assembly of Parties shall select eleven persons to be members of a panel from which presidents of tribunals shall be selected, and shall select an alternate for each such member. Members and alternates shall serve for the period prescribed in paragraph (a) of this Article. If a member becomes unavailable to serve on the panel, he shall be replaced by his alternate.

(c) For the purpose of designating a chairman, the panel shall be convened to meet by the executive organ as soon as possible after the panel has been selected. The quorum for a meeting of the panel shall be nine of the eleven members. The panel shall designate one of its members as its chairman by a decision taken by the affirmative votes of at least six members, cast in one or, if necessary, more than one secret ballot. The chairman so designated shall hold office as chairman for the rest of his period of office as a member of the panel. The cost of the meeting of the panel shall be regarded as an administrative cost of INTELSAT for the purpose of Article 8 of the Operating Agreement.

(d) If both a member of the panel and the alternate for that member become unavailable to serve, the Assembly of Parties shall fill the vacancies thus created from the list referred to in paragraph (a) of this Article. If, however, the Assembly of Parties does not meet within ninety days subsequent to the occurrence of the vacancies, they shall be filled by selection by the Board of Governors from the list referred to in paragraph (a) of this Article, with each Governor having one vote. A person selected to replace a member or alternate whose term of office has not expired shall hold office for the remainder of the term of his predecessor. Vacancies in the office of the chairman of the panel shall be filled by the panel by designation of one of its members in accordance with the procedure prescribed in paragraph (c) of this Article.

(e) In selecting the members of the panel and the alternates in accordance with paragraph (b) or (d) of this Article, the Assembly of Parties or the Board of Governors shall seek to ensure that the composition of the panel will always be able to reflect an adequate geographical representation, as well as the principal legal systems as they are represented among the Parties.

(f) Any panel member or alternate serving on an arbitral tribunal at the expiration of his term shall continue to serve until the conclusion of any arbitral proceeding pending before such tribunal.

(g) If, during the period between the date of entry into force of this Agreement and the establishment of the first panel and alternates pursuant to the provisions of paragraph (b) of this Article, a legal dispute arises between the disputants mentioned in Article 1 of this Annex the panel as constituted in accordance with paragraph (b) of Article 3 of the Supplementary Agreement on Arbitration dated 4 June, 1965, shall be the panel for use in connection with the settlement of that dispute. That panel shall act in accordance with the provisions of this Annex for the purposes of Article XVIII of this Agreement, and Article 20 of, and the Annex to, the Operating Agreement.

Article 4

(a) Any petitioner wishing to submit a legal dispute to arbitration shall provide each respondent and the executive organ with a document which contains:

(i) A statement which fully describes the dispute being submitted for arbitration, the reasons why each respondent is required to participate in the arbitration, and the relief being requested;

(ii) A statement which sets forth why the subject matter of the dispute comes within the competence of a tribunal to be constituted in accordance with this

Annex, and why the relief being requested can be granted by such tribunal if it finds in favor of the petitioner;

(iii) A statement explaining why the petitioner has been unable to achieve a settlement of the dispute within a reasonable time by negotiation or other means short of arbitration;

(iv) In the case of any dispute for which, pursuant to Article XVIII of this Agreement or Article 20 of the Operating Agreement, the agreement of the disputants is a condition for arbitration in accordance with this Annex, evidence of such agreement; and

(v) The name of the person designated by the petitioner to serve as a member of the tribunal.

(b) The executive organ shall promptly distribute to each Party and Signatory, and to the chairman of the panel, a copy of the document provided pursuant to paragraph (a) of this Article.

Article 5

(a) Within sixty days from the date copies of the document described in paragraph (a) of Article 4 of this Annex have been received by all the respondents, the side of the respondents shall designate an individual to serve as a member of the tribunal. Within that period, the respondents may, jointly or individually, provide each disputant and the executive organ with a document stating their responses to the document referred to in paragraph (a) of Article 4 of this Annex and including any counter-claims arising out of the subject matter of the dispute. The executive organ shall promptly furnish the chairman of the panel with a copy of any such document.

(b) In the event of a failure by the side of the respondents to make such a designation within the period allowed, the chairman of the panel shall make a designation from among the experts whose names were submitted to the executive organ pursuant to paragraph (a) of Article 3 of this Annex.

(c) Within thirty days after the designation of the two

members of the tribunal, they shall agree on a third person selected from the panel constituted in accordance with Article 3 of this Annex, who shall serve as the president of the tribunal. In the event of failure to reach agreement within such period of time, either of the two members designated may inform the chairman of the panel, who, within ten days, shall designate a member of the panel other than himself to serve as president of the tribunal.

(d) The tribunal is constituted as soon as the president is selected.

Article 6

(a) If a vacancy occurs in the tribunal for reasons which the president or the remaining members of the tribunal decide are beyond the control of the disputants, or are compatible with the proper conduct of the arbitration proceedings, the vacancy shall be filled in accordance with the following provisions:

   (i) If the vacancy occurs as a result of the withdrawal of a member appointed by a side to the dispute, then that side shall select a replacement within ten days after the vacancy occurs;

   (ii) If the vacancy occurs as a result of the withdrawal of the president of the tribunal or of another member of the tribunal appointed by the chairman, a replacement shall be selected from the panel in the manner described in paragraph (c) or (b) respectively of Article 5 of this Annex.

(b) If a vacancy occurs in the tribunal for any reason other than as described in paragraph (a) of this Article or if a vacancy occurring pursuant to that paragraph is not filled, the remainder of the tribunal shall have the power, notwithstanding the provisions of Article 2 of this Annex, upon the request of one side, to continue the proceedings and give the final decision of the tribunal.

Article 7

(a) The tribunal shall decide the date and place of its sittings.

(b) The proceedings shall be held in private and all material presented to the tribunal shall be confidential, except that INTELSAT and the Parties whose designated Signatories and the Signatories whose designating Parties are disputants in the proceedings shall have the right to be present and shall have access to the material presented. When INTELSAT is a disputant in the proceedings, all Parties and all Signatories shall have the right to be present and shall have access to the material presented.

(c) In the event of a dispute over the competence of the tribunal, the tribunal shall deal with this question first, and shall give its decision as soon as possible.

(d) The proceedings shall be conducted in writing, and each side shall have the right to submit written evidence in support of its allegations of fact and law. However, oral arguments and testimony may be given if the tribunal considers it appropriate.

(e) The proceedings shall commence with the presentation of the case of the petitioner containing its arguments, related facts supported by evidence and the principles of law relied upon. The case of the petitioner shall be followed by the counter-case of the respondent. The petitioner may submit a reply to the counter-case of the respondent. Additional pleadings shall be submitted only if the tribunal determines they are necessary.

(f) The tribunal may hear and determine counter-claims arising directly out of the subject matter of the dispute, provided the counter-claims are within its competence as defined in Article XVIII of this Agreement and Article 20 of, and the Annex to, the Operating Agreement.

(g) If the disputants reach an agreement during the proceedings, the agreement shall be recorded in the form of a decision of the tribunal given by consent of the disputants.

(h) At any time during the proceedings, the tribunal may terminate the proceedings if it decides the dispute is beyond its competence as defined in Article XVIII of the Agreement, and Article 20 of, and the Annex to, the Operating Agreement.

(i) The deliberations of the tribunal shall be secret.

(j) The decisions of the tribunal shall be presented in writing and shall be supported by a written opinion. Its rulings and decisions must be supported by at least two members. A member dissenting from the decision may submit a separate written opinion.

(k) The tribunal shall forward its decision to the executive organ, which shall distribute it to ail Parties and Signatories.

(l) The tribunal may adopt additional rules of procedure, consistent with those established by this Annex, which are necessary for the proceedings.

Article 8

If one side fails to present its case, the other side may call upon the tribunal to give a decision in its favor. Before giving its decision, the tribunal shall satisfy itself that it has competence and that the case is well-founded in fact and in law.

Article 9

(a) Any Party whose designated Signatory is a disputant in a case shall have the right to intervene and become an additional disputant in the case. Intervention shall be made by giving notice thereof in writing to the tribunal and to the other disputants.

(b) Any other Party, any Signatory or INTELSAT, if it considers that it has a substantial interest in the decision of the case, may petition the tribunal for permission to intervene and become an additional disputant in the case. If the tribunal determines that the petitioner has a substantial interest in the decision of the case, it shall grant the petition.

Article 10

Either at the request of a disputant, or upon its own initiative, the tribunal may appoint such experts as it deems necessary to assist it.

Article 11

Each Party, each Signatory and INTELSAT shall provide all

information determined by the tribunal, either at the request of a disputant or upon its own initiative, to be required for the handling and determination of the dispute.

Article 12

During the course of its consideration of the case, the tribunal may, pending the final decision, indicate any provisional measures which it considers would preserve the respective rights of the disputants.

Article 13

- (a) The decision of the tribunal shall be based on
  - (i) This Agreement and the Operating Agreement; and
  - (ii) Generally accepted principles of law.
- (b) The decision of the tribunal, including any reached by agreement of the disputants pursuant to paragraph (g) of Article 7 of this Annex, shall be binding on all the disputants and shall be carried out by them in good faith. In a case in which INTELSAT is a disputant, and the tribunal decides that a decision of one of its organs is null and void as not being authorized by or in compliance with this Agreement and the Operating Agreement, the decision of the tribunal shall be binding on all Parties and Signatories.
- (c) In the event of a dispute as to the meaning or scope of its decision, the tribunal shall construe it at the request of any disputant.

Article 14

Unless the tribunal determines otherwise because of the particular circumstances of the case, the expenses of the tribunal, including the remuneration of the members of the tribunal, shall be borne in equal shares by each side. Where a side consists of more than one disputant, the share of that side shall be apportioned by the tribunal among the disputants on that side. Where INTELSAT is a disputant, its expenses associated with the arbitration shall be regarded as an administrative cost of INTELSAT for the purpose of Article 8 of the Operating Agreement.

ANNEX D
TRANSITION PROVISIONS

1. Continuity of INTELSAT Activities

Any decision of the Interim Communications Satellite Committee taken pursuant to the Interim Agreement or the Special Agreement and which is in effect as of the termination of those Agreements shall remain in full force and effect, unless and until it is modified or repealed by, or in implementation of, the terms of this Agreement or the Operating Agreement.

2. Management

During the period immediately following entry into force of this Agreement, the Communications Satellite Corporation shall continue to act as the manager for the design, development, construction, establishment, operation and maintenance of the INTELSAT space segment pursuant to the same terms and conditions of service which were applicable to its role as manager pursuant to the Interim Agreement and the Special Agreement. In the discharge of its functions it shall be bound by all the relevant provisions of this Agreement and the Operating Agreement and shall in particular be subject to the general policies and specific determinations of the Board of Governors, until:

(i) The Board of Governors determines that the executive organ is ready to assume responsibility for performance of all or certain of the functions of the executive organ pursuant to Article XII of this Agreement, at which time the Communications Satellite Corporation shall be relieved of its responsibility for performance of each such function as it is assumed by the executive organ; and

(ii) The management services contract referred to in subparagraph (a)(ii) of Article XII of this Agreement takes effect, at which time the provisions of this paragraph shall cease to have effect with respect to those functions within the scope of that contract.

3. Regional Representation

During the period between entry into force of this Agreement and the date of assumption of office by the Secretary General, the entitlement, consistent with paragraph (c) of Article IX of this Agreement, of any group of Signatories seeking representation on the Board of Governors, pursuant to subparagraph (a) (iii) of Article IX of this Agreement, shall become effective upon receipt by the Communications Satellite Corporation of a written request from such group.

4. Privileges and Immunities

The Parties to this Agreement which were parties to the Interim Agreement shall extend to the corresponding successor persons and bodies until such times as the Headquarters Agreement and the Protocol, as the case may be, enter into force as provided for in Article XV of this Agreement, those privileges, exemptions and immunities which were extended by such Parties, immediately prior to entry into force of this Agreement, to the International Telecommunications Satellite Consortium, to the signatories to the Special Agreement and to the Interim Communications Satellite Committee and to representatives thereto.

OPERATING AGREEMENT RELATING TO
THE INTERNATIONAL TELECOMMUNICATIONS
SATELLITE ORGANIZATION "INTELSAT"

Preamble

The Signatories to this Operating Agreement,
    Considering that the States Parties to the Agreement Relating to the International Telecommunications Satellite Organization "INTELSAT" have undertaken therein to sign or to designate a telecommunications entity to sign this Operating Agreement,
    Agree as follows:

Article 1: Definitions

(a)   For the purpose of this Operating Agreement:

     (i) "Agreement" means the Agreement Relating to the International Telecommunications Satellite Organization "INTELSAT";

     (ii) "Amortization" includes depreciation; and

    (iii) "Assets" includes every subject of whatever nature to which a right of ownership can attach, as well as contractual rights.

  (b) The definitions in Article I of the Agreement shall apply to this Operating Agreement.

Article 2: Rights and Obligations of Signatories

Each Signatory acquires the rights provided for Signatories in the Agreement and this Operating Agreement and undertakes to fulfill the obligations placed upon it by those Agreements.

Article 3: Transfer of Rights and Obligations

  (a) As of the date the Agreement and this Operating Agreement enter into force and subject to the requirements of Article 19 of this Operating Agreement:

     (i) All of the property and contractual rights and all other rights, including rights in and to the space segment, owned in undivided shares by the signatories to the Special Agreement pursuant to the Interim Agreement and the Special Agreement as of such date, shall be owned by INTELSAT;

    (ii) All of the obligations and liabilities undertaken or incurred by or on behalf of the signatories to the Special Agreement collectively in carrying out the provisions of the Interim Agreement and the Special Agreement which are outstanding as of, or arise from acts or omissions prior to, such date shall become obligations and liabilities of INTELSAT. However, this subparagraph shall not apply to any such obligation or liability arising from actions or decisions taken after the opening for signature of the Agreement which, after the entry into force of the Agreement, could not have been taken by the Board of Governors without prior authorization of the Assembly of Parties pursuant to paragraph (f) of Article III of the Agreement.

(b) INTELSAT shall be the owner of the INTELSAT space segment and of all other property acquired by INTELSAT.

(c) The financial interest in INTELSAT of each Signatory shall be equal to the amount arrived at by the application of its investment share to the valuation effected pursuant to Article 7 of this Operating Agreement.

Article 4: Financial Contributions

(a) Each Signatory shall make contributions to the capital requirements of INTELSAT, as determined by the Board of Governors in accordance with the terms of the Agreement and this Operating Agreement, in proportion to its investment share as determined pursuant to Article 6 of this Operating Agreement and shall receive capital repayment and compensation for use of capital in accordance with the provisions of Article 8 of this Operating Agreement.

(b) Capital requirements shall include all direct and indirect costs for the design, development, construction and establishment of the INTELSAT space segment and for other INTELSAT property, as well as requirements for contributions by Signatories pursuant to paragraph (f) of Article 8 and paragraph (b) of Article 18 of this Operating Agreement. The Board of Governors shall determine the financial requirements of INTELSAT which shall be met from capital contributions from the Signatories.

(c) Each Signatory, as user of the INTELSAT space segment, as well as all other users, shall pay appropriate utilization charges established in accordance with the provisions of Article 8 of this Operating Agreement.

(d) The Board of Governors shall determine the schedule of payments required pursuant to this Operating Agreement. Interest at a rate to be determined by the Board of Governors shall be added to any amount unpaid after the date designated for payment.

Article 5: Capital Ceiling

(a) The sum of the net capital contributions of the Signatories and of the outstanding contractual capital commitments of INTELSAT shall be subject to a ceiling. This sum shall consist of the cumulative capital contributions made by the signatories to the Special Agreement, pursuant to Articles 3 and 4 of the Special Agreement, and by the Signatories to this Operating Agreement, pursuant to Article 4 of this Operating Agreement, less the cumulative capital repaid to them pursuant to the Special Agreement and to this Operating Agreement, plus the outstanding amount of contractual capital commitments of INTELSAT.

(b) The ceiling referred to in paragraph (a) of this Article shall be 500 million U.S. dollars or the amount authorized pursuant to paragraph (c) or (d) of this Article.

(c) The Board of Governors may recommend to the Meeting of Signatories that the ceiling in effect under paragraph (b) of this Article be increased. Such recommendation shall be considered by the Meeting of Signatories, and the increased ceiling shall become effective upon approval by the Meeting of Signatories.

(d) However, the Board of Governors may increase the ceiling up to ten percent above the limit of 500 million U.S. dollars or such higher limits as may be approved by the Meeting of Signatories pursuant to paragraph (c) of this Article.

Article 6: Investment Shares

(a) Except as otherwise provided in this Article, each Signatory shall have an investment share equal to its percentage of all utilization of the INTELSAT space segment by all Signatories.

(b) For the purpose of paragraph (a) of this Article, utilization of the INTELSAT space segment by a Signatory shall be measured by dividing the space segment utilization charges payable by the Signatory to INTELSAT by the number of days for which charges were payable during the six-month period prior to the effective date of a determination of investment shares pursuant to subparagraph (c) (i), (c) (ii) or (c) (v) of this Article. However, if the number of days for which charges were payable by a Signatory for utilization during such six-month period was less than ninety days, such charges shall not be taken into account in determining investment shares.

(c) Investment shares shall be determined effective as of:

    (i) The date of entry into force of this Operating Agreement;

    (ii) The first day of March of each year, provided that if this Operating Agreement enters into force less than six months before the succeeding first day of March, there shall be no determination under this subparagraph effective as of that date;

    (iii) The date of entry into force of this Operating Agreement for a new Signatory;

    (iv) The effective date of withdrawal of a Signatory from INTELSAT; and

    (v) The date of request by a Signatory for whom INTELSAT space segment utilization charges have, for the first time, become payable by that Signatory for utilization through its own earth station, provided that such date of request is not less than ninety days following the date the space segment utilization charges became payable.

(d) (i) Any Signatory may request that, if any determination of investment shares made pursuant to paragraph (c) of this Article would result in its investment share exceeding its quota or investment share, as the case may be, held immediately prior to such determination, it be allocated a lesser investment share, provided that such investment share shall not be less than its final quota held pursuant to the Special Agreement or than its investment share held immediately prior to the determination, as the case may be. Such requests shall be deposited with INTELSAT and shall indicate the reduced investment share desired. INTELSAT shall give prompt notification of such requests to all Signatories, and such requests shall be honored to the extent that other Signatories accept greater investment shares.

(ii) Any Signatory may notify INTELSAT that it is prepared to accept an increase in its investment share in order to accommodate requests for lesser investment shares made pursuant to subparagraph (i) of this paragraph and up to what limit, if any. Subject to such limits, the total amount of reduction in investment shares requested pursuant to subparagraph (i) of this paragraph shall be distributed among the Signatories which have accepted, pursuant to this subparagraph, greater investment shares, in proportion to the investment shares held by them immediately prior to the applicable adjustment.

(iii) If reductions requested pursuant to subparagraph (i) of this paragraph cannot be wholly accommodated among the Signatories which have accepted greater investment shares pursuant to subparagraph (ii) of this paragraph, the total amount of accepted increases shall be allocated, up to the limits indicated by each Signatory accepting a greater investment share pursuant to this paragraph, as reductions to those Signatories which requested lesser investment shares pursuant to subparagraph (i) of this paragraph, in proportion to the reductions requested by them under subparagraph (i) of this paragraph.

(iv) Any Signatory which has requested a lesser or accepted a greater investment share pursuant to this paragraph shall be deemed to have accepted the decrease or increase of its investment share, as determined pursuant to this paragraph, until the next determination of investment shares pursuant to subparagraph (c) (ii) of this Article.

(v) The Board of Governors shall establish appropriate procedures with regard to notification of requests by Signatories for lesser investment shares made pursuant to subparagraph (i) of this paragraph, and notification by Signatories which are prepared to accept increases in their investment shares pursuant to subparagraph (ii) of this paragraph.

(e) For the purposes of composition of the Board of Governors and calculation of the voting participation of Governors, the investment shares determined pursuant to subparagraph (c) (ii) of this Article shall take effect from the first day of the ordinary meeting of the Meeting of Signatories following such determination.

(f) To the extent that an investment share is determined pursuant to subparagraph (c) (iii) or (c) (v) or paragraph (h) of this Article, and to the extent necessitated by withdrawal of a Signatory, the investment shares of all other Signatories shall be adjusted in the proportion that their respective investment shares, held prior to this adjustment, bear to each other. On the withdrawal of a Signatory, investment shares of 0.05 per cent determined in accordance with the-provisions of paragraph (h) of this Article shall not be increased.

(g) Notification of the results of each determination of investment shares, and of the effective date of such determination shall be promptly furnished to all Signatories by INTELSAT.

(h) Notwithstanding any provision of this Article, no Signatory shall have an investment share of less than 0.05 per cent of the total investment shares.

Article 7: Financial Adjustments between Signatories

(a) On entry into force of this Operating Agreement and thereafter at each determination of investment shares, financial adjustments shall be made between Signatories, through INTELSAT, on the basis of a valuation effected pursuant to paragraph (b) of this Article. The amounts of such financial adjustments shall be determined with respect to each Signatory by applying to such valuation:

(i) On entry into force of this Operating Agreement, the difference, if any, between the final quota of each Signatory held pursuant to the Special Agreement and its initial investment share determined pursuant to Article 6 of this Operating Agreement;

(ii) At each subsequent determination of investment shares, the difference, if any, between the new investment share of each Signatory and its investment share prior to such determination.

(b) The valuation referred to in paragraph (a) of this Article shall be effected as follows:

  (i) Deduct from the original cost of all assets as recorded in INTELSAT accounts as of the date of adjustment, including any capitalized return or capitalized expenses, the sum of:

    (a) The accumulated amortization as recorded in INTELSAT accounts as of the date of adjustment, and

    (b) Loans and other accounts payable by INTELSAT as of the date of adjustment;

  (ii) Adjust the results obtained pursuant to subparagraph (i) of this paragraph by:

    (a) Adding or deducting, for the purpose of the financial adjustments on entry into force of this Operating Agreement, an amount representing any deficiency or excess, respectively, in the payment by INTELSAT of compensation for use of capital relative to the cumulative amount due pursuant to the Special Agreement, at the rate or rates of compensation for use of capital in effect during the periods in which the relevant rates were applicable, as established by the Interim Communications Satellite Committee pursuant to Article 9 of the Special Agreement. For the purpose of assessing the amount representing any deficiency or excess in payment, compensation due shall be calculated on a monthly basis and relate to the net amount of the elements described in subparagraph (i) of this paragraph;

    (b) Adding or deducting, for the purpose of each subsequent financial adjustment a further amount representing any deficiency or excess, respectively, in the payment by INTELSAT of compensation for use of capital from the time of entry into force of this Operating Agreement to the effective date of valuation, relative to the cumulative amount due pursuant to this Operating Agreement, at the rate or rates of compensation for use of capital in effect during the periods in which the relevant rates were applicable, as established by the Board of Governors pursuant to Article 8 of this Operating Agreement. For the purpose of assessing the amount representing any deficiency or excess in payment, compensation due shall be calculated on a monthly basis and relate to the net amount of the elements described in subparagraph (i) of this paragraph.

(c) Payments due from and to Signatories pursuant to the provisions of this Article shall be effected by a date designated by the Board of Governors. Interest at a rate to be determined by the Board of Governors shall be added to any amount unpaid after that date, except that, with respect to payments due pursuant to subparagraph (a)

(i)   of this Article, interest shall be added from the date of entry into force of this Operating Agreement. The rate of interest referred to in this paragraph shall be equal to the rate of interest determined by the Board of Governors pursuant to paragraph (d) of Article 4 of this Operating Agreement.

Article 8: Utilization Charges and Revenues

(a) The Board of Governors shall specify the units of measurement of INTELSAT space segment utilization relative to various types of utilization and, guided by such general rules as may be established by the Meeting of Signatories pursuant to Article VIII of the Agreement, shall establish INTELSAT space segment utilization charges. Such charges shall have the objective of covering the operating, maintenance and administrative costs of INTELSAT, the provision of such operating funds as the Board of Governors may determine to be necessary, the amortization of investment made by Signatories in INTELSAT and compensation for use of the capital of Signatories.

(b) For the utilization of capacity available for the purposes of specialized telecommunications services, pursuant to paragraph (d) of Article III of the Agreement, the Board of Governors shall establish the charge to be paid for the utilization of such services. In doing so it shall comply with the provisions of the Agreement and this Operating Agreement and in particular paragraph (a) of this Article, and shall take into consideration the costs associated with the provision of the specialized telecommunications services as well as an adequate part of the general and administrative costs of INTELSAT. In the case of separate satellites or associated facilities financed by INTELSAT pursuant to paragraph (e) of Article V of the Agreement, the Board of Governors shall establish the charges to be paid for the utilization of such services. In doing so, it shall comply with the provisions of the Agreement and this Operating Agreement and in particular paragraph (a) of this Article, so as to cover fully the costs directly resulting from the design, development, construction, and provision of such separate satellites and associated facilities as well as an adequate part of the general and administrative costs of INTELSAT.

(c) In determining the rate of compensation for use of the capital of Signatories, the Board of Governors shall include an allowance for the risks associated with investment in INTELSAT and, taking into account such allowance, shall fix the rate as close as possible to the cost of money in the world markets.

(d) The Board of Governors shall institute any appropriate sanctions in cases where payments of utilization charges shall have been in default for three months or longer.

(e) The revenues earned by INTELSAT shall be applied, to the extent that such revenues allow, in the following order of priority:

    (i) To meet operating, maintenance and dministrative costs;

    (ii) To provide such operating funds as the Board of Governors may determine to be necessary;

    (iii) To pay to Signatories, in proportion to their respective investment shares, sums representing a repayment of capital in the amount of the provisions for amortization established by the Board of Governors and recorded in the INTELSAT accounts;

(iv) To pay to a Signatory which has withdrawn from INTELSAT such sums as may be due to it pursuant to Article 21 of this Operating Agreement; and

(v) To pay to Signatories, in proportion to their respective investment shares, the available balance towards compensation for use of capital.

(f) To the extent, if any, that the revenues earned by INTELSAT are insufficient to meet INTELSAT operating, maintenance and administrative costs, the Board of Governors may decide to meet the deficiency by using INTELSAT operating funds, by overdraft arrangements, by raising a loan, by requiring Signatories to make capital contributions in proportion to their respective investment shares or by any combination of such measures.

Article 9: Transfer of Funds

(a) Settlement of accounts between Signatories and INTELSAT in respect of financial transactions pursuant to Articles 4, 7 and 8 of this Operating Agreement shall be so arranged as to minimize both transfers of funds between Signatories and INTELSAT and the amount of funds held by INTELSAT over and above any operating funds determined by the Board of Governors to be necessary.

(b) All payments between Signatories and INTELSAT pursuant to this Operating Agreement shall be made in U.S. dollars or in currency freely convertible into U.S. dollars.

Article 10: Overdrafts and Loans

(a) For the purpose of meeting financial deficiencies, pending the receipt of adequate INTELSAT revenues or of capital contributions by Signatories pursuant to this Operating Agreement, INTELSAT may, with the approval of the Board of Governors, enter into overdraft arrangements.

(b) Under exceptional circumstances and for the purpose of financing any activity undertaken by INTELSAT, or of meeting any liability incurred by INTELSAT, pursuant to paragraph (a), (b) or (c) of Article III of the Agreement or to this Operating Agreement, INTELSAT may raise loans upon decision of the Board of Governors. The outstanding amounts of such loans shall be considered as contractual capital commitments for the purpose of Article 5 of this Operating Agreement. The Board of Governors shall, in accordance with subparagraph (a) (xiv) of Article X of the Agreement, report fully to the Meeting of Signatories with respect to the reasons for its decision to raise any loan and the terms and conditions under which such a loan was raised.

Article 11: Excluded Costs

The following shall not form part of the costs of INTELSAT:

   (i)   Taxes on income derived from INTELSAT of any of the Signatories;

  (ii)   Design and development expenditure on launchers and launching facilities except expenditure incurred for the adaptation of launchers and launching facilities in connection with the design, development, construction and establishment of the INTELSAT space segment; and

 (iii)   The costs of representatives of Parties and Signatories incurred in attending meetings of the Assembly of Parties, of the Meeting of Signatories, of the Board of Governors or any other meetings of INTELSAT.

Article 12: Audit

The accounts of INTELSAT shall be audited annually by independent auditors appointed by the Board of Governors. Any Signatory shall have the right of inspection of INTELSAT accounts.

Article 13: International Telecommunication Union

In addition to observing the relevant regulations of the International Telecommunication Union, INTELSAT shall, in the design, development, construction and establishment of the

INTELSAT space segment and in the procedures established for regulating the operation of the INTELSAT space segment and of the earth stations, give due consideration to the relevant recommendations and procedures of the International Telegraph and Telephone Consultative Committee, the International Radio Consultative Committee and the International Frequency Registration Board.

Article 14: Earth Station Approval

(a) Any application for approval of an earth station to utilize the INTELSAT space segment shall be submitted to INTELSAT by the Signatory designated by the Party in whose territory the earth station is or will be located or, with respect to earth stations located in a territory not under the jurisdiction of a party, by a duly authorized telecommunications entity.

(b) Failure by the Meeting of Signatories to establish general rules, pursuant to subparagraph (b) (v) of Article VIII of the Agreement, or the Board of Governors to establish criteria and procedures, pursuant to subparagraph (a) (vi) of Article X of the Agreement, for approval of earth stations shall not preclude the Board of Governors from considering or acting upon any application for approval of an earth station to utilize the INTELSAT space segment.

(c) Each Signatory or telecommunications entity referred to in paragraph (a) of this Article shall, with respect to earth stations for which it has submitted an application, be responsible to INTELSAT for compliance of such stations with the rules and standards specified in the document of approval issued to it by INTELSAT, unless, in the case of a Signatory which has submitted an application, its designating Party assumes such responsibility, with respect to all or some of the earth stations not owned or operated by such Signatory.

Article 15: Allotment of Space Segment Capacity

(a) Any application for allotment of INTELSAT space segment capacity shall be submitted to INTELSAT by a Signatory or, in the case of a territory not under the jurisdiction of a Party, by a duly authorized telecommunications entity.

(b) In accordance with the terms and conditions established by the Board of Governors pursuant to Article X of the Agreement, allotment of INTELSAT space segment capacity shall be made to a Signatory or, in the case of a territory not under the jurisdiction of a Party, to the duly authorized telecommunications entity making the application.

(c) Each Signatory or telecommunications entity to, which an allotment has been made pursuant to paragraph (b) of this Article shall be responsible for compliance with all the terms and conditions established by INTELSAT with respect to such allotment, unless, in the case of a Signatory which has submitted an application, its designating Party assumes such responsibility for allotments made with respect to all or some of the earth stations not owned or operated by such Signatory.

Article 16: Procurement

(a) All contracts relating to the procurement of goods and services required by INTELSAT shall be awarded in accordance with Article XIII of the Agreement, Article 17 of this Operating Agreement and the procedures, regulations, terms and conditions established by the Board of Governors pursuant to the provisions of the Agreement and this Operating Agreement.

The services to which this Article refers are those provided by juridical persons.

(b) The approval of the Board of Governors shall be required before:

   (i) The issuing of requests for proposals or invitations to tender for contracts which are expected to exceed 500,000 U.S. dollars in value;

   (ii) The awarding of any contract to a value exceeding 500,000 U.S. dollars.

(c) In any of the following circumstances, the Board of Governors may decide to procure goods and services otherwise than on the basis of responses to open international invitations to tender:

    (i) Where the estimated value of the contract does not exceed 50,000 U.S. dollars or any such higher amount as the Meeting of Signatories may decide in the light of proposals by the Board of Governors;

    (ii) Where procurement is required urgently to meet an emergency situation involving the operational viability of the INTELSAT space segment;

    (iii) Where the requirement is of a predominantly administrative nature best suited to local procurement; and

    (iv) Where there is only one source of supply to a specification which is necessary to meet the requirements of INTELSAT or where the sources of supply are so severely restricted in number that it would be neither feasible nor in the best interest of INTELSAT to incur the expenditure and time involved in open international tender, provided that where there is more than one source they will all have the opportunity to bid on an equal basis.

(d) The procedures, regulations, terms and conditions referred to in paragraph (a) of this Article shall provide for the supply of full and timely information to the Board of Governors. Upon request from any Governor, the Board of Governors shall be able to obtain, with respect to all contracts, any information necessary to enable that Governor to discharge his responsibilities as a Governor.

Article 17: Inventions and Technical Information

(a) INTELSAT, in connection with any work performed by it or on its behalf, shall acquire in inventions and technical information those rights, but no more than those rights, necessary in the common interests of INTELSAT and the Signatories in their capacity as such. In the case of work done under contract, any such rights obtained shall be on a non-exclusive basis.

(b) For the purposes of paragraph (a) of this Article, INTELSAT, taking into account its principles and objectives, the rights and obligations of the Parties and Signatories under the Agreement and this Operating

Agreement and generally accepted industrial practices, shall, in connection with any work performed by it or on its behalf involving a significant element of study, research or development, ensure for itself:

(i) The right without payment to have disclosed to it all inventions and technical information generated by work performed by it or on its behalf;

(ii) The right to disclose and have disclosed to Signatories and others within the jurisdiction of any Party and to use and authorize and have authorized Signatories and such others to use such inventions and technical information:

(a) Without payment, in connection with the INTELSAT space segment and any earth station operating in conjunction therewith, and

(b) For any other purpose, on fair and reasonable terms and conditions to be settled between Signatories or others within the jurisdiction of any Party and the owner or originator of such inventions and technical information or any other duly authorized entity or person having a property interest therein.

(c) In the case of work done under contract, the implementation of paragraph (b) of this Article shall be based on the retention by contractors of ownership of rights in inventions and technical information generated by them.

(d) INTELSAT shall also ensure for itself the right, on fair and reasonable terms and conditions, to disclose and have disclosed to Signatories and others within the jurisdiction of any Party, and to use and authorize and have authorized Signatories and such others to use, inventions and technical information directly utilized in the execution of work performed on its behalf but not included in paragraph (b) of this Article, to the extent that the person who has performed such work is entitled to grant such right and to the extent that such disclosure and use is necessary for the effective exercise of rights obtained pursuant to paragraph (b) of this Article.

(e) The Board of Governors may, in individual cases, where exceptional circumstances warrant, approve a deviation from the policies prescribed in subparagraph (b) (ii) and paragraph (d) of this Article where in the course of negotiations it is demonstrated to the Board of Governors that failure to deviate would be detrimental to the interests of INTELSAT and, in the case of subparagraph (b) (ii), that adherence to these policies would be incompatible with prior contractual obligations entered into in good faith by a prospective contractor with a third party.

(f) The Board of Governors may also, in individual cases, where exceptional circumstances warrant, approve a deviation from the policy prescribed in paragraph (c) of this Article where all of the following conditions are met:

  (i) It is demonstrated to the Board of Governors that failure to deviate would be detrimental to the interests of INTELSAT,

  (ii) It is determined by the Board of Governors that INTELSAT should be able to ensure patent protection in any country, and

  (iii) Where, and to the extent that, the contractor is unable or unwilling to ensure such protection on a timely basis.

(g) In determining whether and in what form to approve any deviation pursuant to paragraphs (e) and (f) of this Article, the Board of Governors shall take into account the interests of INTELSAT and all Signatories and the estimated financial benefits to INTELSAT resulting from such deviation.

(h) With respect to inventions and technical information in which rights were acquired under the Interim Agreement and the Special Agreement, or are acquired under the Agreement and this Operating Agreement other than pursuant to paragraph (b) of this Article, INTELSAT, to the extent that it has the right to do so, shall upon request:

(i) Disclose or have disclosed such inventions and technical information to any Signatory, subject to reimbursement of any payment made by or required of INTELSAT in respect of the exercise of such right of disclosure;

(ii) Make available to any Signatory the right to disclose or have disclosed to others within the jurisdiction of any Party and to use and authorize or have authorized such others to use such inventions and technical information:

   (a) Without payment, in connection with the INTELSAT space segment or any earth station operating in conjunction therewith, and

   (b) For any other purpose, on fair and reasonable terms and conditions to be settled between Signatories or others within the jurisdiction of any Party and INTELSAT or the owner or originator of such inventions and technical information or any other duly authorized entity or person having a property interest therein, and subject to reimbursement of any payment made by or required of INTELSAT in respect of the exercise of such rights.

(i) To the extent that INTELSAT acquires the right pursuant to subparagraph (b) (i) of this Article to have inventions and technical information disclosed to it, it shall keep each Signatory which so requests informed of the availability and general nature of such inventions and technical information. To the extent that INTELSAT acquires rights pursuant to the provisions of this Article to make inventions and technical information available to Signatories and others in the jurisdiction of Parties, it shall make such rights available upon request to any Signatory or its designee.

(j) The disclosure and use, and the terms and conditions of disclosure and use, of all inventions and technical information in which INTELSAT has acquired any rights shall be on a non-discriminatory basis with respect to all Signatories and their designees.

Article 18: Liability

(a) Neither INTELSAT nor any Signatory, in its capacity as such, nor any director, officer or employee of any of them nor any representative to any organ of INTELSAT acting in the performance of their functions and within the scope of their authority, shall be liable to, nor shall any claim be made against any of them by, any Signatory or INTELSAT for loss or damage sustained~by reason of any unavailability, delay or faultiness of telecommunications services provided or to be provided pursuant to the Agreement or this Operating Agreement.

(b) If INTELSAT or any Signatory, in its capacity as such, is required, by reason of a binding decision rendered by a competent tribunal or as a result of a settlement agreed to or concurred in by the Board of Governors, to pay any claim, including any costs and expenses associated therewith, which arises out of any activity conducted or authorized by INTELSAT pursuant to the Agreement or to this Operating Agreement, to the extent that the claim is not satisfied through indemnification, insurance or other financial arrangements, the Signatories shall, notwithstanding any ceiling established by or pursuant to Article 5 of this Operating Agreement, pay to INTELSAT the amount unsatisfied on such claim in proportion to their respective investment shares as of the date the payment by INTELSAT of such claim is due.

(c) If such a claim is asserted against a Signatory, that Signatory, as a condition of payment by INTELSAT of the claim pursuant to paragraph (b) of this Article, shall without delay provide INTELSAT with notice thereof, and shall afford INTELSAT the opportunity to advise and recommend on or to conduct the defense or other disposition of the claim and, to the extent permitted by the law of the jurisdiction in which the claim is brought, to become a party to the proceeding either with such Signatory or in substitution for it.

Article 19: Buy-Out

(a) Consonant with the provisions of Articles IX and XV of the Interim Agreement, the Board of Governors shall, as soon as practicable and not later than three months after entry into force of this Operating Agreement, determine, in accordance with paragraph (d) of this Article, the financial status in relation to INTELSAT of each signatory to the Special Agreement for which, in its capacity as a State, or for whose State the Agreement, on its entry into force, had neither entered into force nor been applied provisionally. The Board of Governors shall notify each such signatory in writing of its financial status and the rate of interest thereon. This rate of interest shall be close to the cost of money in world markets.

(b) A signatory may accept the assessment of its financial status and the rate of interest as notified pursuant to paragraph (a) of this Article or as may otherwise have been agreed between the Board of Governors and this signatory. INTELSAT shall pay to such signatory, in U.S. dollars or in another currency freely convertible into U.S. dollars, within ninety days of such acceptance, or within such greater period as may be mutually agreed, the amount so accepted, together with interest thereon from the date of entry into force of this Operating Agreement to the date of payment.

(c) If there is a dispute between INTELSAT and a signatory as to the amount or the rate of interest, which cannot be settled by negotiation within the period of one year from the date of notification pursuant to paragraph (a) of this Article, the amount and rate of interest notified shall remain the standing offer by INTELSAT to settle the matter, and the corresponding funds shall be set aside at the disposal of such signatory. Provided that a mutually acceptable tribunal can be found, INTELSAT shall refer the matter to arbitration if the signatory so requests. Upon receipt of the decision of the tribunal, INTELSAT shall pay to the signatory the amount decided by the tribunal in U. S. dollars or in another currency freely convertible into U. S. dollars.

(d) For the purpose of paragraph (a) of this Article, the financial status shall be determined as follows:

(i) Multiply the final quota held by the signatory pursuant to the Special Agreement by the amount established from the valuation effected pursuant to paragraph (b) of Article 7 of this Operating Agreement as of the date of entry into force of this Operating Agreement; and

(ii) From the resulting product deduct any amounts due from that signatory as of the date of entry into force of this Operating Agreement.

(e) No provision of this Article shall:

(i) Relieve a signatory described in paragraph (a) of this Article of its share of any obligations incurred by or on behalf of the signatories to the Special Agreement collectively as the result of acts or omissions in the implementation of the Interim Agreement and the Special Agreement prior to the date of entry into force of this Operating Agreement; or

(ii) Deprive such a signatory of any rights acquired by it, in its capacity as such, which would otherwise continue after the termination of the Special Agreement and for which the signatory has not already been compensated pursuant to the provisions of this Article.

Article 20: Settlement of Disputes

(a) All legal disputes arising in connection with the rights and obligations under the Agreement or this Operating Agreement between Signatories with respect to each other, or between INTELSAT and a Signatory or Signatories, if not otherwise settled within a reasonable time, shall be submitted to arbitration in accordance with the provisions of Annex C to the Agreement.

(b) All such disputes arising between a Signatory and a State or telecommunications entity which has ceased to be a Signatory, or between INTELSAT and a State or telecommunications entity which has ceased to be a Signatory, and which arise after such State or telecommunications entity ceased to be a Signatory, if not otherwise settled within a reasonable time, shall be submitted to arbitration, and may be submitted to arbitration in accordance with the provisions of Annex C to the Agreement provided the disputants in any given dispute so agree. If a State or telecommunications entity ceases to be a Signatory after an arbitration in which it is a disputant has commenced, such arbitration shall be continued and concluded in accordance with the provisions of Annex C to the Agreement, or, as the case may be, with the other provisions under which the arbitration is being conducted.

(c) All legal disputes arising in connection with agreements or contracts that INTELSAT may conclude with any Signatory shall be subject to the provisions on settlement of disputes contained in such agreements or contracts. In the absence of such provisions, such disputes, if not otherwise settled within a reasonable time, shall be submitted to arbitration in accordance with the provisions of Annex C to the Agreement.

(d) If upon entry into force of this Operating Agreement, any arbitration is in progress pursuant to the Supplementary Agreement on Arbitration dated 4 June, 1965, the provisions of that Agreement shall remain in force with respect to such arbitration until its conclusion. If the Interim Communications Satellite Committee is a party to any such arbitration, INTELSAT shall replace it as a party.

Article 21: Withdrawal

(a) Within three months after the effective date of withdrawal of a Signatory from INTELSAT pursuant to Article XVI of the Agreement, the Board of Governors shall notify the Signatory of the evaluation by the Board of Governors of its financial status in relation to INTELSAT as of the effective date of its withdrawal and of the proposed terms of settlement pursuant to paragraph (c) of this Article.

(b) The notification pursuant to paragraph (a) of this Article shall include a statement of:

   (i) The amount payable by INTELSAT to the Signatory, calculated by multiplying the investment share held by the Signatory as of the effective date of its withdrawal by the amount established from a valuation effected pursuant to paragraph (b) of Article 7 of this Operating Agreement as of that date;

   (ii) Any amounts to be paid by the Signatory to INTELSAT, pursuant to paragraph (g), (i) or (k) of Article XVI of the Agreement, representing its share of capital contributions for contractual commitments specifically authorized prior to the receipt by the appropriate authority of notice of its decision to withdraw or, as the case may be, prior to the effective date of its withdrawal, together with the proposed schedule for the payments to meet the said contractual commitments; and

   (iii) Any amounts due from the Signatory to INTELSAT as of the effective date of its withdrawal.

(c) The amounts referred to in subparagraphs (b)(i) and (b)(ii) of this Article shall be repaid by INTELSAT to the Signatory over a period of time consistent with the period over which other Signatories will be repaid their capital contributions, or over such lesser period as the Board of Governors may consider appropriate. The Board of Governors shall determine the rate of interest to be paid to or by the Signatory in respect of any amounts which may, from time to time, be outstanding for settlement.

(d) In its evaluation pursuant to subparagraph (b)(ii) of this Article, the Board of Governors may decide to relieve the Signatory in whole or in part of its responsibility for contributing its share of the capital contributions necessary to meet both contractual commitments specifically authorized and liabilities arising from acts or omissions prior to the receipt of notice of withdrawal or, as the case may be, prior to the effective date of withdrawal of the Signatory pursuant to Article VI of the Agreement.

(e)   Except as may be decided by the Board of Governors
      pursuant to paragraph (d) of this Article, no provision of
      this Article shall:
      (i) Relieve a Signatory referred to in paragraph (a) of this
           Article of its share of any non-contractual obligations
           of INTELSAT arising from acts or omissions in the
           implementation of the Agreement and the Operating
           Agreement prior to the receipt of notice of its decision
           to withdraw or, as the case may be, prior to the
           effective date of its withdrawal; or
      (ii) Deprive such a Signatory of any rights acquired by it,
           in its capacity as such, which would otherwise
           continue after the effective date of its withdrawal, and
           for which the Signatory has not already been
           compensated pursuant to the provisions of this Article.

Article 22: Amendments

(a)   Any Signatory, the Assembly of Parties or the Board of
      Governors may propose amendments to this Operating
      Agreement. Proposed amendments shall be submitted to
      the executive organ, which shall distribute them promptly
      to all Parties and Signatories.
(b)   The Meeting of Signatories shall consider each proposed
      amendment at its first ordinary meeting following its
      distribution by the executive organ, or at an earlier
      extraordinary meeting convened in accordance with the
      provisions of Article VIII of the Agreement, provided that
      the proposed amendment has been distributed by the
      executive organ at least ninety days before the opening
      date of the meeting. The Meeting of Signatories shall
      consider any views and recommendations which it
      receives from the Assembly of Parties or the Board of
      Governors with respect to a proposed amendment.
(c)   The Meeting of Signatories shall take decisions on each
      proposed amendment in accordance with the provisions
      relating to quorum and voting contained in Article VIII of
      the Agreement. It may modify any proposed amendment,
      distributed in accordance with paragraph (b) of this
      Article, and may also take decisions on any amendment

not so distributed but directly consequential to a proposed or modified amendment.

(d) An amendment which has been approved by the Meeting of Signatories shall enter into force in accordance with paragraph (e) of this Article after the Depositary has received notice of approval of the amendment from either:

   (i) Two-thirds of the Signatories which were Signatories as of the date upon which the amendment was approved by the Meeting of Signatories, provided that such two-thirds include Signatories which then held at least two-thirds of the total investment shares; or

   (ii) A number of Signatories equal to or exceeding eighty-five per cent of the total number of Signatories which were Signatories as of the date upon which the amendment was approved by the Meeting of Signatories, regardless of the amount of investment shares which such Signatories then held.

Notification of the approval of an amendment by a Signatory shall be transmitted to the Depositary by the Party concerned, and such a notification shall signify the acceptance by the Party of such amendment.

(e) The Depositary shall notify all the Signatories as soon as it has received the approvals of the amendment required by paragraph (d) of this Article for the entry into force of an amendment. Ninety days after the date of issue of this notification, the amendment shall enter into force for all Signatories, including those that have not yet approved it and have not withdrawn from INTELSAT.

(f) Notwithstanding the provisions of paragraphs (d) and (e) of this Article, an amendment shall not enter into force later than eighteen months after the date it has been approved by the Meeting of Signatories.

Article 23: Entry into Force

(a) This Operating Agreement shall enter into force for a Signatory on the date on which the Agreement enters into force, in accordance with paragraphs (a) and (d) or

paragraphs (b) and (d) of Article XX of the Agreement, for
the Party concerned.

(b)   This Operating Agreement shall be applied provisionally
for a Signatory on the date on which the Agreement is
applied provisionally, in accordance with paragraphs (c)
and (d) of Article XX of the Agreement, for the Party
concerned.

(c)   This Operating Agreement shall continue in force for as
long as the Agreement is in force.

Article 24: Depositary

(a)   The Government of the United States of America shall be
the Depositary for this Operating Agreement, the texts of
which in English, French and Spanish are equally
authentic. This Operating Agreement shall be deposited
in the archives of the Depositary, with which shall also be
deposited notifications of approval of amendments, of
substitution of a Signatory pursuant to paragraph (f) of
Article XVI of the Agreement, and of withdrawals from
INTELSAT.

(b)   The Depositary shall transmit certified copies of the texts
of this Operating Agreement to all Governments and all
designated telecommunications entities which have signed
it, and to the International Telecommunication Union, and
shall notify those Governments, designated
telecommunications entities, and the International
Telecommunication Union, of signatures to this Operating
Agreement, of commencement of the sixty-day period
referred to in paragraph (a) of Article XX of the Agreement,
of the entry into force of this Operating Agreement, of
notifications of approval of amendments and of the entry
into force of amendments to this Operating Agreement.
Notice of the commencement of the sixty-day period shall
be issued on the first day of that period.

(c)   Upon entry into force of this Operating Agreement, the
Depositary shall register it with the Secretariat of the
United Nations in accordance with Article 102 of the
Charter of the United Nations.

In Witness Whereof, the undersigned duly authorized thereto have signed this Operating Agreement.

Done at Washington, on the 20th day of August, one thousand nine hundred and seventy-one.

CONVENTION ON
THE INTERNATIONAL MARITIME SATELLITE
ORGANIZATION (INMARSAT) WITH
ANNEX AND OPERATING AGREEMENT (1976);
AS AMENDED 1985; WITH PROTOCOL (1981)

Entry into Force: 16 July, 1979

The States Parties to this Convention

Considering the principle set forth in Resolution 1721 (XVI) of the General Assembly of the United Nations that communication by means of satellites should be available to the nations of the world as soon as practicable on a global and non-discriminatory basis,

Considering the relevant provisions of the Treaty on Principles Governing the Activities of States in the Exploration and Use of Outer Space, Including the Moon and Other Celestial Bodies, concluded on 27 January, 1967, and in particular article 1, which states that outer space shall be used for the benefit and in the interests of all countries,

Taking into account that a very high proportion of world trade is dependent upon ships,

Being aware that considerable improvements to the maritime distress and safety systems and to the communication link between ships and between ships and their management as well as between crew or passengers on board and persons on shore can be made by using satellites,

Determined, to this end, to make provision for the benefit of ships of all nations through the most advanced suitable space technology available, for the most efficient and economic facilities possible consistent with the most efficient and equitable use of the radio frequency spectrum and of satellite orbits,

Recognizing that a maritime satellite system comprises mobile earth stations and land earth stations, as well as the space segment,

Affirming that a maritime satellite system shall also be open for aeronautical communication for the benefit of aircraft of all nations,

Agree as follows:

Article 1: Definitions

For the purposes of this Convention:

(a) "Operating Agreement" means the Operating Agreement on the International Maritime Satellite Organization (INMARSAT), including its annex.

(b) "Party" means a State for which this Convention has entered into force.

(c) "Signatory" means either a Party or an entity designated in accordance with article 2(3), for which the Operating Agreement has entered into force.

(d) "Space segment" means the satellites, and the tracking, telemetry, command, control, monitoring and related facilities and equipment required to support the operation of these satellites.

(e) "INMARSAT space segment" means the space segment owned or leased by INMARSAT.

(f) "Ship" means a vessel of any type operating in the marine environment. It includes inter alia hydrofoil boats, air-cushion vehicles, submersibles, floating craft and platforms not permanently moored.

(g) "Property" means anything that can be the subject of a right of ownership, including contractual rights.

(h) "Aircraft" means any machine that can derive support in the atmosphere from the reactions of the air other than the reactions of the air against the earth's surface.

Article 2: Establishment of INMARSAT

1. The International Maritime Satellite Organization (INMARSAT), herein referred to as "the Organization", is hereby established.

2. The Operating Agreement shall be concluded in conformity with the provisions of this Convention and shall be opened for signature at the same time as this Convention.

3. Each Party shall sign the Operating Agreement or shall

designate a competent entity, public or private, subject to the jurisdiction of that Party, which shall sign the Operating Agreement.

4. Telecommunications administrations and entities may, subject to applicable domestic law, negotiate and enter directly into appropriate traffic agreements with respect to their use of telecommunications facilities provided pursuant to this Convention and the Operating Agreement, as well as with respect to services to be furnished to the public, facilities, division of revenues and related business arrangements.

Article 3: Purpose

1. The purpose of the Organization is to make provision for the space segment necessary for improving maritime communications and, as practicable, aeronautical communications, thereby assisting in improving communications for distress and safety of life, communications for air traffic services, the efficiency and management of ships and aircraft, maritime and aeronautical public correspondence services and radio-determination capabilities.

2. The Organization shall seek to serve all areas where there is need for maritime and aeronautical communications.

3. The Organization shall act exclusively for peaceful purposes.

Article 4: Relations between a Party and its Designated Entity

Where a Signatory is an entity designated by a Party:

(a) Relations between the Party and the Signatory shall be governed by applicable domestic law.

(b) The Party shall provide such guidance and instructions as are appropriate and consistent with its domestic law to ensure that the Signatory fulfils its responsibilities.

(c) The Party shall not be liable for obligations arising under the Operating Agreement. The Party shall, however, ensure that the Signatory, in carrying out its obligations within the Organization, will not act in a manner which violates obligations which the Party has accepted under this Convention or under related international agreements.

(d) If the Signatory withdraws or its membership is terminated the Party shall act in accordance with article 29(3) or 30(6).

Article 5: Operational and Financial Principles of the Organization

1. The Organization shall be financed by the contributions of Signatories. Each Signatory shall have a financial interest in the Organization in proportion to its investment share which shall be determined in accordance with the Operating Agreement.

2. Each Signatory shall contribute to the capital requirements of the Organization and shall receive capital repayment and compensation for use of capital in accordance with the Operating Agreement.

3. The Organization shall operate on a sound economic and financial basis having regard to accepted commercial principles.

Article 6: Provision of Space Segment

The Organization may own or lease the space segment.

Article 7: Access to Space Segment

1. The INMARSAT space segment shall be open for use by ships and aircraft of all nations on conditions to be determined by the Council. In determining such conditions, the Council shall not discriminate among ships or aircraft on the basis of nationality.

2. The Council may, on a case-by-case basis, permit access to the INMARSAT space segment by earth stations located on structures operating in the marine environment other than ships, if and as long as the operation of such earth stations will not significantly affect the provision of service to ships or aircraft.

3. Earth stations on land communicating via the INMARSAT space segment shall be located on land territory under the jurisdiction of a Party and shall be wholly owned by Parties or entities subject to their jurisdiction. The Council may authorize otherwise if it finds this to be in the interests of the Organization.

Article 8: Other Space Segments

1. A Party shall notify the Organization in the event that it or any person within its jurisdiction intends to make provision for, or initiate the use of, individually or jointly, separate space segment facilities to meet any or all of the maritime purposes of the INMARSAT space segment, to insure technical compatibility and to avoid significant economic harm to the INMARSAT system.

2. The Council shall express its views in the form of a recommendation of a non-binding nature with respect to technical compatibility and shall provide its views to the Assembly with respect to economic harm.

3. The Assembly shall express its views in the form of recommendations of a non-binding nature within a period of nine months from the date of commencing the procedures provided for in this article. An extraordinary meeting of the Assembly may be convened for this purpose.

4. The notification pursuant to paragraph (1), including the provision of pertinent technical information, and subsequent consultations with the Organization, shall take into account the relevant provisions of the Radio Regulations of the International Telecommunication Union.

5. This article shall not apply to the establishment, acquisition, utilization or continuation of separate space segment facilities for national security purposes, or which were contracted for, established, acquired or utilized prior to the entry into force of this Convention.

Article 9: Structure

The organs of the Organization shall be:

(a) The Assembly.

    (b)   The Council.
    (c)   The Directorate headed by a Director General.

Article 10: Assembly — Composition and Meetings

1.   The Assembly shall be composed of all the Parties.
2.   Regular sessions of the Assembly shall be held once every two years. Extraordinary sessions shall be convened upon the request of one-third of the Parties or upon the request of the Council.

Article 11: Assembly — Procedure

1.   Each Party shall have one vote in the Assembly.
2.   Decisions on matters of substance shall be taken by a two-thirds majority, and on procedural matters by a simple majority, of the Parties present and voting. Parties which abstain from voting shall be considered as not voting.
3.   Decisions whether a question is procedural or substantive shall be taken by the Chairman. Such decisions may be overruled by a two-thirds majority of the Parties present and voting.
4.   A quorum for any meeting of the Assembly shall consist of a majority of the Parties.

Article 12: Assembly — Functions

1.   The functions of the Assembly shall be to:
    (a) Consider and review the activities, purposes, general policy and long-term objectives of the Organization and express views and make recommendations thereon to the Council.
    (b) Ensure that the activities of the Organization are consistent with this Convention and with the purposes and principles of the United Nations Charter, as well as with any other treaty by which the Organization becomes bound in accordance with its decision.
    (c) Authorize, on the recommendation of the Council, the establishment of additional space segment facilities the special or primary purpose of which is to provide

radiodetermination, distress or safety services. However, the space segment facilities established to provide maritime and aeronautical public correspondence services can be used for telecommunications for distress, safety and radiodetermination purposes without such authorization.

(d) Decide on other recommendations of the Council and express views on reports of the Council.

(e) Elect four representatives on the Council in accordance with article 13(1)(b).

(f) Decide upon questions concerning formal relationships between the Organization and States, whether Parties or not, and international organizations.

(g) Decide upon any amendment to this Convention pursuant to article 34 or to the Operating Agreement pursuant to article XVIII thereof.

(h) Consider and decide whether membership be terminated in accordance with article 30.

(i) Exercise any other functions conferred upon it in any other article of this Convention or the Operating Agreement.

2. In performing its functions the Assembly shall take into account any relevant recommendations of the Council.

Article 13: Council — Composition

1. The Council shall consist of twenty-two representatives of Signatories as follows:

(a) Eighteen representatives of those Signatories, or groups of Signatories not otherwise represented, which have agreed to be represented as a group, which have the largest investment shares in the Organization. If a group of Signatories and a single Signatory have equal investment shares, the latter shall have the prior right. If by reason of two or more Signatories having equal investment shares the number of representatives on the Council would exceed twenty-two, all shall nevertheless, exceptionally, be represented.

   (b) Four representatives of Signatories not otherwise represented on the Council, elected by the Assembly, irrespective of their investment shares, in order to ensure that the principle of just geographical representation is taken into account, with due regard to the interests of the developing countries. Any Signatory elected to represent a geographical area shall represent each Signatory in that geographical area which has agreed to be so represented and which is not otherwise represented on the Council. An election shall be effective as from the first meeting of the Council following that election, and shall remain effective until the next ordinary meeting of the Assembly.

   2.   Deficiency in the number of representatives on the Council pending the filling of a vacancy shall not invalidate the composition of the Council.

Article 14: Council—Procedure

   1.   The Council shall meet as often as may be necessary for the efficient discharge of its functions, but not less than three times a year.

   2.   The Council shall endeavor to take decisions unanimously. If unanimous agreement cannot be reached, decisions shall be taken as follows: Decisions on substantive matters shall be taken by a majority of the representatives on the Council representing at least two-thirds of the total voting participation of all Signatories and groups of Signatories represented on the Council. Decisions on procedural matters shall be taken by a simple majority of the representatives present and voting, each having one vote. Disputes whether a specific matter is procedural or substantive shall be decided by the Chairman of the Council. The decision of the Chairman may be overruled by a two-thirds majority of the representatives present and voting, each having one vote. The Council may adopt a different voting procedure for the election of its officers.

   3.   (a) Each representative shall have a voting participation equivalent to the investment share or shares he represents.

However, no representative may cast on behalf of one Signatory more than 25 per cent of the total voting participation in the Organization except as provided in sub-paragraph (b)(iv).

(b) Notwithstanding article V(9), (10) and (12) of the Operating Agreement:

    (i) If a Signatory represented on the Council is entitled, based on its investment share to a voting participation in excess of 25 per cent of the total voting participation in the Organization, it may offer to other Signatories any or all of its investment share in excess of 25 per cent.

    (ii) Other Signatories may notify the Organization that they are prepared to accept any or all of such excess investment share. If the total of the amounts notified to the Organization does not exceed the amount available for distribution, the latter amount shall be distributed by the Council to the notifying Signatories in accordance with the amounts notified. If the total of the amounts notified does exceed the amount available for distribution, the latter amount shall be distributed by the Council as may be agreed among the notifying Signatories, or, failing agreement, in proportion to the amounts notified.

    (iii) Any such distribution shall be made by the Council at the time of determinations of investment shares pursuant to article V of the Operating Agreement. Any distribution shall not increase the investment share of any Signatory above 25 per cent.

    (iv) To the extent that the investment share of the Signatory in excess of 25 per cent offered for distribution is not distributed in accordance with the procedure set forth in this paragraph, the voting participation of the representative of the Signatory may exceed 25 per cent.

(c) To the extent that a Signatory decides not to offer its excess investment share to other Signatories, the corresponding voting participation of that Signatory in excess of 25 per cent shall be distributed equally to all other representatives on the Council.

4. A quorum for any meeting of the Council shall consist of a majority of the representatives on the Council, representing at least two-thirds of the total voting participation of all Signatories and group of Signatories represented on the Council.

Article 15: Council—Functions

The Council shall have the responsibility, having due regard for the views and recommendations of the Assembly, to make provision for the space segment necessary for carrying out the purposes of the Organization in the most economic, effective and efficient manner consistent with this Convention and the Operating Agreement. To discharge this responsibility, the Council shall have the power to perform all appropriate functions, including:

(a) Determination of maritime and aeronautical satellite telecommunications requirements and adoption of policies, plans, programmes, procedures and measures for the design, development, construction, establishment, acquisition by purchase or lease operation, maintenance and utilization of the INMARSAT space segment, including the procurement of any necessary launch services to meet such requirements.

(b) Adoption and implementation of management arrangements which shall require the Director General to contract for technical and operational functions whenever this is more advantageous to the Organization.

(c) Adoption of criteria and procedures for approval of earth stations on land, on ships, on aircraft, and on structures in the marine environment for access to the INMARSAT space segment and for verification and monitoring of performance of earth stations having access to and utilization of the INMARSAT space segment. For earth stations on ships and aircraft, the criteria should be in sufficient detail for use by national licensing authorities, at their discretion, for type-approval purposes.

(d) Submission of recommendations to the Assembly in

accordance with article 12(1)(c).

(e) Submission to the Assembly of periodic reports on the activities of the Organization, including financial matters.

(f) Adoption of procurement procedures, regulations and contract terms and approval of procurement contracts consistent with this Convention and the Operating Agreement.

(g) Adoption of financial policies, approval of the financial regulations, annual budget and annual financial statements, periodic determination of charges for use of the INMARSAT space segment, and decisions with respect to all other financial matters including investment shares and capital ceiling consistent with this Convention and the Operating Agreement.

(h) Determination of arrangements for consultation on a continuing basis with bodies recognized by the Council as representing shipowners, aircraft operators, maritime and aeronautical personnel and other users of maritime and aeronautical telecommunications.

(i) Designation of an arbitrator where the Organization is a party to an arbitration.

(j) Exercise of any other functions conferred upon it in any other Article of this Convention or the Operating Agreement or any other function appropriate for the achievement of the purposes of the Organization.

Article 16: Directorate

1. The Director General shall be appointed, from among candidates proposed by Parties or Signatories through Parties, by the Council, subject to confirmation by the Parties. The Depositary shall immediately notify the Parties of the appointment. The appointment is confirmed unless within sixty days of the notification more than one-third of the Parties have informed the Depositary in writing of their objection to the appointment. The Director General may assume his functions after appointment and pending confirmation.

2. The term of office of the Director General shall be six years. However, the Council may remove the Director General

earlier on its own authority. The Council shall report the reasons for the removal to the Assembly.

3. The Director General shall be the chief executive and legal representative of the Organization and shall be responsible to and under the direction of the Council.

4. The structure, staff levels and standard terms of employment of officials and employees and of consultants and other advisers to the Directorate shall be approved by the Council.

5. The Director General shall appoint the members of the Directorate. The appointment of senior officials reporting directly to the Director General shall be approved by the Council.

6. The paramount consideration in the appointment of the Director General and other personnel of the Directorate shall be the necessity of ensuring the highest standards of integrity, competency and efficiency.

Article 17: Representation at Meetings

All Parties and Signatories which, under this Convention or the Operating Agreement are entitled to attend and/or participate at meetings of the Organization shall be allowed to attend and/or participate at such meetings as well as any other meeting held under the auspices of the Organization, regardless of where the meeting may take place. The arrangements made with any host country, shall be consistent with these obligations.

Article 18: Costs of Meetings

1. Each Party and Signatory shall meet its own costs of representation at meetings of the Organization.

2. Expenses of meetings of the Organization shall be regarded as an administrative cost of the Organization. However, no meeting of the Organization shall be held outside its headquarters, unless the prospective host agrees to defray the additional expenditure involved.

Article 19: Establishment of Utilization Charges

1. The Council shall specify the units of measurement for

the various types of utilization of the INMARSAT space segment and shall establish charges for such utilization. These charges shall have the objective of earning sufficient revenues for the Organization to cover its operating, maintenance, and administrative costs, the provision of such operating funds as the Council may determine to be necessaiy, the amortization of investment made by Signatories, and compensation for use of capital in accordance with the Operating Agreement.

2. The rates of utilization charge for each type of utilization shall be the same for ail Signatories for that type of utilization.

3. For entities, other than Signatories, which are authorized in accordance with article 7 to utilize the INMARSAT space segment, the Council may establish rates of utilization charge different from those established for Signatories. The rates for each type of utilization shall be the same for all such entities for that type of utilization.

Article 20: Procurement

1. The procurement policy of the Council shall be such as to encourage, in the interests of the Organization, world-wide competition in the supply of goods and services. To this end:

    (a) Procurement of goods and services required by the Organization, whether by purchase or lease, shall be effected by the award of contracts, based on responses to open international invitations to tender.

    (b) Contracts shall be awarded to bidders offering the best combination of quality, price and the most favourable delivery time.

    (c) If there are bids offering comparable combinations of quality, price and the most favourable delivery time, the Council shall award the contract so as to give effect to the procurement policy set out above.

2. In the following cases the requirement of open international tender may be dispensed with under procedures adopted by the Council, provided that in so doing the Council shall encourage in the interests of the

Organization world-wide competition in the supply of goods and services:

(a) The estimated value of the contract does not exceed 50,000 US dollars and the award of the contract would not by reason of the application of the dispensation place a contractor in such a position as to prejudice at some later date the effective exercise by the Council of the procurement policy set out above. To the extent justified by changes in world prices, as reflected by relevant price indices, the Council may revise the financial limit.

(b) Procurement is required urgently to meet an emergency situation.

(c) There is only one source of supply to a specification which is necessary to meet the requirements of the Organization or the sources of supply are so severely restricted in number that it would be neither feasible nor in the best interest of the Organization to incur the expenditure and time involved in open international tender provided that where there is more than one source they will have an opportunity to bid on an equal basis.

(d) The requirement is of an administrative nature for which it would be neither practicable nor feasible to undertake open international tender.

(e) The procurement is for personal services.

Article 21: Inventions and Technical Information

1. The Organization, in connexion with any work performed by it or on its behalf at its expense, shall acquire in inventions and technical information those rights, but no more than those rights, which are necessary in the common interests of the Organization and of the Signatories in their capacity as such. In the case of work done under contract any such rights obtained shall be on a non-exclusive basis.

2. For the purpose of paragraph (1) the Organization, taking into account its principles and objectives and generally accepted industrial practices, shall, in connexion with such

work involving a significant element of study, research or development ensure for itself:

(a) The right to have disclosed to it without payment all inventions and technical information generated by such work.

(b) The right to disclose and to have disclosed to Parties and Signatories and others within the jurisdiction of any Party such inventions and technical information, and to use and to authorize and to have authorized Parties and Signatories and such others to use such inventions and technical information without payment in connexion with the INMARSAT space segment and any earth station on land, ship or aircraft operating in conjunction therewith.

3. In the case of work done under contract, ownership of the rights in inventions and technical information generated under the contract shall be retained by the contractor.

4. The Organization shall also ensure for itself the right, on fair and reasonable terms and conditions, to use and to have used inventions and technical information directly utilized in the execution of work performed on its behalf but not included in paragraph (2), to the extent that such use is necessary for the reconstruction or modification of any product actually delivered under a contract financed by the Organization, and to the extent that the person who has performed such work is entitled to grant such right.

5. The Council may in individual cases approve a deviation from the policies prescribed in paragraphs (2)(b) and (4), where in the course of negotiation it is demonstrated to the Council that failure to deviate would be detrimental to the interests of the Organization.

6. The Council may also, in individual cases where exceptional circumstances warrant, approve a deviation from the policy prescribed in paragraph (3) where all the following conditions are met:

(a) It is demonstrated to the Council that failure to deviate would be detrimental to the interests of the Organization.

(b) The Council determines that the Organization should be able to ensure patent protection in any country.

(c) Where, and to the extent that, the contractor is unable or unwilling to ensure such patent protection within the time required.

7. With respect to inventions and technical information in which rights are acquired by the Organization otherwise than pursuant to paragraph (2), the Organization, to the extent that it has the right to do so, shall upon request:

(a) Disclose or have disclosed such inventions and technical information to any Party or Signatory subject to reimbursement of any payment made by or required of the Organization in respect of the exercise of this right of disclosure.

(b) Make available to any Party or Signatory the right to disclose or have disclosed to others within the jurisdiction of any Party and to use and to authorize and to have authorized such others to use such inventions and technical information:

(i) Without payment in connexion with the INMARSAT space segment or any earth station on land, ship or aircraft operating in conjunction therewith.

(ii) For any other purpose, on fair and reasonable terms and conditions to be settled between Signatories or others within the jurisdiction of any Party and the Organization or the owner of the inventions and technical information or any other authorized entity or person having a property interest therein, and subject to reimbursement of any payment made by or required of the Organization in respect of the exercise of these rights.

8. The disclosure and use, and the terms and conditions of disclosure and use, of all inventions and technical information in which the Organization has acquired any rights shall be on a non-discriminatory basis with respect to all Signatories and others within the jurisdiction of Parties.

9. Nothing in this article shall preclude the Organization, if desirable, from entering into contracts with persons subject to domestic laws and regulations relating to the disclosure of technical information.

Article 22: Liability

Parties are not, in their capacity as such, liable for the acts and obligations of the Organization, except in relation to non-Parties or natural or juridical persons they might represent in so far as such liability may follow from treaties in force between the Party and the non-Party concerned. However, the foregoing does not preclude a Party which has been required to pay compensation under such a treaty to a non-Party or to a natural or juridical person it might represent from invoking any rights it may have under that treaty against any other Party.

Article 23: Excluded Costs

Taxes on income derived from the Organization by any of the Signatories shall not form part of the costs of the Organization.

Article 24: Audit

The accounts of the Organization shall be audited annually by an independent Auditor appointed by the Council. Any Party or Signatory shall have the right to inspect the accounts of the Organization.

Article 25: Legal Personality

The Organization shall have legal personality and shall be responsible for its acts and obligations. For the purpose of its proper functioning, it shall, in particular, have the capacity to contract, to acquire, lease, hold and dispose of movable and immovable property, to be a party to legal proceedings and to conclude agreements with States or international organizations.

Article 26: Privileges and Immunities

1. Within the scope of activities authorized by this Convention, the Organization and its property shall be exempt in all States Parties to this Convention from all national income and direct national property taxation and from customs duties on communication satellites and

components and parts for such satellites to be launched for use in the INMARSAT space segment. Each Party undertakes to use its best endeavours to bring about, in accordance with the applicable domestic procedure, such further exemption from income and direct property taxation and customs duties as is desirable, bearing in mind the particular nature of the Organization.

2. All Signatories acting in their capacity as such, except the Signatory designated by the Party in whose territory the headquarters is located, shall be exempt from national taxation on income earned from the Organization in the territory of that Party.

3. (a) As soon as possible after the entry into force of this Convention, the Organization shall conclude, with any Party in whose territory the Organization establishes its headquarters, other offices or installations, an agreement to be negotiated by the Council and approved by the Assembly, relating to the privileges and immunities of the Organization, its Director General, its staff, of experts performing missions for the Organization and of representatives of Parties and Signatories whilst in the territory of the host Government for the purpose of exercising their functions.

    (b) The agreement shall be independent of this Convention and shall terminate by agreement between the host Government and the Organization or if the headquarters of the Organization are moved from the territory of the host Government.

4. All Parties other than a Party which has concluded an agreement referred to in paragraph (3) shall as soon as possible after the entry into force of this Convention conclude a Protocol on the privileges and immunities of the Organization, its Director General, its staff, of experts performing missions for the Organization and of representatives of Parties and Signatories whilst in the territory of Parties for the purposes of exercising their functions. The Protocol shall be independent of this Convention and shall prescribe the conditions for its termination.

Article 27: Relationship with Other International Organizations

The Organization shall co-operate with the United Nations and its bodies dealing with the Peaceful Uses of Outer Space and Ocean Area, its Specialized Agencies, as well as other international organizations, on matters of common interest. In particular the Organization shall take into account the relevant international standards, regulations, resolutions, procedures and recommendations of the International Maritime Organization and the International Civil Aviation Organization. The Organization shall observe the relevant provisions of the International Telecommunication Convention and regulations made thereunder, and shall in the design, development, construction and establishment of the INMARSAT space segment and in the procedures established for regulating the operation of the INMARSAT space segment and of earth stations give due consideration to the relevant resolutions, recommendations and procedures of the organs of the International Telecommunication Union.

Article 28: Notification to the International Telecommunication Union

Upon request from the Organization, the Party in whose territory the Headquarters of the Organization is located shall co-ordinate the frequencies to be used for the space segment and shall, on behalf of each Party that consents, notify the International Telecommunication Union of the frequencies to be so used and other information, as provided for in the Radio Regulations annexed to the International Telecommunication Convention.

Article 29: Withdrawal

1. Any Party or Signatory may by written notification to the Depositary withdraw voluntarily from the Organization at any time. Once a decision has been made under applicable domestic law that a Signatory may withdraw, notice of the withdrawal shall be given in writing to the Depositary by the Party which has designated the Signatory, and the notification shall signify the acceptance

by the Party of the withdrawal. Withdrawal of a Party, in its capacity as such, shall entail the simultaneous withdrawal of any Signatory designated by the Party or of the Party in its capacity as Signatory, as the case may be.

2. Upon receipt by the Depositary of a notice to withdraw, the Party giving notice and any Signatory which it has designated, or the Signatory in respect of which notice has been given, as the case may be, shall cease to have any rights of representation and any voting rights in any organ of the Organization and shall incur no obligation after the date of such receipt. However, a withdrawing Signatory shall remain responsible, unless otherwise decided by the Council pursuant to article XIII of the Operating Agreement, for contributing its share of the capital contributions necessary to meet contractual commitments specifically authorized by the Organization before the receipt and liabilities arising from acts or omissions before the receipt. Except with respect to such capital contributions and except with respect to article 31 of this Convention and article XVI of the Operating Agreement, withdrawal shall become effective and this Convention and/or the Operating Agreement shall cease to be in force for the Party and/or Signatory three months after the date of receipt by the Depositary of the written notification referred to in paragraph (1).

3. If a Signatory withdraws, the Party which designated it shall, before the effective date of withdrawal and with effect from that date, designate a new Signatory, assume the capacity of a Signatory in accordance with paragraph (4), or withdraw. If the Party has not acted by the effective date, it shall be considered to have withdrawn as from that date. Any new Signatory shall be responsible for all the outstanding capital contributions of the previous Signatory and for the proportionate share of any capital contributions necessary to meet contractual commitments specifically authorized by the Organization, and liabilities arising from acts or omissions, after the date of receipt of the notice.

4. If for any reason a Party desires to substitute itself for its

designated Signatory or to designate a new Signatory, it shall give written notice to the Depositary. Upon assumption by the new Signatory of all the outstanding obligations, as specified in the last sentence of paragraph (3), of the previously designated Signatory and upon signature of the Operating Agreement, that Agreement shall enter into force for the new Signatory and shall cease to be in force for the previous Signatory.

Article 30: Suspension and Termination

1. Not less than one year after the Directorate has received written notice that a Party appears to have failed to comply with any obligation under this Convention, the Assembly, after considering any representations made by the Party, may decide, if it finds that the failure to comply has in fact occurred and that such failure impairs the effective operation of the Organization, that the membership of the Party is terminated. This Convention shall cease to be in force for the Party as from the date of the decision or at such later date as the Assembly may determine. An extraordinary session of the Assembly may be convened for this purpose. The termination shall entail the simultaneous withdrawal of any Signatory designated by the Party or of the Party in its capacity as Signatory, as the case may be. The Operating Agreement shall cease to be in force for the Signatory on the date on which this Convention ceases to be in force for the Party concerned, except with respect to capital contributions necessary to meet contractual commitments specifically authorized by the Organization before the termination and liabilities arising from acts or omissions before the termination, and except with respect to article 31 of this Convention and article XVI of the Operating Agreement.

2. If any Signatory, in its capacity as such, fails to comply with any obligation under this Convention or the Operating Agreement, other than obligations under article III(1) of the Operating Agreement and the failure has not been remedied within three months after the Signatory has been notified in writing of a resolution of the Council

taking note of the failure to comply, the Council, after considering any representations made by the Signatory and, if applicable, the Party concerned may suspend the rights of the Signatory. If, after an additional three months and after consideration of any representations made by the Signatory and, if applicable, the Party, the Council finds that the failure to comply has not been remedied, the Assembly may decide on the recommendation of the Council that the membership of the Signatory is terminated. Upon the date of such decision, the termination shall become effective and the Operating Agreement shall cease to be in force for that Signatory.

3. If any Signatory fails to pay any amount due from it pursuant to article III(1) of the Operating Agreement within four months after the payment has become due, the rights of the Signatory under this Convention and the Operating Agreement shall be automatically suspended. If within three months after the suspension the Signatory has not paid all sums due or the Party which has designated it has not made a substitution pursuant to article 29(4), the Council, after considering any representations made by the Signatory or by the Party which has designated it, may decide that the membership of the Signatory is terminated. From the date of such decision, the Operating Agreement shall cease to be in force for the Signatory.

4. During the period of suspension of the rights of a Signatory pursuant to paragraphs (2) or (3), the Signatory shall continue to have all the obligations of a Signatory under this Convention and the Operating Agreement.

5. A Signatory shall incur no obligation after termination, except that it shall be responsible for contributing its share of the capital contributions necessary to meet contractual commitments specifically authorized before the termination and liabilities arising from acts or omissions before the termination, and except with respect to article 31 of this Convention and article XVI of the Operating Agreement.

6. If the membership of a Signatory is terminated, the Party which designated it shall, within three months from the

date of the termination and with effect from that date, designate a new Signatory, assume the capacity of a Signatory in accordance with article 29(4), or withdraw. If the Party has not acted by the end of that period, it shall be considered to have withdrawn as from the date of termination, and this Convention shall cease to be in force for the Party as from that date.

7. Whenever this Convention has ceased to be in force for a Party, settlement between the Organization and any Signatory designated by that Party or that Party in its capacity as Signatory, shall be accomplished as provided in article XIII of the Operating Agreement.

Article 31: Settlement of Disputes

1. Disputes arising between Parties, or between Parties and the Organization relating to rights and obligations under this Convention should be settled by negotiation between the parties concerned. If within one year of the time any party has requested settlement, a settlement has not been reached and if the parties to the dispute have not agreed to submit it to the International Court of Justice or to some other procedure for settling disputes, the dispute may, if the parties to the dispute consent, be submitted to arbitration in accordance with the annex to this Convention. Any decision of an arbitral tribunal in a dispute between Parties, or between Parties and the Organization, shall not prevent or affect a decision of the Assembly pursuant to article 30(1), that the Convention shall cease to be in force for a Party.

2. Unless otherwise mutually agreed, disputes arising between the Organization and one or more Parties under agreements concluded between them, if not settled by negotiation within one year of the time any party has requested settlement, shall, at the request of any party to the dispute, be submitted to arbitration in accordance with the annex to this Convention.

3. Disputes arising between one or more Parties and one or more Signatories in their capacity as such, relating to rights and obligations under this convention or the Operating

Agreement may be submitted to arbitration in accordance with the annex to this Convention if the Party or Parties and the Signatory or Signatories involved agree to such arbitration.

4. This article shall continue to apply to a Party or Signatory which ceases to be a Party or Signatory, in respect of disputes relating to rights and obligations arising from its having been a Party or Signatory.

Article 32: Signature and Ratification

1. This Convention shall remain open for signature in London until entry into force and shall thereafter remain open for accession. All States may become Parties to the Convention by:
    (a) Signature not subject to ratification, acceptance or approval, or
    (b) Signature subject to ratification, acceptance or approval, followed by ratification, acceptance or approval, or
    (c) Accession.
2. Ratification, acceptance, approval or accession shall be effected by the deposit of the appropriate instrument with the Depositary.
3. On becoming a Party to this Convention, or at any time thereafter, a State may declare, by written notification to the Depositary, to which Registers of ships, to which aircraft operating under its authority, and to which land earth stations under its jurisdiction, the Convention shall apply.
4. No State shall become a Party to this Convention until it has signed, or the entity it has designated, has signed the Operating Agreement. (5) Reservations cannot be made to this Convention or the Operating Agreement.

Article 33: Entry into Force

1. This Convention shall enter into force sixty days after the date on which States representing 95 per cent of the initial investment shares have become Parties to the Convention.

2. Notwithstanding paragraph (1), if the Convention has not entered into force within thirty-six months after the date it was opened for signature, it shall not enter into force.
3. For a State which deposits an instrument of ratification, acceptance, approval or accession after the date on which the Convention has entered into force, the ratification, acceptance, approval or accession shall take effect on the date of deposit.

Article 34: Amendments

1. Amendments to this Convention may be proposed by any Party. Proposed amendments shall be submitted to the Directorate, which shall inform the other Parties and Signatories. Three months' notice is required before consideration of an amendment by the Council, which shall submit its views to the Assembly within a period of six months from the date of circulation of the amendment. The Assembly shall consider the amendment not earlier than six months thereafter, taking into account any views expressed by the Council. This period may, in any particular case, be reduced by the Assembly by a substantive decision.
2. If adopted by the Assembly, the amendment shall enter into force one hundred and twenty days after the Depositary has received notices of acceptance from two-thirds of those States which at the time of adoption by the Assembly were Parties and represented at least two thirds of the total investment shares. Upon entry into force, the amendment shall become binding upon all Parties and Signatories, including those which have not accepted it.

Article 35: Depositary

1. The Depositary of this Convention shall be the Secretary-General of the International Maritime Organization.
2. The Depositary shall promptly inform all signatory and acceding States and all Signatories of:
   (a) Any signature of the Convention.
   (b) The deposit of any instrument of ratification,

acceptance, approval or accession.
(c) The entry into force of the Convention.
(d) The adoption of any amendment to the Convention and its entry into force.
(e) Any notification of withdrawal.
(f) Any suspension or termination.
(g) Other notifications and communications relating to the Convention.
3. Upon entry into force of the Convention the Depositary shall transmit a certified copy to the Secretariat of the United Nations for registration and publication in accordance with Article 102 of the Charter of the United Nations.

In Witness Whereof the undersigned, duly authorized by their respective Governments, have signed this Convention.

Done at London this third day of September one thousand nine hundred and seventy-six in the English, French, Russian and Spanish languages, all the texts being equally authentic, in a single original which shall be deposited with the Depositary, who shall send a certified copy to the Government of each of the States which were invited to attend the International Conference on the Establishment of an International Maritime Satellite System and to the Government of any other State which signs or accedes to this Convention.

ANNEX
PROCEDURES FOR
THE SETTLEMENT OF DISPUTES REFERRED TO
IN ARTICLE 31 OF THE CONVENTION AND
ARTICLE XVI OF THE OPERATING AGREEMENT

Article 1

Disputes cognizable pursuant to article 31 of the Convention or article XVI of the Operating Agreement shall be dealt with by an arbitral tribunal of three members.

Article 2

Any petitioner or group of petitioners wishing to submit a dispute to arbitration shall provide each respondent and the Directorate with a document containing:

(a) A full description of the dispute, the reasons why each respondent is required to participate in the arbitration, and the measures being requested.

(b) The reasons why the subject matter of the dispute comes within the competence of a tribunal and why the measures requested can be granted if the tribunal finds in favour of the petitioner.

(c) An explanation why the petitioner has been unable to achieve a settlement of the dispute by negotiation or other means short of arbitration.

(d) Evidence of the agreement or consent of the disputants when this is a condition for arbitration.

(e) The name of the person designated by the petitioner to serve as a member of the tribunal.

The Directorate shall promptly distribute a copy of the document to each Party and Signatory.

Article 3

1. Within sixty days from the date copies of the document described in article 2 have been received by all the respondents, they shall collectively designate an individual to serve as a member of the tribunal. Within that period, the respondents may jointly or individually provide each disputant and the Directorate with a document stating their individual or collective responses to the document referred to in article 2 and including any counterclaims arising out of the subject matter of the dispute.

2. Within thirty days after the designation of the two members of the tribunal, they shall agree on a third arbitrator. He shall not be of the same nationality as, or resident in the territory of, any disputant, or in its service.

3. If either side fails to nominate an arbitrator within the period specified or if the third arbitrator is not appointed within the period specified, the President of the

International Court of Justice, or, if he is prevented from acting or is of the same nationality as a disputant, the Vice-President, or, if he is prevented from acting or is of the same nationality as a disputant, the senior judge who is not of the same nationality as any disputant, may at the request of either disputant, appoint an arbitrator or arbitrators as the case requires.

4. The third arbitrator shall act as president of the tribunal.
5. The tribunal is constituted as soon as the president is selected.

Article 4

1. If a vacancy occurs in the tribunal for any reason which the president or the remaining members of the tribunal decide is beyond the control of the disputants, or is compatible with the proper conduct of the arbitration proceedings, the vacancy shall be filled in accordance with the following provisions:

    (a) If the vacancy occurs as a result of the withdrawal of a member appointed by a side to the dispute, then that side shall select a replacement within ten days after the vacancy occurs.

    (b) If the vacancy occurs as a result of the withdrawal of the president or of a member appointed pursuant to article 3(3), a replacement shall be selected in the manner described in paragraph (2) or (3), respectively, of article 3.

2. If a vacancy occurs for any other reason, or if a vacancy occurring pursuant to paragraph (1) is not filled, the remainder of the tribunal shall have the power, notwithstanding article 1, upon request of one side, to continue the proceedings and give the final decision of the tribunal.

Article 5

1. The tribunal shall decide the date and place of its meetings.
2. The proceedings shall be held in private and all material presented to the tribunal shall be confidential. However,

the Organization and any Party which has designated a Signatory which is a disputant in the proceedings shall have the right to be present and shall have access to the material presented. When the Organization is a disputant in the proceedings, all Parties and all Signatories shall have the right to be present and shall have access to the material presented.

3. In the event of a dispute over the competence of the tribunal, the tribunal shall deal with that question first.

4. The proceedings shall be conducted in writing, and each side shall have the right to submit written evidence in support of its allegations of fact and law. However, oral arguments and testimony may be given if the tribunal considers it appropriate.

5. The proceedings shall commence with the presentation of the case of the petitioner containing its arguments, related facts supported by evidence and the principles of law relied upon. The case of the petitioner shall be followed by the counter-case of the respondent. The petitioner may submit a reply to the counter-case of the respondent and the respondent may submit a rejoinder. Additional pleadings shall be submitted only if the tribunal determines they are necessary.

6. The tribunal shall hear and determine counter-claims arising directly out of the subject matter of the dispute, if the counter-claims are within its competence as defined in article 31 of the Convention and article XVI of the Operating Agreement.

7. If the disputants reach an agreement during the proceedings, the agreement shall be recorded in the form of a decision of the tribunal given by consent of the disputants.

8. At any time during the proceedings, the tribunal may terminate the proceedings if it decides the dispute is beyond its competence as defined in article 31 of the Convention or article XVI of the Operating Agreement.

9. The deliberations of the tribunal shall be secret.

10. The decisions of the tribunal shall be presented in writing and shall be supported by a written opinion. Its rulings and decisions must be supported by at least two members.

A member dissenting from the decision may submit a separate written opinion.

11. The tribunal shall forward its decision to the Directorate, which shall distribute it to all Parties and Signatories.
12. The tribunal may adopt additional rules of procedure, consistent with those established by this annex, which are appropriate for the proceedings.

Article 6

If one side fails to present its case, the other side may call upon the tribunal to give a decision on the basis of its presentation. Before giving its decision, the tribunal shall satisfy itself that it has competence and that the case is well-founded in fact and in law.

Article 7

1. Any Party whose Signatory is a disputant shall have the right to intervene and become an additional disputant. Intervention shall be made by written notification to the tribunal and to the other disputants.
2. Any other Party, any Signatory or the Organization may apply to the tribunal for permission to intervene and become an additional disputant. The tribunal shall grant permission if it determines that the applicant has a substantial interest in the case.

Article 8

The tribunal may appoint experts to assist it at the request of a disputant or on its own initiative.

Article 9

Each Party, each Signatory and the Organization shall provide all information which the tribunal, at the request of a disputant or on its own initiative, determines to be required for the handling and determination of the dispute.

Article 10

Pending the final decision, the tribunal may indicate any provisional measures which it considers ought to be taken to preserve the respective rights of the disputants.

Article 11

1. The decision of the tribunal shall be in accordance with international law and be based on:
   (a) The Convention and the Operating Agreement.
   (b) Generally accepted principles of law.
2. The decision of the tribunal, including any reached by agreement of the disputant pursuant to article 5(7), shall be binding on all the disputants, and shall be carried out by them in good faith. If the Organization is a disputant, and the tribunal decides that a decision of any organ of the Organization is null and void as not being authorized by or in compliance with the Convention and the Operating Agreement, the decision of the tribunal shall be binding on all Parties and Signatories.
3. If a dispute arises as to the meaning or scope of its decision, the tribunal shall construe it at the request of any disputant.

Article 12

Unless the tribunal determines otherwise because of the particular circumstances of the case, the expenses of the tribunal, including the remuneration of the members of the tribunal, shall be borne in equal shares by each side. Where a side consists of more than one disputant, the tribunal shall apportion the share of that side among the disputants on that side. Where the Organization is a disputant, its expenses associated with the arbitration shall be regarded as an administrative cost of the Organization.

OPERATING AGREEMENT ON
THE INTERNATIONAL MARITIME SATELLITE
ORGANIZATION (INMARSAT)

The Signatories to this Operating Agreement,

Considering that the States Parties to the Convention on the International Maritime Satellite Organization (INMARSAT) have undertaken therein to sign, or to designate a competent entity to sign, this Operating Agreement,

Agree as follows:

Article I: Definitions

1. For the purposes of this Agreement:
   (a) "Convention" means the Convention on the International Maritime Satellite Organization (INMARSAT) including its annex.
   (b) "Organization" means the International Maritime Satellite Organization (INMARSAT) established by the Convention.
   (c) "Amortization" includes depreciation; it does not include compensation for use of capital.
2. The definitions in article 1 of the Convention shall apply to this Agreement.

Article II: Rights and Obligations of Signatories

1. Each Signatory acquires the rights provided for Signatories in the Convention and this Agreement and undertakes to fulfil the obligations placed upon it by these two instruments.
2. Each Signatory shall act consistently with all provisions of the Convention and this Agreement.

Article III: Capital Contributions

1. In proportion to its investment share, each Signatory shall make contributions to the capital requirements of the Organization and shall receive capital repayment and compensation for use of capital, as determined by the Council in accordance with the Convention and this Agreement.
2. Capital requirements shall include:
   (a) All direct and indirect costs of the design, development, Acquisition, construction and

establishment of the INMARSAT space segment, of the acquisition of contractual rights by means of lease, and of other property of the Organization.

(b) Funds required for operating, maintenance and administrative costs of the Organization pending availability of revenues to meet such costs, and pursuant to article VIII(3).

(c) Payments by Signatories pursuant to article XI.

3. Interest at a rate to be determined by the Council shall be added to any amount unpaid after the scheduled date for payment determined by the Council.

4. If, during the period up to the first determination of investment shares on the basis of utilization pursuant to article V, the total amount of capital contributions which Signatories are required to pay in any financial year exceeds 50 per cent of the capital ceiling established by or pursuant to article IV, the Council shall consider the adoption of other arrangements, including temporary debt financing, to permit those Signatories which so desire to pay the additional contributions in subsequent years by instalments. The Council shall determine the rate of interest to apply in such cases, reflecting the additional costs to the Organization.

Article IV: Capital Ceiling

The sum of the net capital contributions of Signatories and of the outstanding contractual capital commitments of the Organization shall be subject to a ceiling. This sum shall consist of the cumulative capital contributions made by Signatories pursuant to article III, less the cumulative capital repaid to them pursuant to this Agreement, plus the outstanding amount of contractual capital commitments of the Organization. The initial capital ceiling shall be 200 million US dollars. The Council shall have authority to adjust the capital ceiling.

Article V: Investment Shares

1. Investment shares of Signatories shall be determined on the basis of utilization of the INMARSAT space segment.

Each Signatory shall have an investment share equal to its percentage of all utilization of the INMARSAT space segment by all Signatories. Utilization of the INMARSAT space segment shall be measured in terms of the charges levied by the Organization for use of the INMARSAT space segment pursuant to article 19 of the Convention and article VIII of this Agreement.

2. For the purpose of determining investment shares, utilization in both directions shall be divided into two equal parts, a ship or aircraft part and a land part. The part associated with the ship or aircraft where the traffic originates or terminates shall be attributed to the Signatory of the Party under whose authority the ship or aircraft is operating. The part associated with the land territory where the traffic originates or terminates shall be attributed to the Signatory of the Party in whose territory the traffic originates or terminates. However, where, for any Signatory, the ratio of the ship and aircraft parts to the land parts exceeds 20:1, that Signatory shall, upon application to the Council, be attributed a utilization equivalent to twice the land part or an investment share of 0.1 per cent, whichever is higher. Structures operating in the marine environment, for which access to the INMARSAT space segment has been permitted by the Council, shall be considered as ships for the purpose of this paragraph.

3. Prior to determination of investment shares on the basis of utilization pursuant to paragraphs (1), (2) and (4), the investment share of each Signatory shall be established in accordance with the annex to this Agreement.

4. The first determination of investment shares based on utilization pursuant to paragraphs (1) and (2) shall be made not less than two nor more than three years from the commencement of operational use of the INMARSAT space segment in the Atlantic, Pacific and Indian Ocean areas, the specific date of determination to be decided by the Council. For the purposes of this first determination, utilization shall be measured over the one-year period prior to such determination.

5. Subsequent to the first determination on the basis of

utilization, investment shares shall be redetermined to be effective:

    (a) Upon one-year intervals after the first determination of investment shares on the basis of utilization, based on the utilization of all Signatories during the previous year.

    (b) Upon the date of entry into force of this Agreement for a new Signatory.

    (c) Upon the effective date of withdrawal or termination of membership of a Signatory.

6. The investment share of a Signatory which becomes a Signatory after the first determination of investment shares on the basis of utilisation, shall be determined by the Council.

7. To the extent that an investment share is determined pursuant to paragraph (5)(b) or (c) or paragraph (8), the investment shares of all other Signatories shall be adjusted in the proportion that their respective investment shares, held prior to this adjustment, bear to each other. On the withdrawal or termination of membership of a Signatory, investment shares of 0.05 per cent determined in accordance with paragraph (8) shall not be increased.

8. Notwithstanding any provisions of this article, no Signatory shall have an investment share of less than 0.05 per cent of the total investment shares.

9. In any new determination of investment shares the share of any Signatory shall not be increased in one step by more than 50 per cent of its initial share, or decreased by more than 50 per cent of its current share.

10. Any unallocated investment shares, after application of paragraphs (2) and (9) shall be made available and apportioned by the Council among Signatories wishing to increase their investment shares. Such additional allocation shall not increase any share by more than 50 per cent of a Signatory's current investment share.

11. Any residual unallocated investment shares, after application of paragraph (10), shall be distributed among the Signatories in proportion to the investment shares which would otherwise have applied after any new determination, subject to paragraphs (8) and (9).

12. Upon application from a Signatory, the Council may allocate to it an investment share reduced from its share determined pursuant to paragraphs (1) to (7) and (9) to (11), if the reduction is entirely taken up by the voluntary acceptance by other Signatories of increased investment shares. The Council shall adopt procedures for the equitable distribution of the released share or shares among Signatories wishing to increase their shares.

Article VI: Financial Adjustments between Signatories

1. At each determination of investment shares after the initial determination upon entry into force of this Agreement, financial adjustments between Signatories shall be carried out through the Organization on the basis of a valuation effected pursuant to paragraph 2.   The amounts of these financial adjustments shall be determined with respect to each Signatory by applying to the valuation the difference, if any, between the new investment share of each Signatory and its investment share prior to the determination.

2. The valuation shall be effected as follows:
   (a) Deduct from the original acquisition cost of all property as recorded in the Organization's accounts as at the date of the adjustment, including all capitalized return and capitalized expenses, the sum of:
      (i) The accumulated amortization as recorded in the Organization's accounts as at the date of adjustment.
      (ii) Loans and other accounts payable by the Organization as at the date of adjustment.
   (b) Adjust the results obtained pursuant to sub-paragraph (a) by adding or deducting a further amount representing any deficiency or excess, respectively, in the payment by the Organization of compensation for use of capital from the entry into force of this Agreement to the effective date of valuation relative to the cumulative amount due pursuant to this Agreement at the rate or rates of compensation for

use of capital in effect during the periods in which the relevant rates were applicable, as established by the Council pursuant to article VIII. For the purpose of assessing the amount representing any deficiency or excess in payment, compensation due shall be calculated on a monthly basis and relate to the net amount of the elements described in sub-paragraph (a).

3. Payments due from and to Signatories pursuant to this article shall be effected by a date decided by the Council. Interest at a rate to be determined by the Council shall be added to any amount unpaid after that date.

Article VII: Payment of Utilization Charges

1. Utilization charges established pursuant to article 19 of the Convention shall be payable by Signatories or authorized telecommunications entities in accordance with arrangements adopted by the Council. These arrangements shall follow as closely as practicable recognized international telecommunications accounting procedures.

2. Unless otherwise decided by the Council, Signatories and authorized telecommunications entities shall be responsible for the provision of information to the Organization to enable the Organization to determine all utilization of the INMARSAT space segment and to determine investment shares. The Council shall adopt procedures for submission of the information to the Organization.

3. The Council shall institute any appropriate sanctions in cases where payments of utilization charges have been in default for four months or longer after the due date.

4. Interest at a rate to be determined by the Council shall be added to any amount unpaid after the scheduled date for payment determined by the Council.

Article VIII: Revenues

1. The revenues earned by the Organization shall normally

be applied, to the extent that such revenues allow, in the following order of priority, unless the Council decides otherwise:

(a) To meet operating, maintenance and administrative costs.

(b) To provide such operating funds as the Council may determine to be necessary.

(c) To pay to Signatories, in proportion to their respective investment shares, sums representing a repayment of capital in the amount of the provisions for amortization established by the Council and recorded in the accounts of the Organization.

(d) To pay to a Signatory which has withdrawn from the Organization or whose membership has been terminated, such sums as may be due to it pursuant to article XIII.

(e) To pay to Signatories, cumulatively in proportion to their respective investment shares, the available balance towards compensation for use of capital.

2. In the determination of the rate of compensation for the use of capital of Signatories, the Council shall include an allowance for the risks associated with investment in INMARSAT and, taking into account such allowance, shall fix the rate as close as possible to the cost of money in the world markets.

3. To the extent that the revenues earned by the Organization are insufficient to meet operating, maintenance and administrative costs of the Organization, the Council may decide to meet the deficiency by using operating funds of the Organization, by overdraft arrangements, by raising a loan, by requiring Signatories to make capital contributions in proportion to their respective current investment shares or by any combination of such measures.

Article IX: Settlement of Accounts

1. Settlement of accounts between Signatories and the Organization in respect of financial transactions pursuant to articles III, VI, VII and VIII shall be arranged in such a

manner that funds transferred between Signatories and the Organization, as well as funds at the Organization's disposal in excess of the operating funds determined by the Council to be necessary, shall be kept at the lowest practicable level.

2. All payments between the Signatories and the Organization pursuant to this Agreement shall be effected in any freely convertible currency acceptable to the creditor.

Article X: DEBT Financing

1. The Organization may, upon decision by the Council, enter into overdraft arrangements for the purpose of meeting financial deficiencies pending receipt of adequate revenues or capital contributions.

2. In exceptional circumstances the Organization may raise loans upon decision by the Council for the purpose of financing any activity undertaken by the Organization in accordance with article 3 of the Convention or for meeting any liability incurred by it. The outstanding amounts of such loans shall be considered as contractual capital commitments for the purpose of Article IV.

Article XI: Liability

1. If the Organization is required by a binding decision rendered by a competent tribunal or as a result of a settlement agreed to or concurred in by the Council, to pay any claim, including any costs or expenses associated therewith, which arises out of any act or obligation of the Organization carried out or incurred in pursuance of the Convention or this Agreement, the Signatories shall, to the extent that the claim is not satisfied by indemnification, insurance or other financial arrangements, pay to the Organization the ~mount unsatisfied on the claim in proportion to their respective investment shares as at the date when the liability arose, notwithstanding any ceiling established by or pursuant to article IV.

2. If a Signatory, in its capacity as such, is required by a

binding decision rendered by a competent tribunal or as a result of a settlement agreed to or concurred in by the Council, to pay any claim, including any costs or expenses associated therewith, which arises out of any act or obligation of the Organization carried out or incurred in pursuance of the Convention or this Agreement, the Organization shall reimburse the Signatory to the extent the Signatory has paid the claim.

3. If such a claim is asserted against a Signatory, that Signatory, as a condition of payment by the Organization, shall without delay notify the Organization of the claim, and shall afford it the opportunity to advise on or to conduct the defence or other disposition of the claim and, to the extent permitted by the law of the jurisdiction in which the claim is brought, to become a party to the proceeding either with the Signatory or in substitution for it.

4. If the Organization is required to reimburse a Signatory under this article, the Signatories shall, to the extent that the reimbursement is not satisfied by indemnification, insurance or other financial arrangements, pay to the Organization the unsatisfied amount of the claimed reimbursement in proportion to their respective investment shares as at the date when the liability arose, notwithstanding any ceiling established by or pursuant to article IV.

Article XII: Exoneration from Liability Arising from the Provision of Telecommunications Services

Neither the Organization, nor any Signatory in its capacity as such, nor any officer or employee of any of them, nor any member of the board of directors of any Signatory, nor any representative to any organ of the Organization acting in the performance of their functions, shall be liable to any Signatory or to the Organization for loss or damage sustained by reason of any unavailability, delay or faultiness of telecommunications services provided or to be provided pursuant to the Convention or this Agreement.

Article XIII: Settlement upon Withdrawal or Termination

1. Within three months after the effective date of withdrawal or termination of the membership of a Signatory pursuant to articles 29 or 30 of the Convention, the Council shall notify the Signatory of the evaluation by the Council of its financial status in relation to the Organization as at the effective date of its withdrawal or termination and of the proposed terms of settlement pursuant to paragraph (3). The notification shall include a statement of:

   (a) The amount payable by the Organization to the Signatory, calculated by multiplying its investment share, as at the effective date of withdrawal or termination, by the amount established from a valuation effected pursuant to article VI as at that date.

   (b) Any amount to be paid by the Signatory to the Organization representing its share of capital contributions for contractual commitments specifically authorized prior to the receipt of notice of decision to withdraw or, as the case may be, prior to the effective date of termination, together with the proposed schedule for payment.

   (c) Any other amounts due from the Signatory to the Organization as at the effective date of withdrawal or termination.

2. In its evaluation pursuant to paragraph (1), the Council may decide to relieve the Signatory in whole or in part of its responsibility for contributing its share of the capital contributions for contractual commitments specifically authorized and liabilities arising from acts or omissions prior to the receipt of notice of decision to withdraw or as the case may be, the effective date of termination.

3. Subject to payment by the Signatory of any amounts due from it under sub-paragraphs (1)(b) and (c), the Organization, taking into account article VIII, shall repay to the Signatory the amounts referred to in sub-paragraphs (1)(a) and (b) over a period consistent with the period over which the remaining Signatories will be repaid their contributions, or sooner if the Council so decides. The

Council shall determine the rate of interest to be paid to or by the Signatory in respect of any amounts which may, from time to time, be outstanding for settlement.

4. Unless the Council decides otherwise, a settlement pursuant to this article shall not relieve the Signatory of its obligation to contribute its share of the non-contractual liabilities arising from acts or omissions of the Organization prior to the date of receipt of notice of decision to withdraw or, as the case may be, prior to the effective date of termination.

5. The Signatory shall not lose any rights acquired by it, in its capacity as such which would otherwise continue after the effective date of withdrawal or termination, and for which it has not been compensated by the settlement pursuant to this article.

Article XIV: Earth Station Approval

1. In order to utilize the INMARSAT space segment, all earth stations shall require approval by the Organization in accordance with criteria and procedures established by the Council pursuant to article 15(c) of the Convention.

2. Any application for such approval shall be submitted to the Organization by the Signatory of the Party in whose territory the earth station on land is or will be located, or by the Party or the Signatory of the Party under whose authority the earth station on a ship or an aircraft or on a structure operating in the marine environment is licensed or, with respect to earth stations located in a territory or on a ship or an aircraft or on a structure operating in the marine environment not under the jurisdiction of a Party, by an authorized telecommunications entity.

3. Each applicant referred to in paragraph (2) shall, with respect to earth stations for which it has submitted an application, be responsible to the Organization for compliance of such stations with the procedures and standards specified by the Organization, unless, in the case of a Signatory which has submitted an application, its designating Party assumes this responsibility.

Article XV: Utilization of the INMARSAT Space Segment

1. Any application for utilization of the INMARSAT space segment shall be submitted to the Organization by a Signatory or, in the case of a territory not under the jurisdiction of a Party, by an authorized telecommunications entity.
2. Utilization shall be authorized by the Organization in accordance with criteria and procedures established by the Council pursuant to article 15(c) of the Convention.
3. Each Signatory or authorized telecommunications entity for which utilization of the INMARSAT space segment has been authorized shall be responsible for compliance with all conditions established by the Organization with respect to such utilization unless, in the case of a Signatory which has submitted an application, its designating Party assumes the responsibility for authorizations made with respect to all or some of the earth stations not owned or operated by that Signatory.

Article XVI: Settlement of Disputes

1. Disputes arising between Signatories, or between Signatories and the Organization, relating to rights and obligations under the Convention or this Agreement, should be settled by negotiation between the parties to the dispute. If within one year of the time any party to the dispute has requested settlement a settlement has not been reached and if a particular procedure for settling disputes has not been agreed between the parties to the dispute, the dispute shall be submitted to arbitration in accordance with the annex to the Convention at the request of any party to the dispute.
2. Unless otherwise mutually agreed, disputes arising between the Organization and one or more Signatories under agreements concluded between them shall be submitted to arbitration in accordance with the annex to the Convention at the request of one of the parties to the dispute within a period of one year from the time that settlement was requested by any party to the dispute.

3.   A Signatory which ceases to be a Signatory shall remain bound by this article in respect of disputes relating to rights and obligations arising from its having been a Signatory of this Agreement.

Article XVII: Entry into Force

1.   This Agreement shall enter into force for a Signatory on the date on which the Convention enters into force for the respective Party in accordance with article 33 of the Convention.

2.   This Agreement shall continue in force for as long as the Convention is in force.

Article XVIII: Amendments

1.   Amendments to this Agreement may be proposed by any Party or Signatory. Proposed amendments shall be submitted to the Directorate, which shall inform the other Parties and Signatories. Three months' notice is required before consideration of an amendment by the Council. During this period the Directorate shall solicit and circulate the views of all Signatories. The Council shall consider amendments within six months from circulation. The Assembly shall consider the amendment not earlier than six months after the approval by the Council. This period may in any particular case be reduced by the Assembly by a substantive decision.

2.   If confirmed by the Assembly after approval by the Council, the amendment shall enter into force one hundred and twenty days after the Depositary has received notice of its approval by two thirds of those Signatories which at the time of confirmation by the Assembly were Signatories and then held at least two thirds of the total investment shares. Notification of approval of an amendment shall be transmitted to the Depositary only by the Party concerned and the transmission shall signify the acceptance by the Party of the amendment. Upon entry into force, the amendment shall become binding upon all Signatories, including those which have not accepted it.

Article XIX: Depositary

1. The Depositary of this Agreement shall be the Secretary-General of the International Maritime Organization.
2. The Depositary shall promptly inform all signatory and acceding States and all Signatories of:
    (a) Any signature of this Agreement.
    (b) The entry into force of this Agreement.
    (c) The adoption of any amendment to this Agreement and its entry into force.
    (d) Any notification of withdrawal.
    (e) Any suspension or termination.
    (f) Other notifications and communications relating to this Agreement.
3. Upon entry into force of this Agreement the Depositary shall transmit a certified copy to the Secretariat of the United Nations for registration and publication in accordance with Article 102 of the Charter of the United Nations.

In Witness Whereof the undersigned, duly authorized, have signed this Agreement.

Done at London this third day of September one thousand nine hundred and seventy-six in the English, French, Russian and Spanish languages, all the texts being equally authentic, in a single original which shall be deposited with the Depositary, who shall send a certified copy to the Government of each of the States which were invited to attend the International Conference on the Establishment of an International Maritime Satellite System, to the Government of any other State which signs or accedes to the Convention and to each Signatory.

ANNEX
INVESTMENT SHARES PRIOR TO
THE FIRST DETERMINATION ON THE BASIS OF
UTILIZATION

(a) The initial investment shares of the signatories of the States listed below shall be as follows:

United States	17.00
United Kingdom	12.00
USSR, Byelorussian SSR and Ukrainian SSR	11.00

Norway	9.50
Japan	8.45
Italy	4.37
France	3.50
Germany, Federal Republic of	3.50
Greece	3.50
Netherlands	3.50
Canada	3.20
Spain	2.50
Sweden	2.30
Denmark	2.10
Australia	2.00
India	2.00
Brazil	1.50
Kuwait	1.48
Poland	1.48
Argentina	0.75
Belgium	0.75
Finland	0.75
German Democratic Republic	0.74
Singapore	0.62
New Zealand	0.44
Bulgaria	0.33
Cuba	0.33
Indonesia	0.33
Iran	0.33
Chile	0.25
Peru	0.25
Switzerland	0.25
Liberia	0.10
Algeria	0.05
Egypt	0.05
Ghana	0.05
Iraq	0.05
Thailand	0.05
Turkey	0.05
United Republic of Cameroon	0.05
TOTAL:	101.45

(b) Any signatory to the Operating Agreement designated by a State listed above may, prior to the entry into force of the Convention and the Operating Agreement, accept an initial investment share higher than that listed in paragraph (a) if:

(i) Other signatories accept a correspondingly lower initial investment share; or

(ii) The Convention and the Operating Agreement have not entered into force twenty-four months after they were opened for signature.

The signatories concerned shall inform the Depositary, who shall prepare and distribute a revised list of initial investment shares to all States included in the list of initial investment shares.

(c) A signatory of a State not listed in paragraph (a), on signing the Operating Agreement prior to its entry into force, shall declare to the Depositary its initial investment share, which shall correspond to its projected proportionate utilization of the INMARSAT space segment. The Depositary shall add the new signatory and its initial investment share to the list of initial investment shares in paragraph (a). The revised list shall be sent to all States included in the list. The initial investment share of the new signatory shall be subject subsequently to approval or adjustment by the Council. If the Council adjusts the share, it shall adjust proportionately the initial investment shares of all Signatories and, subsequently, the investment shares of all Signatories.

(d) Upon entry into force of the Operating Agreement, the investment shares of Signatories shall be determined by adjusting the initial investment shares of Signatories proportionately so that the sum of all investment shares amounts to 100 per cent.

(e) The initial investment share of any Signatory which is not included in the list in paragraph (a) and which signs the Operating Agreement after its entry into force, and for any Signatory included in the list of initial investment shares for which the Operating Agreement has not entered into force thirty-six months after it was opened for signature, shall be determined by the Council and shall be included in a revised list of initial investment shares of all Signatories.

(f) When a new Party enters the Organization or when a Party withdraws from the Organization or its membership is terminated, the investment shares of all Signatories shall be determined by adjusting proportionately the initial investment shares of all Signatories so that the sum of all investment shares amounts to 100 per cent.

(g) Investment shares of 0.05 per cent determined in accordance with paragraph (8) of article V of the Operating Agreement, shall not be increased pursuant to paragraphs (c), (d), (e) and (f) of this annex.

PROTOCOL ON THE PRIVILEGES AND IMMUNITIES OF THE INTERNATIONAL MARITIME SATELLITE ORGANIZATION (INMARSAT)

The States Parties to this Protocol:

Having regard to the Convention and the Operating Agreement on the International Maritime Satellite Organization (INMARSAT) opened for signature at London on 3 September, 1976 and, in particular, to Articles 25 and 26(4) of the Convention;

Taking note that INMARSAT has concluded a Headquarters Agreement with the Government of the United Kingdom of Great Britain and Northern Ireland on 25 February, 1980;

Considering that the aim of this Protocol is to facilitate the achievement of the purpose of INMARSAT and to ensure the efficient performance of its functions;

Have agreed as follows:

Article 1: Use of Terms

For the purposes of this Protocol:

(a) "Convention" means the Convention on the International Maritime Satellite Organization (INMARSAT), including its Annex, opened for signature at London on 3 September, 1976;

(b) "Operating Agreement" means the Operating Agreement on the International Maritime Satellite Organization (INMARSAT), including its Annex, opened for signature at London on 3 September,1976;

(c) "Party to the Convention" means a State for which the Convention is in force;

(d) "Headquarters Party" means the Party to the Convention in whose territory INMARSAT has established its headquarters;

(e) "Signatory" means either a Party to the Protocol or an entity designated by a Party to the Protocol for which the Operating Agreement is in force;

(f) "Party to the Protocol" means a State for which this Protocol is in force;

(g) "Staff member" means the Director General and any person employed full time by INMARSAT and subject to its staff regulations;

(h) "Representatives" in the case of Parties to the Protocol, the Headquarters Party and Signatories means representatives to INMARSAT and in each case means heads of delegations, alternates and advisers;

(i) "Archives" includes all manuscripts, correspondence, documents, photographs, films, optical and magnetic recordings, data recordings, graphic representations and computer programmes, belonging to or held by INMARSAT;

(j) "Official activities" of INMARSAT means activities carried out by the Organization in pursuance of its purpose as defined in the Convention and includes its administrative activities;

(k) "Expert" means a person other than a staff member appointed to carry out a specific task for or on behalf of INMARSAT and at its expense;

(l) "INMARSAT space segment" means the satellites, and tracking, telemetry, command, control, monitoring and related facilities and equipment required to support the operation of these satellites, which are owned or leased by INMARSAT;

(m) "Property" means anything that can be the subject of a right of ownership, including contractual rights.

Article 2: Immunity of INMARSAT from Jurisdiction And Execution

1. Unless it has expressly waived immunity in a particular case, INMARSAT shall, within the scope of its official

activities, have immunity from jurisdiction except in respect of:

(a) Its commercial activities;

(b) A civil action by a third party for damage arising from an accident caused by a motor vehicle or other means of transport belonging to, or operated on behalf of, INMARSAT, or in respect of a traffic offence involving such means of transport;

(c) The attachment, pursuant to the final order of a court of law, of the salaries and emoluments, including pension rights, owed by INMARSAT to a staff member, or a former staff member;

(d) A counter-claim directly connected with judicial proceedings initiated by INMARSAT.

2. Notwithstanding paragraph (1), no action shall be brought in the course of Parties to the Protocol against INMARSAT by Parties to the Convention, Signatories or persons acting for or deriving claims from any of them, relating to rights and obligations under the Convention or Operating Agreement.

3. (a) The INMARSAT space segment, wherever located and by whomsoever held, shall be immune from any search, restraint, requisition, seizure, confiscation expropriation, sequestration or execution, whether by executive, administrative or judicial action.

(b) All other property and assets of INMARSAT, wherever located and by whomsoever held, shall enjoy the immunity set out in paragraph (3)(a), except in respect of:

(i) An attachment or execution in order to satisfy a final judgement or order of a court of law that relates to any proceedings that may be brought against INMARSAT pursuant to paragraph (1);

(ii) Any action taken in accordance with the law of the State concerned which is temporarily necessary in connection with the prevention of and investigation into accidents involving motor vehicles or other means of transport belonging to, or operated on behalf of, INMARSAT;

(iii) Expropriation in respect of real property for

public purposes and subject to prompt payment of fair compensation, provided that such expropriation shall not prejudice the functions and operations of INMARSAT.

Article 3: Inviolability of Archives

The archives of INMARSAT shall be inviolable wherever located and by whomsoever held.

Article 4: Exemption from Taxes and Duties

1. Within the scope of its official activities, INMARSAT and its property and income shall be exempt from all national direct and other taxes not normally incorporated in the price of goods and services.
2. If INMARSAT, within the scope of its official activities, acquires goods or uses services of substantial value, and if the price of these goods or services includes taxes or duties, Parties to the Protocol shall, whenever possible, take appropriate measures to remit or reimburse the amount of such taxes or duties.
3. Within the scope of its official activities, INMARSAT shall be exempt from customs duties, taxes and related charges on the INMARSAT space segment and on equipment connected with the launching of satellites for use in the INMARSAT space segment.
4. Goods acquired by INMARSAT within the scope of its official activities shall be exempt from all prohibitions and restrictions on import or export.
5. No exemption shall be accorded in respect of taxes and duties which represent charges for specific services rendered.
6. No exemption shall be accorded in respect of goods acquired by, or services provided to, INMARSAT for the personal benefit of staff members.
7. Goods exempted under this Article shall not be transferred, hired out or lent, permanently or temporarily, or sold, except in accordance with conditions laid down by the Party to the Protocol which granted the exemption.

8. Payments from INMARSAT to Signatories pursuant to the Operating Agreement shall be exempt from national taxes by any Party to the Protocol, other than the Party which has designated the Signatory.

Article 5: Funds, Currency and Securities

INMARSAT may receive and hold any kind of funds, currency or securities and dispose of them freely for any of its official activities. It may hold accounts in any currency to the extent required to meet its obligations.

Article 6: Official Communications and Publications

1. With regard to its official communications and transfer of all its documents, INMARSAT shall enjoy in the territory of each Party to the Protocol treatment not less favourable than that generally accorded to equivalent intergovernmental organizations in the matter of priorities, rates and taxes on mails and all forms of telecommunications, as far as may be compatible with any international agreements to which that Party to the Protocol is a party.

2. With regard to its official communications, INMARSAT may employ all appropriate means of communication, including messages in code or cypher. Parties to the Protocol shall not impose any restriction on the official communications of INMARSAT or on the circulation of its official publications. NO censorship shall be applied to such communications and publications.

3. INMARSAT may install and use a radio transmitter only with the consent of the Party to the Protocol concerned.

Article 7: Staff Members

1. Staff members shall enjoy the following privileges and immunities:
    (a) Immunity from jurisdiction, even after they have left the service of INMARSAT, in respect of acts, including words spoken or written, done by them in the exercise

of their official functions; this immunity shall not, however, apply in the case of a traffic offence committed by a staff member, or in the case of damage caused by a motor vehicle or other means of transport belonging to or driven by him;

(b) Exemption, together with members of their families forming part of their respective households, from any obligations in respect of national service, including military service;

(c) Inviolability for all their official papers related to the exercise of their functions within the scope of the official activities of INMARSAT;

(d) Exemption, together with members of their families forming part of their respective households, from immigration restrictions and alien registration;

(e) The same treatment in the matter of currency and exchange control as is accorded to staff members of intergovernmental organizations;

(f) Together with members of their families forming part of their respective households, the same facilities as to repatriation in time of international crisis as are accorded to staff members of intergovernmental organizations;

(g) The right to import free of duty their furniture and personal effects, including a motor vehicle, at the time of first taking up their post in the State concerned, and the right to export them free of duty on termination of their functions in that State, in both cases in accordance with the laws and regulations of the State concerned. However, except in accordance with such laws and regulations, goods which have been exempted under this sub-paragraph shall not be transferred, hired out or lent, permanently or temporarily, or sold.

2. Salaries and emoluments paid by INMARSAT to staff members shall be exempt from income tax from the date upon which such staff members have begun to be liable for a tax imposed on their salaries by INMARSAT for the latter's benefit. Parties to the Protocol may take these salaries and emoluments into account for the purpose of

assessing the amount of taxes to be applied to income from other sources. Parties to the Protocol are not required to grant exemption from income tax in respect of pensions and annuities paid to former staff members.

3. Provided that staff members are covered by an INMARSAT social security scheme, INMARSAT and its staff members shall be exempt from all compulsory contributions to national social security schemes. This exemption does not preclude any voluntary participation in a national social security scheme in accordance with the law of the Party to the Protocol concerned; neither does it oblige a Party to the Protocol to make payments of benefits under social security schemes to staff members who are exempt under the provisions of this paragraph.

4. The Parties to the Protocol shall not be obliged to accord to their nationals or permanent residents the privileges and immunities referred to in sub-paragraphs (b), (d), (e), (f) and (g) of paragraph (1).

Article 8: Director General

1. In addition to the privileges and immunities provided for staff members under Article 7, the Director General shall enjoy:
   (a) Immunity from arrest and detention;
   (b) Immunity from civil and administrative jurisdiction and execution enjoyed by diplomatic agents, except in the case of damage caused by a motor vehicle or other means of transport belonging to or driven by him;
   (c) Full immunity from criminal jurisdiction, except in the case of a traffic offence caused by a motor vehicle or other means of transport belonging to, or driven by him, subject to sub-paragraph (a) above.

2. The Parties to the Protocol shall not be obliged to accord to their nationals or permanent residents the immunities referred to in this Article.

Article 9: Representatives of Parties

1. Representatives of the Parties to the Protocol and

representatives of the Headquarters Party shall enjoy, while exercising their official functions and in the course of their journeys to and from their place of meeting, the following privileges and immunities:

(a) Immunity from any form of arrest or detention pending trial;

(b) Immunity from jurisdiction, even after the termination of their mission, in respect of acts, including words spoken or written, done by them in the exercise of their official functions; however, there shall be no immunity in the case of a traffic offence committed by a representative, or in the case of damage caused by a motor vehicle or other means of transport belonging to or driven by him;

(c) Inviolability for all their official papers;

(d) Exemption, together with members of their families forming part of their respective households, from immigration restrictions and alien registration;

(e) The same treatment in the matter of currency and exchange control as is accorded to representatives of foreign governments on temporary official missions;

(f) The same treatment in the matter of customs as regards their personal luggage as is accorded to representatives of foreign governments on temporary official missions.

2. The provisions of paragraph (1) shall not apply in relations between a Party to the Protocol and its representatives. Further, the provisions of paragraphs (a), (d), (e) and (f) of paragraph (1) shall not apply in relations between a Party to the Protocol and its nationals or permanent residents.

Article 10: Representatives of Signatories

1. Representatives of Signatories and representatives of the Signatory of the Headquarters Party shall, while exercising their official functions in relation to the work of INMARSAT and in the course of their journeys to and from their place of meeting, enjoy the following privileges and immunities:

    (a) Immunity from jurisdiction, even after the termination of their mission, in respect of acts, including words spoken or written, done by them in the exercise of their official functions; however, there shall be no immunity in the case of a traffic offence committed by a representative, or in the case of damage caused by a motor vehicle or other means of transport belonging to or driven by him;

    (b) Inviolability for all their official papers;

    (c) Exemption, together with members of their families forming part of their respective households, from immigration restrictions and alien registration.

2. The provisions of paragraph (1) shall not apply in relations between a Party to the Protocol and the representative of the Signatory designated by it. Further, the provisions of subparagraph (c) of paragraph (1) shall not apply in relations between a Party to the Protocol and its nationals or permanent residents.

Article 11: Experts

1. Experts, while exercising their official functions in relation to the work of INMARSAT, and in the course of their journeys to and from the place of their missions, shall enjoy the following privileges and immunities:

    (a) Immunity from jurisdiction, even after the termination of their mission, in respect of acts, including words spoken or written, done by them in the exercise of their official functions; however, there shall be no immunity in the case of damage caused by a motor vehicle or other means of transport belonging to or driven by him;

    (b) Inviolability for all their official papers;

    (c) The same treatment in the matter of currency and exchange control as is accorded to the staff members of intergovernmental organizations;

    (d) Exemption, together with members of their families forming part of their respective households, from immigration restrictions and alien registration;

    (e) The same facilities as regards their personal luggage

as are accorded to experts of other intergovernmental organizations.

2. The parties to the Protocol shall not be obliged to accord to their nationals or permanent residents the privileges and immunities referred to in sub-paragraphs (c), (d), and (e) of paragraph (1).

Article 12: Notification of Staff Members and Experts

The Director General of INMARSAT shall at least once every year notify the Parties to the Protocol of the names and nationalities of the staff members and experts to whom the provisions of Articles 7, 8 and 11 apply.

Article 13: Waiver

1. The privileges, exemptions and immunities provided for in this Protocol are not granted for the personal benefit of individuals but for the efficient performance of their official functions.

2. If, in the view of the authorities listed below, privileges and immunities are likely to impede the course of justice, and in all cases where they may be waived without prejudice to the purposes for which they have been accorded, these authorities have the right and duty to waive such privileges and immunities:

   (a) The Parties to the Protocol in respect of their representatives and representatives of their Signatories;

   (b) The Council in respect of the Director General of INMARSAT;

   (c) The Director General of INMARSAT in respect of staff members and experts;

   (d) The Assembly, convened if necessary in extraordinary session, in respect of INMARSAT.

Article 14: Assistance to Individuals

The Parties to the Protocol shall take all appropriate measures to facilitate entry, stay and departure of representatives, staff members and experts.

Article 15: Observance of Laws and Regulations

INMARSAT, and all persons enjoying privileges and immunities under this Protocol, shall, without prejudice to the other provisions thereof, respect the laws and regulations of the Parties to the Protocol concerned and co-operate at all times with the competent authorities of those Parties in order to ensure the observance of their laws and regulations.

Article 16: Precautionary Measures

Each Party to the Protocol retains the right to take all precautionary measures necessary in the interest of its security.

Article 17: Settlement Of Disputes

Any dispute between Parties to the Protocol or between INMARSAT and a Party to the Protocol concerning the interpretation or application of the Protocol shall be settled by negotiation or by some other agreed method. If the dispute is not settled within twelve (12) months, the parties concerned may, by common agreement, refer the dispute for decision to a tribunal of three arbitrators. One of the arbitrators shall be chosen by each of the parties to the dispute, and the third, who shall be the Chairman of the tribunal, shall be chosen by the first two arbitrators.

Should the first two arbitrators fail to agree upon the third within two months of their own appointment, the third arbitrator shall be chosen by the President of the International Court of Justice. The tribunal shall adopt its own procedures and its decisions shall be final and binding on the parties to the dispute.

Article 18: Complementary Agreements

INMARSAT may conclude with any Party to the Protocol complementary agreements to give effect to the provisions of this Protocol as regards such Party to the Protocol to ensure the efficient functioning of INMARSAT.

Article 19: Signature, Ratification and Accession

1. This Protocol shall be open for signature at London from 1 December, 1981 to 31 May, 1982.
2. All Parties to the Convention, other than the Headquarters Party, may become Parties to this Protocol by:
   (a) Signature not subject to ratification, acceptance or approval; or
   (b) Signature subject to ratification, acceptance or approval, followed by ratification, acceptance or approval; or
   (c) Accession.
3. Ratification, acceptance, approval or accession shall be effected by the deposit of the appropriate instrument with the Depositary.
4. Reservations to this Protocol may be made in accordance with international law.

Article 20: Entry into Force and Duration of Protocol

1. This Protocol shall enter into force on the thirtieth day after the date on which ten Parties to the Convention have fulfilled the requirements of paragraph (2) of Article 19.
2. This Protocol shall cease to be in force if the Convention ceases to be in force.

Article 21: Entry into Force and Duration for a State

1. For a State which has fulfilled the requirements of paragraph 2 of Article 19 after the date of entry into force of this Protocol, the Protocol shall enter into force on the thirtieth day after the date of signature or of the deposit of such instrument with the Depositary respectively.
2. Any Party to the Protocol may denounce this Protocol by giving written notice to the Depositary. The denunciation shall become effective twelve (12) months after the date of receipt of the notice by the Depositary or such longer period as may be specified in the notice.
3. A Party to the Protocol shall cease to be a Party to the Protocol on the date that it ceases to be a Party to the Convention.

Article 22: Depositary

1. The Director General of INMARSAT shall be the Depositary of this Protocol.
2. The Depositary shall, in particular, promptly notify all Parties to the Convention of:
   (a) Any signature of the Protocol;
   (b) The deposit of any instrument of ratification, acceptance, approval or accession;
   (c) The date of entry into force of this Protocol;
   (d) The date when a State has ceased to be a Party to this Protocol;
   (e) Any other communications relating to this Protocol.
3. Upon entry into force of this Protocol, the Depositary shall transmit a certified copy of the original to the Secretariat of the United Nations for registration and publication in accordance with Article 102 of the Charter of the United Nations.

Article 23: Authentic Texts

This Protocol is established in a single original in the English, French, Russian and Spanish languages, all the texts being equally authentic, and shall be deposited with the Director General of INMARSAT who shall send a certified copy to each Party to the Convention.

In Witness Whereof the undersigned, duly authorized for that purpose by their respective Governments, have signed this Protocol.

Done at London this first day of December one thousand nine hundred and eighty-one.

AMENDMENTS TO THE CONVENTION ON THE INTERNATIONAL MARITIME SATELLITE ORGANISATION (INMARSAT)

Preamble

At the end of the Preamble, the following new paragraph is added:
Affirming that a maritime satellite system shall also be open

for aeronautical communication for the benefit of aircraft of all nations,

Article 1: Definitions

In Article 1, the following new paragraph (h) is added:
  (h) "Aircraft" means any machine that can derive support in the atmosphere from the reactions of the air other than the reactions of the air against the earth's surface.

Article 3: Purpose

Article 3, paragraphs (1) and (2) are replaced by the following text:

1. The purpose of the Organization is to make provision for the space segment necessary for improving maritime communications and, as practicable, aeronautical communications, thereby assisting in improving communications for distress and safety of life, communications for air traffic services, the efficiency and management of ships and aircraft, maritime and aeronautical public correspondence services and radiodetermination capabilities.
2. The Organization shall seek to serve all areas where there is need for maritime and aeronautical communications.

Article 7: Access to Space Segment

Article 7, paragraphs (1) and (2) are replaced by the following test:

1. The INMARSAT space segment shall be open for use by ships and aircraft of all nations on conditions to be determined by the Council. In determining such conditions, the Council shall not discriminate among ships or aircraft on the basis of nationality.
2. The Council may, on a case-by-case basis, permit access to the INMARSAT space segment by earth stations located on structures operating in the marine environment other than ships, if and as long as the operation of such earth stations will not significantly affect the provision of service to ships or aircraft.

Article 8: Other Space Segments

Article 8, paragraph (1) is replaced by the following text:

1. A Party shall notify the Organization in the event that it or any person within its jurisdiction intends to make provision for, or initiate the use of, individually or jointly, separate space segment facilities to meet any or all of the maritime purposes of the INMARSAT space segment, to insure technical compatibility and to avoid significant economic harm to the INMARSAT system.

Article 12: Assembly—Functions

Article 12, sub-paragraph (1)(c) is replaced by the following text:

(c) Authorize, on the recommendation of the Council, the establishment of additional space segment facilities the special or primary purpose of which is to provide radiodetermination, distress or safety services. However, the space segment facilities established to provide maritime and aeronautical public correspondence services can be used for telecommunications for distress, safety and radiodetermination purposes without such authorization.

Article 15: Council—Functions

Article 15, paragraphs (a), (c) and (h) are replaced by the following text:

(a) Determination of maritime and aeronautical satellite telecommunications requirements and adoption of policies, plans, programmes, procedures and measures for the design, development, construction, establishment, acquisition by purchase or lease operation, maintenance and utilization of the INMARSAT space segment, including the procurement of any necessary launch services to meet such requirements.

(c) Adoption of criteria and procedures for approval of earth

stations on land, on ships, on aircraft, and on structures
in the marine environment for access to the INMARSAT
space segment and for verification and monitoring of
performance of earth stations having access t o and
utilization of the INMARSAT space segment. For earth
stations on ships and aircraft, the criteria should be in
sufficient detail for use by national licensing authorities,
at their discretion, for type-approval purposes.

(h) Determination of arrangements for consultation on a
continuing basis with bodies recognized by the Council
as representing shipowners, aircraft operators, maritime
and aeronautical personnel and other users of maritime
and aeronautical telecommunications.

Article 21: Inventions and Technical Information

Article 21, sub paragraphs (2)(b) and (7)(b)(i) are replaced by the
following text:

2(b) The right to disclose and to have disclosed to Parties and
Signatories and others within the jurisdiction of any Party
such inventions and technical information, and to use and
to authorize and to have authorized Parties and Signatories
and such others to use such inventions and technical
information without payment in connexion with the
INMARSAT space segment and any earth station on land,
ship or aircraft operating in conjunction therewith.

(7)(b (i) Without payment in connexion with the INMARSAT space
segment or any earth station on land, ship or aircraft
operating in conjunction therewith.

Article 27: Relationship with other International Organizations

Article 27 is replaced by the following text:

The Organization shall co-operate with the United Nations
and its bodies dealing with the Peaceful Uses of Outer Space and
Ocean Area, its Specialised Agencies, as well as other international
organizations, on matters of common interest. In particular the
Organization shall take into account the relevant international
standards, regulations, resolutions, procedures and

recommendations of the International Maritime Organization and the International Civil Aviation Organization. The Organization shall observe the relevant provisions of the International Telecommunication Convention and regulations made thereunder, and shall in the design, development, construction and establishment of the INMARSAT space segment and in the procedures established for regulating the operation of the INMARSAT space segment and of earth stations give due consideration to the relevant resolutions, recommendations and procedures of the organs of the International Telecommunication Union.

Article 32: Signature and Ratification

Article 32, paragraph (3) is replaced by the following text:

3. On becoming a Party to this Convention, or at any time thereafter, a State may declare, by written notification to the Depositary, to which Registers of ships, to which aircraft operating under its authority, and to which land earth stations under its jurisdiction, the Convention shall apply.

Article 35: Depositary

Article 35, paragraph (1) us replaced by the following text:

(1) The Depositary of this Convention shall be the Secretary-General of the International Maritime Organization.
Amendments to the Operating Agreement on the International Maritime Satellite Organization (INMARSAT)

4

High Seas and International Seabed

GENERAL INTRODUCTION TO LOS

The term United Nations Convention on Law of the Sea (UNCLOS, also called simply the Law of the Sea or LOS) refers to several United Nations events and one treaty. The events the term refers to are the (First) United Nations Convention on Law of the Sea, the Second United Nations Convention on Law of the Sea, and the Third United Nations Convention on Law of the Sea. The treaty resulting from the Third United Nations Convention on Law of the Sea also bears the name United Nations Convention on Law of the Sea and is the most recent major development in international law governing the oceans. The treaty provided new universal legal controls for the management of marine natural resources and the control of pollution. Its Secretariat resides within the United Nations Division for Ocean Affairs and the Law of the Sea.

Historical Background

The LOS was needed owing to the weakness of the older 'freedom of the seas' concept, dating from the 17th century: national rights were limited to a specified belt of water extending from a nation's coastlines, usually three (3) nautical miles, according to the 'cannon shot' rule developed by the Dutch jurist Cornelius Bynkershoek. All water beyond national boundaries was considered international waters-free to all nations, but belonging to none of them (the *mare liberum* principle promulgated by Grotius).

Into the 20th century many nations expressed a need to extend national claims, in order to include mineral resources, to protect fish stocks, and to have the means to enforce pollution controls. This was recognized by the League of Nations, and a conference was held in 1930 at the Hague, but did not result in any agreements.

One nation that undermined the 'freedom of the seas' principle was the United States, when in 1945 President Truman unilaterally extended his nation's control, to cover all the natural resources of their continental shelf. Other nations were quick to emulate the USA. Between 1946 and 1950, Argentina, Chile, Peru, and Ecuador all extended their sovereign rights to a 200 nautical miles distance—so as to cover their Humboldt Current fishing grounds. Other nations extended their territorial seas to 12 nautical miles.

By 1967 only 25 nations still used the old three nautical miles limit, 66 nations had set a 12 nautical miles territorial limit, and eight had set a 200 nautical miles limit. For the latest table of maritime claims, as compiled by the United Nations, see 3]. According to that table, as of 30 June, 2006, only a handful of countries use the old 3 miles limit (Jordan, Palau, and Singapore). It also used in certain Australian islands, an area of Belize, some Japanese straits, certain areas of Papua New Guinea, and a few UK dependencies, such as Anguilla.

UNCLOS I

In 1956, the United Nations held its first Conference on the Law of the Sea ("UNCLOS I") at Geneva, Switzerland. UNCLOS I resulted in four treaties concluded in 1958:

- Convention on the Territorial Sea and Contiguous Zone, entry into force: 10 September, 1964
- Convention on the Continental Shelf, entry into force: 10 une, 1964
- Convention on the High Seas, entry into force: 30 September, 1962
- Convention on Fishing and Conservation of Living Resources of the High Seas.

Although UNCLOS I was considered a success, it left open the important issue of breadth of territorial waters.

The Second United Nations Conference on Law of the Sea (UNCLOS II)

The United Nations followed this in 1960 with its second

Convention on the Law of the Sea ("UNCLOS II"). UNCLOS II did not result in any international agreements. During the six-week conference at Geneva, UNCLOS II did not achieve much. Generally speaking, the developing countries participated only as clients, allies, or dependents of United States or the former Soviet Union; there was no voice for countries of the third world or the developing nations.

The Third United Nations Conference on Law of the Sea (UNCLOS III)

The issue of varying claims of territorial waters was raised in the UN in 1967 by Arvid Pardo, of Malta, and in 1973 the *Third United Nations Conference on the Law of the Sea* was convened in New York to write a new treaty covering the oceans. The conference lasted until 1982 and over 160 nations participated. The conference was conducted under a process of consensus rather than majority vote in an attempt to reduce the possibility of groups of nation-states dominating the negotiations. The convention came into force on 16 November, 1994, one year after the sixtieth state, Guyana, signed it.

The convention introduced a number of provisions. The most significant issues covered were setting limits, navigation, archipelagic status and transit regimes, exclusive economic zones (EEZ), continental shelf jurisdiction, deep seabed mining, the exploitation regime, protection of the marine environment, scientific research, and settlement of disputes.

The convention set the limit of various areas, measured from a carefully defined baseline, as follows:

Internal Waters

Covers all water and waterways on the landward side of the baseline. The coastal nation is free to set laws, regulate any use, and use any resource. Foreign vessels have no right of passage within internal waters.

Territorial Waters

Out to 12 nautical miles from the baseline, the coastal state is free to set laws, regulate any use, and use any resource. Vessels were given the right of "innocent passage" through any territorial waters, with strategic straits allowing the passage of military craft as "transit passage", in that naval vessels are allowed to maintain postures that would be illegal in territorial waters. "Innocent Passage" is defined by the convention as passing through waters in expeditious and continuous manner, which is not "prejudicial to the peace, good order or the security" of the coastal state. Fishing, polluting, weapons practice, spying are not "innocent." Nations can also temporarily suspend innocent passage in specific areas of their territorial seas, if doing so is essential for the protection of its security.

Contiguous Zone

Beyond the 12 nautical mile limit there was a further 12 nautical miles or 24 nautical miles from the territorial sea baselines limit, the "contiguous zone", in which area a state could continue to enforce laws regarding activities such as smuggling or illegal immigration.

Exclusive Economic Zones (EEZ)

Extends 200 nautical miles from the baseline. Within this area, the coastal nation has sole exploitation rights over all natural resources. The EEZ were introduced to halt the increasingly heated clashes over fishing rights, although oil was also becoming important. The success of an offshore oil platform in the Gulf of Mexico in 1947 was soon repeated elsewhere in the world, by 1970 it was technically feasible to operate in waters 4000 metres deep. Foreign nations have the freedom of navigation and overflight, subject to the regulation of the coastal states. Foreign states may also lay submarine pipes and cables.

Archipelagic Waters

The convention set the definition of Archipelagic States in Part IV, which also define how the state can draw its territorial borders. A baseline is drawn between the outermost points of the outermost islands, subject to these points being sufficiently close to one another. All waters inside this baseline is described as *Archipelagic*

Waters and are included as part of the state's territory and territorial waters. This baseline is also used to chart its territorial waters 12 nautical miles from the baseline and EEZ 200 nautical miles from the baseline.

Continental Shelf

Continental shelf is defined as natural prolongation of the land territory to the continental margin's outer edge, or 200 nautical miles from the coastal state's baseline, whichever is greater. State's continental shelf may exceed 200 nautical miles until the natural prolongation ends, but it may never exceed 350 nautical miles, and 100 nautical miles beyond 2,500 meter isobath, which is a line connecting the depth of 2,500 meters. States have the right to harvest mineral and non-living material in the subsoil of its continental shelf, to the exclusion of others.

Aside from its provisions defining ocean boundaries, the convention establishes general obligations for safeguarding the marine environment and protecting freedom of scientific research on the high seas, and also creates an innovative legal regime for controlling mineral resource exploitation in deep seabed areas beyond national jurisdiction, through an International Seabed Authority.

Landlocked states are given a right of access to and from the sea, without taxation of traffic through transit states.

Part XI

Part XI of the Convention provides for a regime relating to minerals on the seabed outside any states territorial waters or EEZ. It establishes an International Seabed Authority (ISA) to authorise seabed exploration and mining and collect and distribute the seabed mining royalty.

The United States strongly objected to the provisions of Part XI of the treaty, on several grounds. The US felt that the provisions of the treaty were not free market friendly and were designed to favour the economic systems of the Communist states. The US felt that the provisions could potentially result in the ISA receiving large revenues from seabed mining, and that there was insufficient controls over what these revenues could be used for. The US was particularly concerned that these revenues could be given to causes which the US opposed, such as the PLO. It was also concerned that the ISA would become a bloated and expensive bureaucracy even if seabed mining never proved to be economically feasible.

Due to Part XI, the US refused to sign the UNCLOS, although they expressed their agreement with the remaining provisions of the treaty. They also expressed the view that even as not a party, it considered many of the remaining provisions as binding upon the United States as a statement of customary international law which it had accepted.

It became clear that the US would not accept the treaty as it stood. It was felt that the treaty would not be successful with such strong opposition from the US. In addition, the fall of the Communism in the late 1980s had removed much of the support for some of the more contentious Part XI provisions. As a result, the United Nations resolved to negotiate an amendment to the treaty to meet the United States' concerns. As a result, the Agreement relating to Part XI was negotiated and agreed upon by the parties to the treaty and the United States. This modified Part XI to remove or soften most of the provisions the US was opposed to. In particular, it limited the size of the ISA bureaucracy and gave the US an effective veto over the dispersal of ISA funds.

Due to the Agreement, the United States government now feels that the UNCLOS (including the modified Part XI provisions) are now acceptable, and no longer opposes ratification. (However, despite this, ratification still has not occurred, due to internal political reasons discussed below.)

US Criticism

"The treaty... would put 70 per cent of the Earth's surface under the despot-loving, corrupt and unaccountable "governance" of the United Nations." — Oliver North

"The United States is simply not going to shoot our way to acceptable resolution of oceans disputes with Canada, Chile, Brazil, India, Italy and other democracies." — J. N. Moore and W. L. Schachte

Libertarians criticize the treaty for creating a tragedy of the commons by designating oceanic resources as the "common heritage of mankind"—essentially public property—instead of privatizing the seabed. According to economic theories promoted by the Property and Environment Research Center and other free market environmentalists, privatization would create incentives for preservation by giving owners an economic interest in protecting the long-term value of their property. If long-term tuna fishing rights were auctioned off, for instance, the owner would have an incentive not to overfish, since depleting the population would lessen returns in future years.

In the United States there is vigorous debate over ratification of the treaty, with criticism coming mainly from political conservatives who consider it antithetical to US national interests. A small group of Republican senators, led by Jim Inhofe of Oklahoma, has blocked American ratification of the treaty, claiming that it would impinge upon US sovereignty. The Bush administration, a majority of the United States Senate, and the Pentagon favor ratification, as do representatives of scientific, international legal scholar, mining, and environmentalist groups.

Arguments

US arguments against the treaty fall into these main categories:

- *National Sovereignty:* The treaty limits US legal authority by granting power to a United Nations-created agency with its own court and bureaucracy, as part of a general expansion of international power, which is not necessarily democratically elected. Ultimately treaty-based laws could be enforced against the US.
- *War on Terror:* The treaty limits US military activities especially relevant to anti-terror operations, such as intelligence collection and submerged travel in coastal waters (Articles 19, 20) and the boarding of ships for anti-terror purposes (Art. 110). Other provisions such as Articles 88 and 301 limit the sea to "peaceful purposes," which is said to restrict all military operations.
- *Navigation Rights not Threatened:* One of the treaty's main selling points, legally recognized navigation rights on, over, and under straits, is unnecessary because these rights are not currently threatened by law or by any military capable of opposing the US.

- *Redistribution of Wealth:* The treaty would force the US to pay taxes to the United Nations, further increasing the UN's power.

- *Redistribution of Technology:* The treaty would force US businesses to turn over economically and militarily relevant technology to other countries.

- *Undesirable Precedent:* The treaty paves the way for increased power of Non-governmental organizations over the US and other nations.

- *Harm to De-militarizing Operations:* The treaty would for the first time require all unmanned ocean vessels, including those used for mine detection to protect ships exercising the right of innocent passage, to navigate on the surface in territorial waters-effectively eliminating their value for such purposes8].

- *Internationalizing Domestic Law:* Some of the treaty's conservation provisions would provide new avenues for non-U.S. environmental organizations to attempt to influence domestic U.S. environmental policies by pursuing legal action in both U.S. and international courts9.

Response

The response to these criticisms is a vigorous denial of their truth. A compilation of arguments by Prof. John Norton Moore of the University of Virginia Law School and Adm. William L. Schachte addresses the criticism as follows:

- *Existing Compliance:* The US already has accepted many parts of the treaty via the UN Charter and the 1958 Geneva Conventions, and by Ronald Reagan's executive order already considers itself bound by the 1982 version of the treaty but for the mining provisions of Part XI.

- *International Law:* The anti-UN arguments against compliance with this treaty apply to *all* international agreements, so that a position that the US must not bind itself in any way is a rejection of the principle of international diplomacy.

- *Straits Rights Needed:* There are more than 100 straits used for navigation, making many countries capable of cutting off waterways crucial to defense and the majority of US trade. A single international regime is a more practical means of enforcing navigation and overflight rights than a collection of two-party agreements with potentially hostile countries.

- *Dispute Settlement:* The International Seabed Authority's jurisdiction applies only to seabed mining, and the Law of the Sea Tribunal offers several alternative forms of arbitration. The treaty offers a peaceful way to resolve disputes with Canada, India, and other nations. In contrast, without treaty compliance the US has no peaceful recourse if another non-signatory party like Iran decides to close its straits to navigation, making war more likely.

- *Military Activities Unrestricted:* The treaty is understood not to apply to wartime or to ban military activities such as the travel of warships, or to restrict any nation's right to self-defense. The Senate made these assertions as well in the proposed advice and consent bill. If military operations such as the Iraq War would be illegal under the treaty, they are already illegal under agreements the US has accepted. Therefore the treaty does not further restrict US military and anti-terror actions. To the extent that the US seeks greater authority to stop, search, and seize vessels on the high seas, it implies that other nations should have the same rights against US ships and crew.

- *Expansion of Authority:* The treaty actually expands US territory and authority by recognizing a 200-mile Exclusive Economic Zone around all coasts, including those of Alaska and Hawaii, roughly doubling the geographic area considered US property.

- *No Taxation:* The International Seabed Authority's "modest revenue sharing provisions... and certain fees" shoud not be considered "taxes," because they represent a sale of access rights similar to land sales, are less than comparable licensing fees charged by countries for coastal mining operations, and go only to the ISA itself rather than to the UN.

- *Necessity for Mining:* The United States presently lacks a developed seabed mining industry and will continue to do so until the treaty is adopted, because American companies refuse to make the necessary billion-dollar-scale investments until they can be assured of internationally recognized, exclusive economic control over mineral deposits.

- *Other Economic Interests:* Fisheries and less prominent industries such as undersea cable layers stand to suffer from US non-compliance, possibly taking their business to other countries.
- *Onerous Mining Provisions Removed:* The ISA, under the 1994 Agreement, has been redesigned to eliminate socialist-style production controls, and it no longer mandates technology transfer.
- *Positive Precedent:* The revised mining provisions now grant the US a permanent veto power over the ISA's spending, a power not shared with any other nation, making the US able to deny funding to the PLO and other disfavored states.
- *Overwhelming Support:* All the major US interest groups including the military, intelligence agencies, and economic, scientific, and environmental groups support the treaty and consider it favorable to US interests.

Overall, Moore and Schachte believe that the defects in the treaty cited by Reagan have been addressed, so that the treaty now represents a large potential gain for US rights and interests with no downside. They consider criticism of the treaty to be founded in ignorance of its actual provisions and in some cases, outright dishonesty.

Signature and ratification

Opened for signature-10 December, 1982.
Entered into force-16 November , 1994.

Parties — (152) Albania, Algeria, Angola, Antigua and Barbuda, Argentina, Armenia, Australia, Austria, The Bahamas, Bahrain, Bangladesh, Barbados, Belgium, Belarus, Belize, Benin, Bolivia, Bosnia and Herzegovina, Botswana, Brazil, Brunei, Bulgaria, Burkina Faso, Burma, Cameroon, Canada, Cape Verde, Chile,

People's Republic of China, Comoros, Democratic Republic of the Congo, Cook Islands, Costa Rica, Côte d'Ivoire, Croatia, Cuba, Cyprus, Czech Republic, Denmark, Djibouti, Dominica, Egypt, Equatorial Guinea, Estonia, European Union, Fiji, Finland, France, Gabon, The Gambia, Georgia, Germany, Ghana, Greece, Grenada, Guatemala, Guinea, Guinea-Bissau, Guyana, Haiti, Honduras, Hungary, Iceland, India, Indonesia, Iraq, , Italy, Jamaica, Japan, Jordan, Kenya, Kiribati, South Korea, Kuwait, Laos, Latvia, Lebanon, Lithuania, Luxembourg, Former Yugoslav Republic of Macedonia, Madagascar, Malaysia, Maldives, Mali, Malta, Marshall Islands, Mauritania, Mauritius, Mexico, Federated States of Micronesia, Monaco, Mongolia, Montenegro, Mozambique, Namibia, Nauru, Nepal, Netherlands, New Zealand, Nicaragua, Nigeria, Niue, Norway, Oman, Pakistan, Palau, Panama, Papua New Guinea, Paraguay, Philippines, Poland, Portugal, Qatar, Romania, Russia, Saint Kitts and Nevis, Saint Lucia, Saint Vincent and the Grenadines, Samoa, São Tomé and Príncipe, Saudi Arabia, Senegal, Serbia, Seychelles, Sierra Leone, Singapore, Slovakia, Slovenia, Solomon Islands, Somalia, South Africa, Spain, Sri Lanka, Sudan, Suriname, Sweden, Tanzania, Togo, Tonga, Trinidad and Tobago, Tunisia, Tuvalu, Uganda, Ukraine, United Kingdom, Uruguay, Vanuatu, Vietnam, Yemen, Zambia, .

Countries that have signed, but not yet ratified—(26) Afghanistan, Bhutan, Burundi, Cambodia, Central African Republic, Chad, Colombia, Republic of the Congo, Dominican Republic, El Salvador, Ethiopia, Iran, North Korea, Lesotho, Liberia, Libya, Liechtenstein, Malawi, Morocco, Niger, Rwanda, Swaziland, Switzerland, Thailand, United Arab Emirates, United States.

Countries that have not signed—(18) Andorra, Azerbaijan, Ecuador, Eritrea, Israel, Kazakhstan, Kyrgyzstan, Moldova, Peru, San Marino, Syria, Tadjikistan, Timor-Leste, Turkey, Turkmenistan, Uzbekistan, Vatican City, Venezuela.

HIGH SEAS FISHING

Introduction

In the decade following the adoption of the 1982 United Nations Convention on the Law of the Sea, fishing on the high seas became a major international problem. The Convention gave all States the freedom to fish without regulations on the high seas, but coastal States, to which the Law of the Sea conferred exclusive economic rights, including the right to fish within 200 miles off their shores, began to complain that fleets fishing on the high seas were reducing catches in their domestic waters.

The problem centred on fish populations that "straddle" the boundaries of countries' 200-mile exclusive economic zones (EEZs), such as cod off Canada's eastern coast and pollack in the Bering Sea, and highly migratory species like tuna and swordfish, which move between EEZs and the high seas.

By the early 1990s, most stocks of commercially valued fish were running low, according to the Food and Agriculture Organization of the United Nations (FAO). As catches became smaller, coastal States complained that the industrial-scale fishing operations of the so-called "distant-water" States on the high seas were undermining their efforts to conserve and revitalize fish stocks within the EEZs.

Reports of violence between fishing vessels from coastal and distant-water States became increasingly frequent, especially during the "cod wars" of the 1970s. Several countries, including Britain and Norway, sent naval ships to protect fishing fleets on the high seas. Spanish fishers clashed with British and French driftnetters in what came to be known as the "tuna wars". Before the UN Agreement on Straddling and Highly Migratory Fish Stocks was finalized in October, 1995, several coastal States had fired shots at foreign fleets. In the northern Atlantic, Canada seized and confiscated a Spanish boat and crew fishing in international waters just beyond the Canadian 200-mile limit.

The coastal States most concerned during the negotiations about the impact of high seas fishing on their domestic harvest include Argentina, Australia, Canada, Chile, Iceland and New Zealand. Six countries are responsible for 90 per cent of "distant-water" fishing: Russia, Japan, Spain, Poland, the Republic of Korea, and Taiwan province of China. The United States also does a significant amount of high-seas fishing, especially for tuna, and in recent years China has become a major fishing nation.

At the Earth Summit—the UN Conference on Environment and Development, held in Rio de Janeiro in June, 1992— Governments called on the United Nations to find ways to conserve

The Law of the Sea was expected to lead to a reduction in the number of distant-water fishing fleets. Instead, companies began to use refrigerated factory trawlers or "mother ships" that allow fleets to travel vast distances from the home country and to stay at sea for longer periods without having to return to shore. The fleets undermine the livelihoods of local fishers and deprive poor people in coastal areas of a primary source of sustenance. As global fish stocks decline, seafood becomes an increasingly expensive item for the rich and a rarity for the poor.

Typically, fleets on the high seas use non-selective fishing equipment, which indiscriminately sweeps up everything in its path—undersize target species and non-target species and other marine life such as mollusks, jellyfish, turtles and porpoises. This "by-catch", currently estimated at 27 million tonnes annually, is thrown back into the ocean and the creatures are usually too damaged to survive.

The Political Issue

The negotiations focused on the conflict between the coastal and distant-water fishing States. By mid-1993, Canada had declared a moratorium on cod fishing off its Atlantic coast until stocks were able to regenerate, putting between 20,000 and 30,000 fishers out of work. In the United States, fisheries for Atlantic haddock, cod and flounder and for Pacific salmon virtually collapsed. Iceland cut back its domestic fishing by 50 per cent because of depleted stocks. Meanwhile, unregulated foreign fleets continued to fish just off these countries' boundaries.

Coastal States argued that the high social and economic cost at home of fishermen out of work in order to preserve fish stocks could not be supported if foreign fleets continued to fish without restrictions on the high seas. Russia mounted military surveillance to keep Chinese, Japanese, Republic of Korea and Polish boats from overfishing pollack in the hotly contested Peanut-Hole, a small area of international water surrounded by Russian seas. In the South Pacific, island States tried to stop Taiwanese and Korean fishers poaching tuna. At the same time, distant-water States pointed to research that suggested coastal States were not sustainably managing stocks within their zones.

At first, many countries were reluctant to accept the need for a legally binding agreement. But as talks progressed, "most coastal States realized the time had come for a meaningful international agreement and the distant-water fishing States understood very well that it was time to either play by a set of internationally agreed upon regulations or face anarchy on the high seas", according to Brian Tobin, who spoke in his capacity as Canada's Minister of Fisheries and Oceans.

What the Agreement Is

Officially, the treaty is the "Agreement for the implementation of the provisions of the UN Convention on the Law of the Sea of 10 December, 1982 relating to the conservation and management of straddling fish stocks and highly migratory fish stocks". It was opened for signing on 4 December, 1995 and will become legally binding after ratification by 30 countries, a process which could take two years. Four years after it takes effect, the United Nations will hold a review conference to examine implementation.

What the Agreement Does

"The freedom to fish on the high seas no longer exists as it did under the old law of the sea. It is no longer a free-for-all", Ambassador Nandan said at the close of negotiations. Governments would be required to cooperate to regulate high seas fishing or their vessels would not be allowed to fish.

The 50-article Agreement legally binds countries to conserve and sustainably manage fish stocks and to settle peacefully any disputes that arise over fishing on the high seas. Specifically, the treaty:

- Establishes the basis for the sustainable management and conservation of the world's fisheries;
- Addresses the problem of inadequate data on fish stocks;
- Provides for the establishment of quotas;
- Calls for the setting up of regional fishing organizations where none exist;
- Tackles problems caused by the persistence of unauthorized fishing;
- Sets out procedures for ensuring compliance with its

provisions, including the right to board and inspect vessels belonging to other States; and

■ Prescribes options for the compulsory and binding peaceful settlement of disputes between States.

Conservation and Management Measures: A Key Role for Regional Organizations

Responsibility for regulating and enforcing sustainable fishing practices falls to the regional fishing organizations, which must also collect, report, verify and exchange data on catches. On the basis of a periodic review of the status of fish stocks, they will allocate quotas for States fishing on the high seas.

The Agreement aims to make the fishing industry more transparent. Fishers are obliged to report, through their Governments to the FAO and regional fishing organizations, the size of catches and the amount of fish they discard. Deliberate under-reporting, which is thought to be widespread, will be monitored by other States, which all have the right to board and inspect vessels to ensure compliance with regional agreement.

Because data for many stocks do not exist or are unreliable, the Agreement calls for Governments to use the "precautionary principle" in devising conservation regimes. Regional organizations have the right to impose quotas or restrictions on fishing if they suspect that a stock is in danger of full exploitation. The precautionary principle, which obliges Governments to act conservatively if there is reason to suspect that serious damage is being done to the environment, underlies all of the Earth Summit agreements.

Only States that agree to adhere to the conservation and management measures adopted by the regional organizations will have access to the fishing grounds administered by those organizations, but boats of all States are subject to the Agreement, whether or not they are party to it. Under international law, a country which does not ratify an international agreement cannot be bound by its provisions. However, the Agreement devolves responsibility for regulating and enforcing sustainable fishing practices to regional organizations, which can take action against any boat that undermines the agreed conservation regime.

Strong Enforcement Mechanisms

Any State that is a member of a regional fisheries organization can enforce the terms of the Agreement against any State wishing to fish in the area. In areas where no regional organizations exist, States concerned about declining fish stocks are expected to organize their establishment. The question of which States are eligible to join regional organizations was left to the organizations to decide.

The Agreement breaks new ground in international law. Most maritime law is enforced by the State that registers the vessel — the "flag State". The Agreement addresses situations where ships on the high seas are too distant from their flag State to be adequately supervised or where the flag State is unwilling or unable to police its vessels. It gives any country that is a member of a regional fishing organization the right to board and inspect vessels of any other States fishing in the area in order to ensure that regional quotas and conservation measures are being followed.

Where there are reasonable grounds for believing that a fishing vessel is violating conservation rules, the inspecting State can notify the flag State. If the flag State does not respond within three working days — during which time the inspectors are permitted to stay on board — the inspecting State can require the vessel to go to the nearest appropriate port for further action. If the flag State feels that enforcement measures have been taken unjustifiably, it can begin dispute-settlement procedures, as outlined in the Agreement.

Dispute Procedures

The Agreement calls for the compulsory and legally binding settlement of high seas fishing disputes by a third party. States can choose from options established under the Law of the Sea, which include appeal to the International Tribunal on the Law of the Sea, the International Court of Justice or an ad hoc tribunal set up to arbitrate particular disputes.

During the negotiations, the right to board and inspect fishing vessels in international waters proved controversial. Distant-water States, including members of the European Union (EU), felt that the issue should be determined by regional fishing organizations.

5

International Freshwater Conservation and Management

INTERNATIONAL FRESHWATER TREATIES DATABASE

A searchable database of summaries and/or the full text of more than 400 international, freshwater-related agreements, covering the years 1820 to 2002. Documents are coded by the basin and countries involved, date signed, treaty topic, allocation measures, conflict resolution mechanisms, and non-water linkages. Both English and non-English language agreements are included. Where available, translations to English of non-English language documents are provided.

The agreements collected relate to international freshwater resources, where the concern is water as a scarce or consumable resource, a quantity to be managed, or an ecosystem to be improved or maintained. Documents concerning navigation rights and tariffs, division of fishing rights, and delineation of rivers as borders or other territorial concerns are not included, unless freshwater as a resource is also mentioned in the document, or physical changes are being made that may impact the hydrology of the river system (e.g., dredging of river bed to improve navigation, straightening of a river's course). In large part, the documents in the database concern: water rights, water allocations, water pollution, principles for equitably addressing water needs, hydropower/reservoir/flood control development, and environmental issues and the rights of riverine ecological systems.

BELLAGIO TREATY

The Bellagio Draft Treaty was developed by a group of experienced legal practitioners and scientists from many parts of the world who came together to identify basic requirements for protection and use of international groundwater supplies. Treaty provisions and international agencies with jurisdiction over groundwater are limited in scope and often unable to address the issues. The goal of the draft treaty is to provide mechanisms for dealing with uncontrolled drawdown, depletion, drought reserves, water quality, protection of recharge areas, and public health emergencies, along with procedures for settling disputes.

The work began upon the joint initiative of Professor Al Utton and Mexican Ambassador Cesar Sepulveda in 1977 who convened a group to study the issues. Many proposals and drafts were circulated over the years and in 1987, a conference was convened in Bellagio, Italy. The notes and tapes from the 1987 meeting became a principal basis for the preparation of the Bellagio Draft Treaty, authored by Professors R.D. Hayton, G. E. Radosevich and Albert E. Utton.

A COMPILATION OF ALL THE INTERNATIONAL FRESHWATER AGREEMENTS ENTERED INTO BY SOUTH AFRICA WITH OTHER STATES
REPORT NO. 1515/1/06
JANUARY, 2006

Executive Summary

This Final Report introduces the background and rationale for the project, followed by a discussion of the core outputs and findings, arguing that the availability of data and knowledge for decision-making is an important step towards good governance of international watercourses. South Africa is party to several international freshwater agreements that confer both rights and responsibilities. Easy access to these agreements will help South Africa's water resource managers to exercise these rights and comply with the responsibilities.

South Africa shares four rivers with its six neighbours—the Incomati, Orange, Limpopo and Maputo. The water in these rivers

transboundary groundwaters and, and for that purpose, to utilize a joint agency; and

Concluding that the best means to achieve the rational management of their transboundary water resources and the protection of the underground environment is to adopt, in principle, an integrated approach including, where appropriate, the conjunctive use of surface water and groundwater in their border region,

Have agreed as follows:

Article I : Definitions

As used in this Agreement:

1. "Aquifer" means a subsurface waterbearing geologic formation from which significant quantities of water may be extracted.
2. "Border region" means the area within approximately kilometers from each side of the mutual boundary as set forth on the annexed map.
3. "The Commission" means the agency designated in Article III, para. 1, of this Agreement.
4. "Conjunctive Use" means the integrated development and management of surface and groundwater as a total water supply system.
5. "Contaminant" means any substance, species or energy which detrimentally affects directly, indirectly, cumulatively or in combination with other substances, human health or safety or agricultural or industrial products or processes, or flora, fauna or an ecosystem.
6. "Contamination" means any detrimental chemical, physical, biological, or temperature change in the content or characteristics of a body of water.
7. "Depletion" means the withdrawal of water from an aquifer at a rate faster than it is recharged, otherwise know as "mining" the water.
8. "Drought" means a condition of abnormal water scarcity in a specific area resulting from natural conditions.
9. "Drought Alert" means the declared condition provided for in Article XII.

10. "Drought Emergency" means the declared emergency provided for in Article XII.
11. "Drought Management Plan" means the plan provided for pursuant to Article XII.
12. "Environmental sensitivity" means vulnerability or susceptibility to changes detrimentally affecting the quality of life or one or more biological or physical systems.
13. "Government(s)" means the governments of the Parties to this Agreement.
14. "Groundwater" means the water in aquifers.
15. "Impairment" means any physical change in an aquifer or its recharge area which significantly reduces or restricts the potential for use of the waters of the aquifer.
16. "Interrelated surface water" means those surface waters in the territory of either Party, the quantity or quality of which is affected by the outflows from, or the inflows to, transboundary groundwater
17. "Pollution" means the introduction of any contaminant by man, directly or indirectly, into groundwaters or surface waters.
18. "Public Health Emergency" means the declared emergency provided for in Article IX.
19. "Recharge" means the addition of water to an aquifer by infiltration of precipitation through the soil or of water from surface streams, lake, or reservoirs, by discharges of water to the land surface, or by injection of water into the aquifer through wells.
20. "Transboundary aquifer" means an aquifer intersected by a common boundary.
21. "Transboundary Groundwater Conservation Area" means an area declared by the Commission pursuant to Article VII.
22. "Transboundary groundwater" means waters in transboundary aquifers.

Article II : General Purposes

1. The Parties recognize their common interest and responsibility in ensuring the reasonable and equitable

development and management of groundwaters in the border region for the well being of their Peoples.

2. Accordingly, the Parties have entered into this Agreement in order to attain the optimum utilization and conservation of transboundary groundwaters and to protect the underground environment. It is also the purpose of the Parties to develop and maintain reliable data and information concerning transboundary aquifers and their waters in order to use and protect these waters in a rational and informed manner.

Article III: The Commission Responsible Under This Agreement

1. The Commission is designated as the Parties' agency to carry out the functions and responsibilities provided for by this Agreement.

2. The Commission shall be authorized a technical staff, which, in collaboration with the technical staffs of the Governments, shall assist the Commission in the accomplishment of its functions and responsibilities.

3. The Commission is authorized to declare Transboundary Groundwater Conservation Areas, Drought Alerts, Drought Emergencies and Public Health Emergencies, and to promulgate the corresponding plans and Depletion Plans, in accordance with the provision of this Agreement.

4. The Commission shall have jurisdiction over such additional matters concerning the border region as are from time to time referred to it by the Governments jointly.

5. The Commission shall prepare and propose to the Governments a budget, conforming insofar as practicable to the budget cycles and procedures of the Governments, covering the projected expenses and capital costs of the Commission's joint operations, plant and staff. The total amount of each budget shall be divided between the Governments in the proportions agreed upon by the Commission and approved by the Governments.

6. The budget for the separate operating costs of each national section shall be the responsibility of the respective Government.

7. The Governments may jointly refer a specific matter

relating to transboundary groundwater to the Commission for investigating or action. Individually Governments may request the Commission's advice relating to transboundary groundwaters on matter originating within the requesting Government's portion of the border region.

8. The Commission shall cause each such referral and request to be taken up and investigated, studied or acted upon, as appropriate. The Commission shall render a report to the Governments on every referral and request taken up.

Article IV: Enforcement and Oversight Responsibilities

1. The enforcement of water quality and quantity measures and related land use controls within the territory of each Party shall be the responsibility of that Party or of its political subdivisions, as appropriate.

2. The Commission shall biennially conduct a review of the water quality and quantity control measures taken within each Party's territory affecting the border region and shall issue a Report containing its assessment of the adequacy and effectiveness of programs for the protection and improvement of the transboundary aquifers and their waters and withdrawal and land use controls, including with respect to any Transboundary Groundwater Conservation Areas, Depletion Plans, Drought Emergency Plans and Health Emergencies. To that end, each Government shall furnish the Commission with the relevant data, information, and studies for use by the Commission in preparing its Report, in accordance with the reporting formats provided by the Commission.

3. In addition to facilitating, as needed, the Commission's oversight responsibilities under paragraph 2, each Government shall make a biennial Report to the Commission specifying the water quality and conservation measures taken; quantities withdrawn, transferred and exchanged, and any problems encountered in carrying out the provisions of this Agreement or in implementation of any of the conservation, depletion and drought management plans and health emergency measures adopted.

Article V: Establishment and Maintenance of the Database

1. The Commission is charged with the creation and maintenance of a comprehensive and unified database pertaining to transboundary groundwaters, in the languages of the Parties. The database shall include an inventory of all transboundary groundwater resources taking into account quantity, quality, aquifer geometry, recharge rates, interaction with surface waters, and other pertinent data and shall identify all transboundary aquifers.

2. The Commission shall carry out studies directly, or through research programs conducted by or with other bodies, public or private:

    (a) to identify inadequacies in available data and to propose remedial action;

    (b) to examine present and potential future uses of said groundwaters, taking into account demographic projections and socio-economic development plants;

    (c) to assess the impact of present and potential development on transboundary groundwaters and related resources;

    (d) to study possible alternative sources of surface water and groundwater for use in the border region, taking into account the quantity and quality of the waters and the potential for the conjunctive use of the available waters; and

    (e) to examine the potential for, and the consequences of, drought, floods, and contamination in the border region.

3. The Parties undertake to facilitate the acquisition of information and data by the Commission on a timely basis in accordance with the Commission's requirements.

4. The Commission shall compile, analyze, and disseminate the data, information and studies and provide the results to the Governments.

Article VI: Water Quality Protection

1. The Parties undertake cooperatively to protect and to

improve, insofar as practicable, the quality of
transboundary aquifers and their waters in conjunction
with their programs for surface water quality control, and
to avoid appreciable harm in or to the territories of the
Parties.

2. The Governments shall promptly inform the Commission
    of any actual or planned, significantly polluting discharge
    into transboundary groundwaters or recharge areas, or of
    other activity with the potential for significant leaching
    into transboundary groundwaters.

3. The Commission shall without delay consider the gravity
    of any situation indicating significant groundwater
    contamination, or the threat thereof, in any part of the
    border region in accordance with the provisions of
    Article VII.

Article VII: Transboundary Groundwater Conservation Areas

1. The Commission shall determine the desirability of
    declaring any area within the border region containing
    transboundary groundwaters to be a Transboundary
    Groundwater Conservation area.

2. In the event that the Commission determines that a
    Transboundary Groundwater Conservation Area is
    desirable, such determination shall be reported to the
    Governments with a draft of the proposed declaration and
    justification therefore, including the delineation of the area
    and its aquifer(s).

3. If no Government files an objection with the Commission
    within one hundred eighty (180) days, the Commission
    shall issue the formal declaration. Any objection(s) filed
    shall specify, with an explanation, the objectionable
    section(s) of the proposed declaration or justification or
    both.

4. Unless an objection requires termination of consideration,
    the Commission shall within ninety (90) days of receipt of
    objections, report to the Governments a revised proposed
    declaration, to be effective within ninety (90) days, unless a
    Government files a subsequent objection with the
    Commission. If no subsequent objection is filed within the

said ninety (90) day period, the formal declaration shall be issued by the Commission. If a subsequent objection is filed within the ninety (90) day period, the Commission shall refer the matter, together with the entire record, to the Governments for resolution by consultation.

5. In making its determination, the Commission shall consider whether:
    (a) groundwater withdrawals exceed or are likely to exceed recharge so as to endanger yield or water quality or are likely to diminish the quantity or quality of interrelated surface waters;
    (b) recharge has been or may become impaired;
    (c) the use of the included aquifer(s) as an important source of drinking water has been, or may become impaired;
    (d) the aquifer(s) have been or may become contaminated; and
    (e) recurring or persistent drought conditions necessitate management of all or some water supplies in the particular area.

6. In making its determination, the Commission shall take into account the impact of the implementation of the declaration under consideration on the sources and uses of water previously allocated by agreements between the Parties or under the Drought Management Plan.

7. The Commission shall periodically review the appropriateness of continuing or modifying Transboundary Groundwater Conservation Areas.

Article VIII: Comprehensive Management Plans

1. For each declared Transboundary Groundwater Conservatoin Area, the Commission shall prepare a Comprehensive Management Plan for the rational development, use, protection and control of the waters in the Transboundary Groundwater Conservation Area.

2. A Comprehensive Management Plan may:
    (a) prescribe measures to prevent, eliminate or mitigate degradation of transboundary groundwater quality and for that purpose may:

     (i) classify transboundary groundwaters according to use and coordinate the formulation of water quality standards;

    (ii) identify toxic and hazardous contaminants in the Area and require a continuing record of such substances from origin to disposal;

  (iii). establish criteria for the safe storage of wastes and maintain an inventory of dumpsites, abandoned as well as active, that have caused or may cause transboundary aquifer pollution;

  (iv) propose a scheme for monitoring water quality conditions including the placement and operation of test wells and for remedial actions where required, including pretreatment and effluent discharge limitations and charges; and

   (v) provide for the establishment where required of protective zones in which land use must be regulated.

(b) allocate the uses of groundwaters and interrelated surface waters taking into account any other allocation(s) previously made applicable within the Transboundary Groundwater Conservation Area.

(c) prescribe measures including pumping limitations, criteria for well placement and number of new wells, retirement of existing wells, imposition of extraction fees, planned depletion regimes or reservations of groundwaters for future use.

(d) arrange, where conditions are favorable, programs of transboundary aquifer recharge.

(e) articulate programs of conjunctive use where appropriate.

(f) prescribe the integration and coordination of water quality and quantity control programs.

(g) include other measures and actions as may be deemed appropriate by the Commission.

3. In making any allocations of water uses within a Comprehensive Management Plan, the Commission shall consider all relevant factors such as:

(a) hydrogeology and meteorology;

(b) existing and planned uses;

(c) environmental sensitivity;
(d) quality control requirements;
(e) socio-economic implications (including dependency);
(f) water conservation practices (including efficiency of water use);
(g) artificial recharge potential; and
(h) comparative costs and implications of alternative sources of supply.

The weight to be given to each factor is to be determined by its importance in comparison with that of the other relevant factors.

4. The Commission shall submit proposed Comprehensive Management Plans to the Governments.
   (a) If no Government files an objection with the Commission within one hundred eighty (180) days, the Commission shall adopt the Plan and monitor its implementation.
   (b) A Government's objections shall specify with an explanation the objectionable portions of the proposed Comprehensive Management Plan.
   (c) Within ninety (90) days of receipt of objections, the Commission shall submit to the Governments a revised proposed Comprehensive Management Plan to be effective within ninety (90) days unless a subsequent objection is filed. If no subsequent objection is filed with the ninety (90) day period, the proposed Comprehensive Management Plan shall be adopted and the Commission shall monitor its implementation. If subsequent objections are filed within the ninety (90) day period, the Commission shall refer the matter, together with the entire record, to the Governments for resolution by consultation.
5. The Commission is authorized to approve advances and exchanges of water consistent with the objectives of the applicable Comprehensive Management Plan.
6. The Commission shall monitor and evaluate the measures taken under the Comprehensive Management Plan and shall propose, as appropriate, modifications thereto.

Article IX: Public Health Emergencies

1. Upon determination by the Commission or any Government that there is an imminent or actual public health hazard involving the contamination of transboundary groundwaters, the Commission shall notify the respective Governments, and may declare a Public Health Emergency for a stated period.
2. In the event that the Public Health Emergency is not mitigated or abated within the initial stated period, the Commission may extend the emergency for such additional period as may be deemed necessary under the circumstances.
3. On the basis of the declaration, the Commission shall have authority to investigate the area of imminent or actual contamination and to prescribe measures to prevent, eliminate or mitigate the public health hazard.
4. The Governments shall provide the indicated information, data, studies and reports concerning public health emergencies as set forth in Paragraphs 2 and 3 of Article IV.

Article X: Planned Depletion

1. The Commission, after evaluation of all relevant considerations, may prepare and, with the consent of the Governments, may approve a plan for the depletion of an aquifer over a calculated period. The plan may apportion the uses and specify the rates and means of extraction of the transboundary groundwaters, and may authorize advances, exchanges and transboundary transfers of water consistent with the objectives of the Depletion Plan.
2. The Governments shall provide the indicated information, data, studies and reports concerning depletion as set forth in Paragraphs 2 and 3 of Article IV.

Article XI: Transboundary Transfers

Nothing in this Agreement shall be so construed as to preclude either short-term or long-term transfers of waters between the Parties under terms and conditions approved by the Commission.

Article XII: Planning for Drought

1. The Commission shall, within two (2) years of the coming into force of this Agreement, complete the preparation of a Drought Management Plan applicable to the border region for activation in the region, or in parts thereof, in the event of drought. The completed Plan shall be submitted to the Governments for standby approval.

2. The Drought Management Plan shall:
   (a) specify the hydrometeorological preconditions for the declaration of a Drought Alert and, thereunder, the conservation measures to be observed by all water users within the border region;
   (b) specify the hydrometerological preconditions for the declaration of a Drought Emergency and, thereunder, the specific measures to be observed by all water users within the border region;
   (c) provide for the monitoring of the hydrometeorological conditions generally in the border region, and compliance with prescribed conservation or other specific measures under any Drought Alert or Drought Emergency; and
   (d) provide for periodic reports to the Governments during any Drought Alert or Drought Emergency, to include any proposed modifications to the Drought Emergency Plan and any modifications made to the prescribed measures under any Drought Alert or Drought Emergency.

3. The Drought Management Plan may:
   (a) designate and reserve certain transboundary aquifers or specific well sites for use in times of drought;
   (b) provide, for the duration of any declared Drought Emergency:
      1. the conjunctive management of groundwater and surface water supplies within or made available to the border region or part(s) thereof governed by the declaration;
      2. increases and reductions in the normal allowable withdrawals and at variance with allocations made under a Comprehensive Management Plan

for a Transboundary Groundwater Conservation Area or by prior agreements between the Parties, maintaining to the extent practicable the established withdrawal ratios between the Parties and an equitable balance of all emergency obligations.

3. authorization to use designated and reserved groundwaters within the border region.

(c) include other structural and nonstructural measures deemed likely to be needed under various drought conditions.

4. The conservation and other specific measures provided in the Plan for Drought Alert declarations or Drought Emergency declarations may be modified or suspended by the Commission to meet the specific requirements of the situation at the time of such declarations and during the time such declarations remain in force.

5. The authority to determine the existence of the preconditions specified in the approved Drought Management Plan and to declare drought alerts and drought emergencies thereunder, in any portion of the border region, is vested in the Commission.

6. The Commission is authorized to modify or terminate a declaration of Drought Alert or of Drought Emergency when the hydrometeorological conditions so warrant.

7. Declarations of Drought Alert and Drought Emergency, and modifications to or termination of the same, shall be immediately communicated to the Governments and published so as to come to the attention of all water users in the border region.

8. The Governments shall provide the indicated information, data, studies and reports concerning drought as set forth in Paragraphs 2 and 3 of Article IV.

Article XIII: Inquiry in the Public Interest

1. The Commission shall by general notice invite written statements and information from all persons professing interest in the groundwater-related conditions and activities in the portion of the border region for which a Transboundary Groundwater Conservation Area declaration, a Comprehensive Management Plan, a Depletion Plan, a trans-boundary transfer, or a Drought Alert or Emergency declaration is under consideration.

2. All submissions received pursuant to Paragraph 1 shall be taken into account by the Commission.

3. Whenever the Commission deems that public interest warrants, it shall schedule and conduct hearings open to the public in appropriate places and facilities in the border region, and shall make and publish a record of such hearings.

4. Any person professing an interest may also petition the Commission at any time requesting the Commission to schedule a hearing or to invite written statements and information concerning groundwater conditions in the border region, or urging the Commission to take a particular action under this Agreement.

5. When deemed useful by the Commission, technical meetings, work-shops and briefings relating to transboundary groundwater matters may be held under the auspices of the Commission or in cooperation with authorities and organizations concerned with the welfare of the border region.

Article XIV: Existing Rights and Obligations

The rights and obligations of the Parties as set forth in prior agreements between the Parties shall not be permanently altered by this Agreement or any measures taken hereunder.

Article XV: Accomodation of Differences

1. The Commission shall expend its best efforts to resolve differences within the Commission with respect to the facts

and circumstances of a situation within the purview of this Agreement. Failure to resolve such differences within six (6) months at the technical level of the Commission shall result in the submission of the difference(s), together with the entire record, to the Governments for resolution by consultation.

2. If after good faith consultations during a period of twelve (12) months the Governments are unable to reach an accommodation of a difference or differences between them concerning the facts and circumstances of a situation within the purview of this Agreement, or with respect to which the Commission has been unable to reach agreement,

   (a) any Government is entitled to invoke this Article to the effect that a commission of inquiry be appointed and charged with a full and impartial study for the purpose of verification of the facts of the situation;

   (b) the Governments shall appoint and instruct the commissioner(s), and defray the expenses of such commissions equally, unless otherwise agreed; and

   (c) in the event the Governments fail to agree upon the implementation of this Paragraph within six (6) months from the date of its formal invocation, the, at the request of any Government shall, after consultation with each Government, appoint the commissioner(s), instruct the same, and apportion the expenses of the commission, as may be required to render the commission operational.

3. A commission of inquiry appointed under this Article shall render a report to the Governments within the terms of its instructions and on the basis of independent and detailed examination of the data and information made available to it by the Governments and the Commission, and may request such additional data and information as the commission of inquiry deems significant for its deliberations and findings.

4. On the basis of the report of a commission of inquiry, the Parties undertake promptly to enter into consultations for the purpose of reaching an agreed accommodation of the difference(s).